Signpost

THE PREMIER COLOUR HOTEL GUIDE

1991 - 52ND EDITION

ISBN 0 901249 20 3

Printed by Ebenezer Baylis & Son Ltd (Printers & Binders)
London Road, Worcester WR5 2JH

Trade Distribution by
W. Foulsham & Co. Ltd., Yeovil Road, Slough, Berks. SL1 4JH
Tel: 0753 38637

**SIGNPOST is Published in the U.S.A.
under the title
PREMIER HOTELS OF GREAT BRITAIN**

SIGNPOST LIMITED. FOUNTAIN COURT, STEELHOUSE LANE, BIRMINGHAM B4 6DT.
Telephone: 021-236 5979 Fax: 021-200 1159

CONTENTS

How to use Signpost

1. **All hotels are listed in two separate indices:**

   (a) On pages 447–453 under the counties in which they are situated.

   (b) On pages 454–460 under the names of the nearest town or village.

2. **The book is divided into sections containing hotels in England, Wales, Scotland and the Islands. In each of these sections the nearest town or village to each hotel appears alphabetically.** For example, Salford Hall at Abbots Salford appears first and the Swallow Chase Hotel, York last in the English section.

3. The type of licence each hotel has is indicated by:

F	—Full
C	—Conditional
CL	—Club
R	—Restaurant
R and R	—Restaurant and Residential

THE *SIGNPOST* TEAM

On the following pages are photographs of the *Signpost* Directors and Inspectors, taken during their travels this Summer.

Our Reader's comments about the hotels featured in this guide are of immense value to the Inspectors and staff concerned, and are always taken into consideration as we plan each edition. We welcome your letters.

Signpost *Inspector Fiona Davison with Trevor Beale, Managing Director of West Lodge Park Hotel, Hadley Wood, Herts.*

Photographed in Ascots Restaurant at the Berkshire Hotel, London, is General Manager Peter Proquitte and Chairman of Signpost *Christopher Carney-Smith (right).*

By the steps of The Ritz, London, Vice President and Managing Director of the Cunard Trafalgar House Group, Terry Holmes (left) with Signpost *Inspector Annie Randolph Dyer and General Manager of The Ritz, David Hopkins.*

Proprietors of Gabriel Court Hotel, Stoke Gabriel, Devon, Michael and Eryl Beacom accompanied by Signpost *Inspector, Tricia Doyle (left).*

At the Saunton Sands Hotel, Devon, Brend Hotel Group Design Manager Tony Atkinson (left), Deputy Manager of the Hotel, John Belchamber and Signpost *Director Freddie Bell-Scott (centre).*

Mrs. Else-Marie Kearney, General Manager at the Cricklade Hotel and Country Club, Nr. Swindon, Wiltshire with her Deputy Manager Roger Lamothe and (standing) Signpost *Inspector John Stenning.*

Peter Chubb, General Manager of Audleys Wood Country House Hotel, Basingstoke, Hants, and Signpost *Inspector, Susan Long.*

Sylvia Adcock, Proprietor of the Stratford House Hotel, Stratford-upon-Avon, and Signpost *Director, Gill Carney-Smith (right).*

Susan Foreman, Signpost *Inspector at the Alexander House, Turners Hill, Sussex, with General Manager Anthony Humphries.*

In the gardens of Graythwaite Manor Hotel, Grange-over-Sands, Cumbria, Olof White (left) Signpost *Inspector with Directors of the Hotel (from left to right) Mrs. Doris Bullough, Mr. Iain Blakemore and Mrs. Marjorie Mascord.*

Proprietors of the Winterbourne Hotel, Bonchurch, Isle of Wight, Terry and Pat O'Connor with Signpost *Inspector Scarlett Edwards-Jones (centre).*

Edward Salmon (right) Signpost *Director photographed at Chateau Valeuse Hotel, St. Brelade's Bay, Jersey, with Rosanne and Claudio Magris, Managers of the Hotel.*

Mr. G. Theo Smith, Proprietor of Pittodrie House Hotel, Pitcaple, Scotland, having coffee with Signpost *Inspector Gillian Sheldon.*

HOLIDAYS IN ENGLAND

An English holiday offers a whole world of enjoyment; England may be a small country, but it packs in an amazing variety of scenery, attractions and entertainment.

Take the seaside for example, we have 6,000 miles of shoreline, enough to stretch from London to Vladivostock.

Billions of pounds have been spent by our resorts over the past few years on providing exciting all-weather facilities: luxurious water worlds, leisure centres and pleasure domes and an exciting array of visitor attractions – from smuggler's caves to sea-life centres, where visitors can watch sharks swimming a few inches away, or stroke a giant eel! Add to that the top-flight evening entertainments, featuring stars of stage, screen and recording studio, and it's clear that today's seaside holiday offers a whole lot more than the bucket and spade stroll along the Prom of yesteryear.

Glorious scenery is a feature of the English countryside that, happily, has not changed: from rugged moorland to majestic forest, from the lush apple orchards and hop gardens of Kent to the serenity of the Lake District, there are landscapes for all tastes, with over 100,000 miles of footpaths to explore – it's surprisingly easy, given our density of population, to get away from it all and enjoy rural isolation.

To make the most of England's wide, open spaces, activity holiday facilities abound – the ideal chance to try out sailing, narrowboating, riding, abseiling, archery, windsurfing or any other outdoor activity you have always yearned to try.

Our heritage of pageantry and palaces, stately homes, castles and gardens is unsurpassed, with literally thousands of historic buildings to visit. Our industrial past, as the cradle of the Industrial Revolution, is now being explored and exploited to the full, at fascinating attractions like Ironbridge Gorge, Wigan Pier, Beamish, and in the mines, mills and factories which are open to the public – seeing how the other half works, or used to work, makes just as compulsive viewing as how the other half lives.

Our glorious maritime past also provides a wealth of attractions, such as Portsmouth's Historic Dockyard where Henry VIII's flagship *Mary Rose*, Nelson 's ship HMS *Victory* and the early Victorian ironclad warship HMS *Warrior* can be seen; Brunel's *Great Britain*, the world's first iron steamship at Bristol, Liverpool's restored Albert Dock with its museums, galleries, shops and restaurants; and the picturesque maritime quarters of Plymouth and Hull.

England is rich in museums – over 1300 of them – covering every conceivable subject from lace to Laurel and Hardy, Whitby jet to jump-jets, and they are no longer the fusty, musty, 'don't touch' places they used to be. Hands-on science centres; the electronic wizardry of London's Museum of the Moving Image and Bradford's National Museum of Photography Film and Television; and the high-tech wonders of the Greater Manchester Museum of Science and Industry all belong to the new generation of museums which make learning exciting.

Best of all, it's so easy to explore the holiday pleasures of England, no fuming at airport, no visa or vaccinations – just pack your bags and go!

For further details contact the English Tourist Board, see page 386.

SALFORD HALL HOTEL

Abbots Salford, Worcs WR11 5UT

Telephone: (0386) 871300 *Fax: 0386 871301*

Stratford-upon-Avon 8, London 103, Oxford 47, Bristol 63, Birmingham 27, Cheltenham 21

F licence; 34 bedrooms, all with en suite bathroom, telephone and TV; room service; baby listening; last orders for dinner 10.00 p.m.; bar meals; special diets; children welcome; no dogs; conferences up to 50; snooker; sauna and solarium; tennis; open all year except 24th December–4th January; all credit cards accepted.

Considerable investment has been made in this Tudor manor house; its restoration and refurbishment have been accomplished to a standard of comfort and luxury that would meet the demands of the most discerning guest. You can see from the photograph that this 15th century hall has a strong architectural significance, and a history to match, with hideaway lounges, including one with a priest hole concealed behind a bookcase. Those interested in our heritage can visit many famous places; Broughton, Kenilworth, Sudeley and Warwick Castles, Ragley Hall, Coughton Court, Hanway House and Snowshill Manor. Public rooms are elegantly furnished, and all the bedrooms, named after historical dignitaries, are individually decorated and equipped, with all the 20th century prerequisites, like colour TV, in-house video, refrigerated mini-bar, hairdryer and trouser press. The Stanford Room Restaurant offers interesting menus, for instance a terrine of turbot filled with tomato and fresh basil, possibly followed by chicken supreme, filled with fresh lobster, served on a bed of sorrel. A comprehensive wine list complements the food, with bottles available from most of the wine-growing countries. Ask for the brochure showing special away breaks, an interesting variety from Rolls Royce touring to the Champagne Balloon experience. Room and breakfast from £70.00 single, £95.00 double.

THE ALDERLEY EDGE HOTEL

Macclesfield Road, Alderley Edge, Cheshire SK9 7BJ

Telephone: (0625) 583 033 *Fax: 0625 586 343*

Airport 7, Manchester 17, M6 12, M56 5, Macclesfield 5, Wilmslow Station 1

F licence; 32 en suite bedrooms (6 ground floor) all with telephone, colour TV and full central heating; night service; last orders 10.30 p.m.; bar meals all day; diets; children welcome, baby listening; dogs allowed; conferences up to 50; many sporting activities by arrangement; Amex, Diners, Access and Barclaycards accepted.

I have known the Alderley Edge for many years but it is only since Mr. Buttery took over in late 1988 that it has become an hotel of international calibre. It is still relatively small, so it retains the personal touch but the standard of the décor, the furnishings and the quality of the cuisine are the equal of all but the most fabulously priced hotels. What other hotel in Great Britain has fish delivered fresh, twice daily? Or can boast a seventeen page wine list which lists 600 wines (from £7.00 to £685.00) including 225 champagnes, many of which can be served by the glass, and yet offer a table d'hôte lunch at under £15.00, and dinner at under £20.00! I think that herein lies the essence of this hotel; there is variety in everything for which you could ask, and from whatever range you choose, you can be assured that the quality will be of the best and that it will be excellent value. The Manchester area has many notable hotels but, dare I say it, this one has the "Edge" on them all. Of importance to the business man is the fact that Manchester airport is only 7 miles away, Junction 6 of the M56 is 6 miles and Junction 19 of the M6 is 9 miles. Of interest to the tourist (if they can tear themselves away from the delights of the hotel!) is the proximity of the Peak District and the lovely countryside of Cheshire and even North Wales. Hotel open all year. Room and breakfast from £88.00.

FAIRLAWNS HOTEL AND RESTAURANT

Aldridge, Walsall, West Midlands WS9 0NU

Telephone: (0922) 55122 *Telex: 339873* *Fax: 0922 743210*

M6 (Junc. 10) 6, Birmingham 7, NEC 12, Lichfield 7, Alton Towers 30

F licence; 36 en suite bedrooms (3 ground floor) all with telephone and col. TV; full central heating; night service; last orders 10 p.m.; bar meals; diets; children welcome; baby listening; dogs accepted; conferences max. 80; golf 1½ miles; Amex, Diners, Visa, Access & Consort cards accepted.

Centrally situated between Sutton Coldfield with its 2,400 acre park, Walsall, famous for its wonderful open market and the lovely city of Lichfield, birthplace of Doctor Samuel Johnson and proud of its beautiful sandstone Cathedral, the Fairlawns Hotel enjoys a delightfully secluded country setting. However, it has easy access to the motorway network being 20 minutes drive from Birmingham City Centre and 25 minutes from the NEC. There are 36 attractive en suite bedrooms which include 6 suites. Some bedrooms are split-level having a sitting room area below and the bedroom above. More bedrooms are planned which will be incorporated into a large leisure complex at the rear. The attractive air-conditioned restaurant has an ever-changing and excellent menu and Chef Stefan Wilkinson uses only the finest quality fresh ingredients. The hotel has superb purpose built self-contained conference rooms offering first class facilities for up to 30 delegates. These comprise 4 main rooms with folding partition screens in the Cedar Suite for separating into syndicate areas, together with 6 bedroom suites, each having a lounge/study area that enables them to be used as extra syndicate rooms or as a base for senior executives. Whether you are planning a quiet night out for two, a wedding, a party or a conference, you will find the Fairlawns has much to offer. This friendly, yet efficient, hotel is managed by Mr. John Pette. Single room and breakfast from £39.50, Double from £65.00. Open all year.

BISHOPFIELD COUNTRY HOUSE HOTEL

Allendale, Hexham, Northumberland NE47 9EJ

Telephone: (043468) 3248 *Fax: 043468 3830*

Hexham 10, Newcastle 30, Carlisle 25, Scotch Corner 50, Lake District 1 hour

R & R licence; 11 en suite bedrooms (2 ground floor), all with telephone, colour TV; last orders 8.00 p.m.; diets; children welcome; baby listening; dogs accepted; conferences max. 30; 3 lounges; golf, tennis, riding, shooting, fishing all nearby; bicycles available; Access credit cards accepted.

For those readers of *Signpost* who enjoy the country way of living, Bishopfield is the epitome of a country house hotel. The outdoor enthusiast, whether actively participating in sports such as fishing, shooting or walking, or more passively observing as a nature lover, has every activity catered for here. For the fishermen there is a stretch of 1½ miles of river trout fishing and salmon fishing is available on the Tyne; shooting is available and for the walker there is a collection service to take you out to your starting point or bring you back to the hotel. For the naturalist, the fifty acres of grounds abound with wildlife and the surrounding countryside is glorious. But do not think that you have to "rough it" here. The hotel, which has been completely refurbished, is owned and personally run by a delightful young family who know how to pamper their guests. The dining room has gained a well deserved reputation locally for its superb cuisine and for its well chosen wine list. This is an hotel I shall stay in as often as possible and I cannot recommend it too highly for those wishing to "get away from it all". Room and breakfast from £27.00 per person, dinner, room and breakfast from £40.00 per person, low season tariff also available. Open all year.

LOWBYER MANOR COUNTRY HOUSE HOTEL

Hexham Road, Alston, Cumbria CA9 3JX

Telephone: (0434) 881230

Hexham 20, Carlisle 28, Penrith 20, Middleton-in-Teesdale 20

R & R licence; 11 en suite bedrooms, 2 on ground floor; full central heating; last orders 8.30 p.m.; bar meals; diets; children welcome; dogs by arrangement; conferences up to 20; dancing at Christmas only; sailing and boating, golf, riding, shooting and fishing all nearby; Visa, Access, Amex and Diners cards welcome.

Although Alston is the highest market town in England, it lies in the sheltered South Tyne Valley. Cobbled streets lead up to the Pennine Moor and Fells and in a well wooded corner of the town, lies this small, friendly hotel. It has been converted from a seventeenth century manor house to give the traveller or holidaymaker the warmth and comfort appreciated after driving over or walking through this superb moorland country. The bedrooms, all with private bathrooms and tea/coffee making facilities are above average for this type of hotel. There is an intimate bar, and the other public rooms are spacious and well furnished. Mr. and Mrs. Hughes, the proprietors, ensure that a warm welcome awaits you and that a meal in their dining room is a very pleasant experience. The food is well prepared and presented. To sum up, this is a quiet country hotel for those wishing to sample the delights of this area of England, or to use as a base for touring the Lake District, Hadrian's Wall or the Pennine Way. Always open. Room and breakfast from £25.50 per night, or £245.00 per week, inclusive of VAT.

PENHALLOW MANOR COUNTRY HOUSE HOTEL

Altarnun, Launceston, Cornwall PL15 7SJ

Telephone: (0208) 86206

Launceston 7, Bodmin 12, A30 ½ mile

F licence (with conditions); 7 bedrooms, all with en suite bathroom; telephone and TV; baby listening; last orders for dinner 9.30 p.m.; bar meals; special diets; children over 8 welcome; dogs by prior arrangement; conferences 15–20 max.; morning coffee and cream teas; riding and fly fishing locally; tennis and leisure centre 7 miles; sea bathing, sailing and boating within 30 minutes' drive; many nearby golf courses – St. Mellion, Launceston, Bodmin and Camelford 7–10 miles; hotel open all year except December; Visa Cards accepted.

Penhallow Manor can be found next to the church in the village of Altarnun, half a mile from the edge of Bodmin Moor. Originally the vicarage, the house was built in 1842, and stands next to the historic church of St. Nonna, known as the "cathedral of the moor". Penhallow was featured in "Jamaica Inn", after a visit by writer, Daphne du Maurier. The drawing room is comfortable and well decorated, whilst in the elegantly furnished dining room guests can enjoy two or four course dinners to suit every appetite. Breakfast is served in the conservatory, and light lunches are also available for guests. There are seven very peaceful bedrooms, all with telephone, colour TV and tea-making facilities, and all are beautifully decorated, with co-ordinated wall paper and fabrics. A well-modernized, self-catering Coach House is available, which includes three double bedrooms with en suite facilities. The sea is just half an hour away, with windsurfing, sailing and fishing at Rock. There are several National Trust Houses nearby as well as golfing, riding and birdwatching. Mr. and Mrs. Gray and family will make you very welcome, and I know you will enjoy the charm and peace of Penhallow Manor. Room and breakfast from £70.00 for two people per night, or £350.00 per week for two.

ALTON HOUSE HOTEL

Normandy Street, Alton, Hampshire GU34 1DW

Telephone: (0420) 80033 *Fax: 0420 89222*

London 54, Guildford 18, Farnham 7, Winchester 17, Southampton 30

F licence; 38 en suite bedrooms (2 ground floor) all with telephone, TV & welcome tray; 2 honeymoon suites, 2 family rooms; room and night service;last orders for dinner 9.30 p.m.; bar meals; special diets; children welcome; guide dogs only accepted; conferences max. 180; tennis, billiards & snooker; outdoor heated swimming pool; sauna and squash courts 300 metres; leisure centre, solarium, gymnasium, golf and riding ½ mile; spa pool 1 mile; shooting and fishing 2 miles; Skirmish 1 mile; 2 acres of gardens; open all year; major credit cards accepted.

The Alton House Hotel is ideally situated for access to the centre of the old market town of Alton. The town retains much of its original charm, and has a fascinating selection of shops. The hotel has an impressive modern Georgian elevation, set back from the road, with 95 car parking spaces. Facilities are really excellent; much thought and attention to detail has created a sophisticated atmosphere throughout the hotel's public rooms, guest rooms, conference facilities and banqueting hall. O'Connors Restaurant is light and very attractive. Excellent cuisine can be enjoyed with varied choice from table d'hôte and à la carte menus. A fine wine list complements the well chosen menus and service is discreet, friendly and attentive. The stylish Old Town Bar is adorned with historic photographs of Alton. The Fountain Lounge is a dramatic focal point of the hotel. An indoor fountain, street lights and picture windows overlooking the wonderful gardens make this room a sheer delight. In the grounds two floodlit tennis courts and a large outdoor heated swimming pool are to be found. Conference facilities are superb. Room and breakfast in the week from £45.00 single, and £60.00 double, weekends from £34.00 single, £44.00 double.

THE GRANGE HOTEL

17/19 London Road, Alton,
Hampshire GU34 4EG

Telephone: (0420) 86565 *Fax: 0420 541 346*

London 54, Guildford 18, Farnham 7

F licence; 34 en suite bedrooms (7 ground floor), all with colour TV, telephone and full central heating; last orders 9.00 p.m.; bar meals; diets by arrangement; baby listening; dogs by prior arrangement; conferences up to 30; outdoor swimming pool; putting green; croquet; all credit cards accepted.

The Grange Hotel is run under the personal direction of the resident proprietors, Andrea and David Levene. Situated on the outskirts of the charming little town of Alton, it is ideally placed for railway buffs to explore the famous Watercress Line running through the lovely Hampshire countryside. Jane Austen's house is a short drive away and well worth a visit. The main reception rooms of the hotel, which feature open wood fires, have all recently been refurbished and the number of bedrooms increased. The restaurant, which overlooks two acres of well tended gardens, is brightened still more by the vases of flowers on all the tables; both à la carte and table d'hôte menus are available. The individually decorated bedrooms (no two are alike), are soft and pretty, and are equipped with trouserpress and hairdryer as well as TV and direct dial telephone. Business meetings, conferences and private functions are all willingly undertaken. Room and breakfast from £45.00 single, £59.50 double. Always open.

KIRKSTONE FOOT HOTEL
Ambleside, Cumbria LA22 9EH

Telephone: (05394) 32232

London 300, Kendal 13, Keswick 17, Penrith 30

R and R licence; 15 en suite bedrooms; full central heating; meals to 8.30 p.m.; diets; children welcome; dogs in annexe only; sailing, boating, golf, tennis, squash, riding and fishing nearby; 13 self-catering units.

The standard of hotels in the Lake District has, over the last few years, improved immensely. The Kirkstone Foot Country House Hotel has, in my opinion, improved more than any other. Since taking over some years ago, Mr. and Mrs. Bateman have brought the standard of comfort and décor in both bedrooms and public rooms to well above that which the most discerning traveller can expect. Recently their daughter Annabel and her husband Andrew have joined the staff, making this a truly family operation. The fresh milk and fine bone china on the bedroom tea tray, the tasteful and comfortable décor throughout and the immaculate gardens all reflect the thought and precision that is applied to the running of this peaceful country house. Then there is the food. The new chef, Victor Sharratt, maintains the same high standards and menus of the past, but now vegetarian and fish dishes are offered as an alternative to the usual roast, to cater for the increase in personal diet awareness. Mr. Bateman, a connoisseur and an organiser of the local wine circle, serves and will advise on the wines from a most comprehensive list. He also rounds off the evening by passing round a most superior port with the cheese. This is without doubt one of the best hotels in this price range that I have ever visited. Dinner, room and breakfast from £35.00 per person per day. See also Bargain Breaks section.

NANNY BROW COUNTRY HOUSE HOTEL

Clappersgate, Ambleside, Cumbria LA22 9NF

Telephone: (05394) 32036. *Fax: 05394 32036*

Ambleside 1, Kendal 13, Manchester 90, Windermere 4, Keswick 18, London 300.

R and R licence; 19 bedrooms, 6 ground floor, all with private bathrooms, radio, room telephone and TV; 8 luxury garden view suites all with own lounge area; dinner 7.30 to 9.00 p.m.; special diets; children welcome; baby listening; dogs in Garden Wing; conferences; solarium and spa bath; lake bathing, sailing and boating 1 mile; tennis 1 mile; indoor swimming pool and squash 2 miles; riding 3 miles; golf 5 miles; fishing on own stretch of River Brathay; uninterrupted views of the valley and mountains; Visa and Access accepted.

I kept hearing good reports of this hotel and on visiting it I found them all to be true. Set on a hill, away from the summer crowds and in five acres of delightful gardens is this elegant Country House. It is now most tastefully and comfortably decorated and furnished, and it offers the peace and quiet for which people look in the Lake District but so seldom find. Add to this that the hotel has won awards for its good food and accommodation, and you have an excellent base from which to tour the area. There are, of course, all the many outdoor sporting activities for which the Lakes are famous, but to me this hotel is one in which to relax amongst the beautiful scenery and to indulge oneself. Bed and breakfast from £48.00 single, to £73.00 per person double; dinner, bed and breakfast from £55.00 single to £80.00 double including VAT. Open all year.

ROTHAY MANOR HOTEL
Ambleside, Cumbria LA22 0EH

Telephone: (05394) 33605 *Fax: 05394 33607*

London 280, Kendal 13, Coniston 8, Keswick 18, Grasmere 5

R and R licence; 15 en suite bedrooms (3 ground floor) all with room telephone, colour TV, radio; 3 suites in lodge in grounds; full central heating; meals to 9.00 p.m.; diets; children welcome; croquet; badminton and golf 5 miles; riding 4 miles; squash 1 mile; sailing and boating ½ mile; tennis and fishing ¼ mile; Amex, Access, Visa, Diners cards accepted.

If you believe, as I do, that one of the main ingredients of civilised life is good food and wine taken in comfortable surroundings, then Rothay Manor is, without doubt, one of the finest venues in which to enjoy that life. Rothay Manor has been voted top of the list by a publication on hotel breakfasts and the excellence of the lunches and dinners complements the sumptuous surroundings. Comfortable antiques all around, fresh flowers in abundance and the feeling of warmth and well-being everywhere. The whole ambience is orchestrated by Nigel and Stephen Nixon and their wives. These impressions were echoed by many of the other guests to whom I spoke and, even from the elegant brochure, you too will begin to feel the atmosphere of Rothay Manor. It seems unnecessary to add that the surrounding mountains, lakes and the air of the Lake District make a superb backdrop and atmosphere in which to indulge these pleasures. Room and breakfast from £63.00 single, £88.00–£98.00 double and suite £126.00. Closed the beginning of January and the first week in February.

WATEREDGE HOTEL

Borrans Road, Ambleside, Cumbria LA22 0EP

Telephone: (05394) 32332 *Fax: 05394 32332*

London 300, Kendal 13, Keswick 17, Penrith 30

R licence; 23 en suite bedrooms (5 ground floor), all with radio, TV and telephone, complementary morning tea and coffee tray; TV lounge; full central heating; diets; children over 7 welcome; dogs not allowed in public rooms or suites; small conferences; lake bathing; sailing and boating; fishing; private jetty for guests' use; Access, Amex and Visa credit cards accepted.

It is not often that one comes across a hotel that has excellent food, is immaculately and comfortably furnished and decorated, and yet is perfectly situated, but the Wateredge Hotel is exactly that. With its gardens running down to Lake Windermere, with its beautiful views from the public rooms, with its delightful bedrooms and delicious meals, it makes an idyllic venue for a holiday in the Lake District. Not only is there the peace and quiet of the hotel itself, but there is the tranquillity of a stroll on the nearby fells to be enjoyed. For those seeking a more active time, there is boating and fishing on the doorstep, there are sporting facilities of all kinds, both indoor and out, in the immediate vicinity. In addition, Ambleside is a lively and bustling town with everything that a holiday maker or tourist could need. The Wateredge is an unpretentious, ''honest to goodness'' hotel which makes any visit to the Lake District well worth while. Dinner, room and breakfast from £48.50 single, £84.00 twin. Closed December and January.

SKELWITH BRIDGE HOTEL

Nr. Ambleside, Cumbria LA22 9NJ

Telephone: (05394) 32115 *Fax: 05394 34254*

London 280, Windermere 7, Kendal 15, Carlisle 48, Manchester 90

F licence; 29 en suite bedrooms, all with TV, radio, direct dial telephone; full central heating; late meals to 9.00 p.m.; diets; children welcome, baby listening; dogs welcome; conferences 10 to 40 persons; sauna, solarium, indoor swimming pool, sailing, boating, tennis, squash, water skiing, all 2 miles; river bathing; golf 5 miles; riding and pony trekking; private river fishing; sail board for hire; hunting fox, hares nearby; Access, Visa credit cards accepted.

This hotel was taken over by Mr. and Mrs. Chamberlain some years ago. Since then it has been continuously improved and has built up a very well deserved reputation for good food and hospitality. The hotel is ideally situated for exploring all that is best in the Lake District. What a delight it is to return to the warmth and comfort of the Skelwith Bridge after, let us say, a strenuous day's walking amongst the superb scenery of Langdale, with its river and pikes, or after fishing or boating on Windermere (only a few minutes away)! The hotel is in fact so centrally situated that any part of the Lake District is within easy reach. The atmosphere of the hotel, originally a 17th century inn, is enhanced by the open fires, the oak beams, the antiques that surround you, and the comfort extended by furnishings which are all in keeping with the décor. The bedrooms are warm and cosy and have all the modern conveniences that travellers and holiday makers have come to expect today. Room and breakfast from £22.00, weekly from £180.00 half board. Dinner £15.95, Sunday lunch £8.25, non residents most welcome. Special breaks available. Open all year.

THE CROWN OF CRUCIS

Ampney Crucis, Cirencester, Gloucestershire GL7 5RS

Telephone: (0285) 851806 *Fax: 0285 851735*

Cheltenham 13, Circencester 2, London 70, Swindon 10, Stratford 35, Burford 15

F licence; 26 bedrooms (14 on ground floor), with private bathrooms, telephone, colour TV and central heating; last orders 10.00 p.m.; bar meals – lunch, and dinner until 10.00 p.m.; diets; children welcome, baby listening; dogs accepted by arrangement; conferences up to 70 welcome; golf and tennis nearby; hotel open all year (except Christmas Day); Credit cards accepted.

You will find The Crown of Crucis a couple of miles out of Cirencester on the A417 Lechlade road. It has got quite a history as it was originally a coaching Inn for people travelling to or from London; now it is in the experienced hands of hotelier Ken Mills and his wife, Tessa. They have in the past few years added on 26 double rooms and large well designed Function Room, all of which surround a garden courtyard. All the rooms are tastefully furnished and thoughtfully equipped. Most overlook the pretty Ampney Brook and the village cricket ground. The restaurant offers a good selection of food from the à la carte menu which is available seven days a week. For a less formal meal, the bar snacks are interesting and varied, and good value, both for lunch and evening meals. The bar has a warm and friendly atmosphere, and in winter log fires burn, adding to the air of cheery welcome. Ampney Crucis is the largest of the four "Ampney" villages, and is typical of the beautiful Cotswold countryside. The Crown of Crucis is an ideal base, whether for touring or business, or just passing through. Room and breakfast from £43.00 single, £54.00 double.

APPLEBY MANOR HOTEL

Appleby-in-Westmorland, Cumbria CA16 6DJ

Telephone: (07683) 51571 *Telex: 94012971*

A1 Scotch Corner 38, M6 (Junctions 38 & 40) 13, Keswick 31, Kendal 25, Ullswater 15, Penrith 13

F licence; 30 en suite bedrooms (10 ground floor), all with telephone, hairdryers, colour TV, video film channel; last orders 9.00 p.m.; diets; children welcome, baby listening; dogs in coach-house bedrooms only; conferences up to 30; games room; snooker and pool; indoor heated swimming pool; jacuzzi; sauna and solarium; leisure centre; squash ½ mile; fishing locally; riding and golf 2 miles; hotel closed only on 3 days of Christmas; Visa, Access, Amex and Diners Cards accepted.

Appleby Manor stands on a hill commanding views of the historic little town, its romantic castle and the sweeping countryside and fells beyond. Within, you will find an old fashioned, friendly courtesy. However, it also offers such modern luxuries as remote control TV, direct dial telephone, a hospitality tray and a leisure centre where you can bake, bubble and bathe to your heart's content. The bedrooms are comfortable, and furnished in keeping with the period of the house and there is a Coach House conversion, offering more contemporary accommodation, which is also suitable for disabled people. After the recent alterations, the new lounge has superb views over Appleby and its Castle. The lovely new dining room is informal and you can relax over a good table d'hôte menu, well presented and satisfying, or choose from one of the three other menus on offer. The wine list offers a good selection of wines from 18 countries and the bar has a broad range of malt whiskies. There is plenty to see and do locally, there are walks to suit all abilities and golf, fishing and riding are available nearby. The border counties, including Hadrian's Wall and the Roman Camps are within easy motoring distance, as are the Lake District, the high Pennines and the Yorkshire Dales. Prices per person start at £32.50 for bed and breakfast, £42.00 for dinner, bed and breakfast; weekly rates from £270.00, including dinner, bed and breakfast.

ROYAL OAK INN

Bongate, Appleby-in-Westmorland,
Cumbria CA16 6UN

Telephone: (07683) 51463

Carlisle 30, Scotch Corner 38, Penrith 13, M6 Junctions 38 & 40–both 13

F licence; 8 bedrooms, 5 with en suite baths, all with colour TV; full central heating; last orders 9.00 p.m.; bar meals; diets by arrangement; children welcome; small meetings catered for; outdoor swimming pool nearby; golf, squash, badminton, riding, shooting, fishing nearby; Access, Amex, Diners, Visa credit cards accepted.

Appleby is the old county town of Westmorland. It is dominated by the castle and full of historic buildings. Close to where the Romans forded the beautiful River Eden and in the oldest part of the town is The Royal Oak Inn. It is believed that parts of the building date back as far as the twelfth century and this long, black and white building retains all of its original charm yet has all the modern conveniences that make travelling today such a pleasure. Comfort and warmth are the keynote here; log fires burn and antiques glow in the public rooms where you can enjoy the peace and quiet and sample the hand-pumped ale or try some of the specially selected malt whiskies. To complete the sense of well being that the Royal Oak imparts, the food is delicious. The most appetising dishes can be chosen from a very varied menu and there is an excellent wine list to complement this. For those exploring Appleby, the Eden Valley, the northern Pennines or even the Lake District and Yorkshire, which are both easily accessible by car, here is a superb venue from which to do so. Room and breakfast from £18.50 single, £25.00 per person double, with en suite facilities. Open all year.

F licence; 19 en suite bedrooms all with telephone, col. TV, full central heating; night service; last orders 9.30 p.m.; bar meals, diets; children welcome; baby listening; conferences max. 20; outdoor heated swimming pool; fishing and squash close by; golf & shooting 4 miles; riding 6 miles; Access and Visa cards accepted.

TUFTON ARMS HOTEL

Appleby-in-Westmorland, Cumbria CA16 6XA

Telephone: (07683) 51593 *Fax: 07683 52761*

Carlisle 36, Kendal 33, Lake District 16

The town of Appleby has grown up around the feet of the castle. Its main street runs down the hill from the castle, and opens into a square, one side of which is dominated by a church with picturesque archways, another by the Tufton Arms itself. For a long time it was a coaching inn, but today it is a first class hotel. Its new owners, the Milsom family, have woken it from years of torpor, renovated every room from cellar to attic, filled it with a comfortable mixture of antique and modern furnishings, and are still full of plans for further improvement. They have created a happy atmosphere, composed of hospitality, enthusiasm and cheerful service. The hotel is a family affair with brothers Nigel and David playing prominent roles. In the dining room, David provides imaginative meals, beautifully cooked and presented, with a good wine list to accompany them. Before dining, guests can enjoy a drink in the warmly decorated panelled bar, or in the elegant and comfortable drawing room. The bedrooms, all very well appointed, offer a variety of accommodation from single rooms to suites. I foresee this hotel becoming very popular with sportsmen, as it offers a variety of fishing and shooting, and Appleby boasts an 18 hole golf course. Add to this, the easy access for the tourist to The Lakes, The Dales and the Border country and you have a unique hotel, offering its guests excellent value. Tariff on application. Hotel open all year.

DWELDAPILTON HALL HOTEL

Appleton-le-Moors, N. Yorkshire YO6 6TF

Telephone: (075 15) 227

London 232, York 33, Whitby 26, Scarborough 24, Thirsk 24, Malton 15

R and R licence; 10 en suite bedrooms, including 2 suites and a four poster, all with TV; full central heating; lift; meals to 8.30 p.m.; diets; no children; dogs welcome; golf 1½ miles, riding 3 miles, fishing by arrangement; Access, Amex, Visa credit cards accepted.

If you are looking for peace and tranquillity away from the usual tourist routes, then here at Dweldapilton Hall is the hotel for which you have been searching. The Hall is an English Country House which has been converted to form a most comfortable hotel with all its bedrooms en suite. There are magnificent views, especially from the elegant lounge with its comfortable furniture and log fire. As the days grow longer and warmer, afternoon tea is served on the terrace. The Hall is situated at the end of the picturesque and historic village of Appleton-le-Moors. Inside, there is a cosy bar serving over 50 brands of whisky, apart from the normal range of drinks. A new chef, using the freshest of ingredients, produces a delicious range of English dishes which are available throughout the day and evening. One day is hardly enough time to enjoy this hotel and its lovely surroundings, and special breaks are available for those wishing to stay longer. Room and breakfast from £38.00. Open all year round.

THE ROYAL BERKSHIRE
Sunninghill, Ascot SL5 0PP

Telephone: (0344) 23322 *Fax: 0344 27100*

London 25, Ascot 1, Windsor 5, Henley 18, Heathrow 15

F licence; 82 en suite rooms (17 ground floor), all with telephone, colour TV, radio, hairdrier, trouser press; suites; 24-hour room and laundry service; late meals to 10.00 p.m.; full central heating; diets; children welcome; dogs welcome; sauna; indoor heated swimming pool; croquet; 2 hard tennis courts; telex, facsimile; all major credit cards accepted.

The Royal Berkshire, a spectacular Queen Anne mansion built in 1705, once the home of the Churchill family, is set in fifteen glorious acres of parkland and formal gardens. The hotel has recently been completely refurbished and the owners, Hilton International, have been careful to retain the individual character and ambience of the building. The furnishings and fittings are luxurious, with much use of natural lighting and pastel colours. The imaginative yet contemporary menu puts local seasonal produce to excellent use, and the Head Chef achieves particularly high standards with the individually prepared dishes. The wine list is comprehensive with examples from the major wine producing nations, as well as a special section for lesser known areas. In addition to the sporting facilities listed here, the hotel is just a mile from Ascot Race Course, and the same distance from both Sunningdale and Wentworth Golf Courses. Smith's Lawn, and Guards Club Polo are only five minutes away, and Virginia Water about two miles. Single bedroom from £100.00, double bedroom from £120.00 inclusive of VAT and service. Open all year.

HOLNE CHASE HOTEL

Nr. Ashburton, Devon TQ13 7NS

Telephone: Poundsgate (036 43) 471 *Fax: 03643 453*

London 192, Plymouth 27, Exeter 19, Torquay 13, Tavistock 19

R and R licence; 14 bedrooms (1 ground floor, 2 annexe), all en suite (13 with bath, 1 with shower); 1 four-poster suite; all with direct dial telephone, tea/coffee making facilities; full room service 7.30 a.m.–10.30 p.m. (not in cottage); porterage; central heating; log fires; drying room; diets; children welcome; dogs welcome; conferences max. 30; salmon trout fishing; riding nearby; golf 6 miles; separate cottage annexe with 2 en suite bedrooms; all major credit cards.

The Holne Chase is an early 19th century house, situated 3 miles west of Ashburton on the Two Bridges and Tavistock road, set in 27 acres of well wooded grounds in the Dartmoor National Park. All the public rooms command fabulous views of the Dart Valley. The owners, Kenneth, Mary and Hugh Bromage, run a friendly and efficient hotel, with an air of good living and minimum formality. All the bedrooms are decorated and equipped to a very high standard and offer many unexpected delights. Thanks to the enthusiastic young chefs and the proprietors' personal supervision, you will be well satisfied with their dishes, which are interesting and presented to a very high standard. During a recent visit I was particularly interested to find how careful buying can still produce an excellent wine list at sensible prices. All who visit Holne Chase will want to come again, for it offers an environment for a peaceful and healthy holiday, inviting to both the young and old, who will be looked after by a staff who are cheerful and attentive. Room and breakfast from £55.00 single, £80.00 double, including VAT. Half board terms and Winter rates available on request. Open all year. English Tourist Board Four Crown commended. A member of Inter Hotels – Relais du Silence.

EASTWELL MANOR

Boughton Lees, Nr. Ashford, Kent TN25 4HR

Telephone: (0233) 635751 Telex: 966281 EMANOR Fax: 0233 635530

London 57, Rye 27, Canterbury 13, Heathrow 61, Gatwick 54, Lydd Airport 16

F licence; 23 en suite bedrooms (4 on ground floor), all with radio, telephone and TV; full central heating; lift; night service; meals to 9.30 p.m.; diets; children welcome; baby listening; conferences; billiards; tennis; shooting; fishing; riding by arrangement; all major credit cards accepted.

Eastwell Manor is 30 minutes drive from Dover and within easy reach of the M2 and M20 motorways, and is convenient for London and the airports. This hotel is renowned for the luxury, space and graciousness of both the bedrooms and the reception rooms. Its restaurant is unsurpassed for excellence of cuisine — superbly presented in beautifully panelled surroundings. The cellars are well stocked with bottles of choice French wine. The Manor is found up a long, winding drive, nestling in 3,000 acres of undulating Kent parkland on the edge of the Northern Downs. A more peaceful setting and delightful hotel would be hard to find. For those who like to venture out there are a multitude of houses, gardens, castles and vistas to be viewed with Canterbury only a stone's throw away — with its beautiful Cathedral and lovely shopping areas. Open all year. Room and breakfast from £85.00 single, £100.00 twin. Special Greatstay Weekend and midweek breaks available for 2 nights or more. See Bargain Breaks section for details.

CHAPEL HOUSE

Atherstone, Warwickshire CV9 1EY

Telephone: (0827) 718949

Burton 15, Coventry 12, Lichfield 10, Birmingham 16, N.E.C. 8

R & R licence; 13 rooms, 11 en suite, 2 with shower, all with radio, direct dial telephone & colour TV, full central heating; last orders 9.30 p.m.; diets; conferences max. 20; Diners, Access and Visa credit cards accepted.

Thirteen years ago, David and Pat Roberts and their four children moved into Chapel House, which was the original Dower House to the old Atherstone Hall. They began by providing good quality overnight accommodation and the Restaurant was started later — in October 1982. Their reputation for good food has grown to such an extent that it is now a small hotel with eleven bedrooms, all of which have the added personal touches of china ornaments and magazines. The drawing room and conservatory both overlook the well-stocked walled garden. There is a new ornamental pool and it is floodlit throughout the year. The restaurant is open to non-residents from Monday until Saturday and the menu is changed on a five-weekly basis. There is a wide choice of freshly prepared food and a four-course dinner will only cost £18.50. House meals are available Monday to Saturday for residents at £10.50 (last orders 7 p.m.). The dining room was the old drawing room back in 1879 and it has been restored in traditional style which reflects the grace and elegance of a bygone era. Atherstone is well placed for easy access to the midland motorways for the M42 is only a couple of miles away and there are many interesting places to visit nearby. Chapel House is found in a quiet corner of this old market town and I found a warm welcome in this family run hotel, but be sure to book in advance. Single room and breakfast from £32.50, double from £48.00. Closed Christmas and Boxing Day. Details of Bargain Breaks on application.

ROSE AND CROWN HOTEL

Bainbridge, Wensleydale, North Yorkshire DL8 3EE

Telephone: (0969) 50225

London 250, Leeds 55, York 60, Newcastle 70

F licence; 12 en suite bedrooms, all with colour TV and full central heating; last orders 9.30 p.m.; bar meals, diets; children welcome; dogs allowed; day conferences up to 100; private functions; pool table; fishing from hotel; Access and Visa cards accepted.

For *Signpost* readers who have had enough of the grand hotel and are looking for a simpler venue from which to explore either Yorkshire, Lancashire or Cumbria, then the Rose and Crown offers the best of alternatives. Situated overlooking the Green and village of Bainbridge in some of the loveliest of English countryside, it surely is in a prime position for a small hotel. Originally built in 1445, the hotel is now run by the Collins family and the personal touch is always evident. The furnishings and décor are warm and comfortable, including log fires and original beamed ceilings. The food, all of which is home made, is prepared from local produce wherever possible, and this is reflected by the number of regional dishes on the menu. The Rose and Crown makes a super base from which to immerse oneself in the immediate surroundings or to tour a vast area containing all that is best in the North of England. Open all year. Room and breakfast start at £29.00 per person and weekly rates for dinner, bed and breakfast, from £280.00.

HASSOP HALL HOTEL

Hassop, Nr. Bakewell, Derbyshire DE4 1NS

Telephone: (062987) 488 *Telex: 378485 HASSOP G* *Fax: 062987 577*

Bakewell 2½, Sheffield 14, Buxton 14, Chesterfield 14

R and R licence; 12 en suite bedrooms, all with radio, telephone, TV; full central heating; lift; phone only night service; meals to 9.30 p.m.; diets; children welcome; dogs at hotel's discretion; small conferences; dancing over New Year; all weather tennis; golf, riding and fishing nearby. Most credit cards accepted.

Mr. and Mrs. Chapman, owners of Hassop Hall Hotel, are justifiably proud of their beautiful and historic home. The original house was mentioned in the Domesday Book and the Chapmans have lived there since 1975. The gardens are beautifully stocked and have breathtaking scenery, including a lake view. Restoration is underway on a magnificent and historic ballroom in the hotel grounds. The elegant bar is reputed to be from Sheffield Castle. The staff are charming and courteous and nothing is too much trouble for them. A conference room is available, also a very special bridal suite. Golf and fishing are nearby, and croquet and a hard tennis court are in the grounds. There are helicopter landing facilities. The excellent dinner menu is most comprehensive, and the wine list varied. From Tuesday to Friday a special two course luncheon is offered at £7.95 including coffee and VAT. Single room from £65.00, twin from £75.00, both plus breakfast which is normally served in the room. Winter breaks are available from 1st November to 31st March. Always open except for 3 days at Christmas.

WAREN HOUSE HOTEL AND RESTAURANT

Waren Mill, Bamburgh, Northumberland NE70 7EE
Telephone: (06684) 581 *Fax: 06684 484*

Berwick 14, Alnwick 14, Newcastle 45, London 350

F licence; 8 en suite bedrooms, all with telephone, colour TV; last orders 8.00 p.m. winter, 8.30 p.m. summer; diets; no children; no dogs; croquet lawn and tennis court; sea-bathing, riding; bird-watching; local sailing and boating; 7 golf courses within 12 miles; shooting and fishing by arrangement; major credit cards accepted.

The North-East coast offers few hotels of distinction, but Waren House is one of those few which can boast of an exceptional quality. For here, where the comfort of the public rooms and the bedrooms, and the cuisine are all unexpectedly good, there is the bonus of that rare ingredient, peace and tranquillity. The Edwardian Suite particularly, provides all the luxury and comfort one would expect from a hotel such as this. It is furnished with antiques which have been in owner, Peter Laverack's family, for over one hundred years, and on arriving here, you can unwind over the complimentary sherry with which the room is provided. Only 2 miles from the bustling A1 trunk road, the hotel's 6 acres of gardens are home to a multitude of birds whose songs harmonize with the calls of the waders, geese and sea-birds on Budle Bay sanctuary. Waren House is a haven for the ornithologist; a visit to the Farn Islands is an experience never to be forgotten. For the historian, the wonders of Lindisfarne and the castles of Bamburgh, Alnwick, Dunstanburgh and Warksworth are only a few minutes drive away. Most of all, however, I would recommend a visit here not only for the delights of the hotel, but for the joy of discovering the wilderness and solitude of this beautiful part of England. Waren House Hotel is situated on the B1342 Bamburgh-Belford road and is just 2 miles from the A1. Room and breakfast from £35.00 per person, double occupancy. Edwardian Suite – minimum stay 2 nights, from £100.00. No smoking rooms available. RAC 3 Star, ETB 4 Crown Commended.

DOWNREW HOUSE

Bishops Tawton, Nr. Barnstaple,
North Devon EX32 0DY

Telephone: (0271) 42497/46673 Fax: 0271 23947

Barnstaple 3, Bideford 8

R & R licence; 12 en suite bedrooms (3 ground floor), all with telephone, colour TV and full central heating; last orders 9.15 p.m.; bar snacks; diets; children over 7 years welcome; dogs allowed; conferences up to 12; games room; billiards; outdoor heated swimming pool; solarium, golf, croquet and tennis; fishing 1 mile; sauna, squash, badminton and leisure centre 3 miles; riding 5 miles; shooting, sea bathing, sailing and boating 8 miles; Visa and Access cards welcome.

Downrew is a small Queen Anne Country House with lodge, 3 miles south of Barnstaple on the slopes of Codden Hill. The original building dates from 1640 and was enlarged in 1705. It stands in 12 acres of meadowland, well kept gardens and has its own 5-hole 15 approach golf course. The resident proprietors have created a wonderfully warm and friendly atmosphere, which is peaceful and relaxing. Care, and attention to detail are the hallmarks of this delightful house, with service of the highest order under the personal supervision of the owners. Downrew House is very comfortable, filled with lovely period furniture. The elegant drawing room with its log fire, overlooks the garden, and adjoins the sitting room. The dining room's magnificent 18ft bow window looks over the lawns, rose beds and the surrounding countryside, towards Dartmoor in the far distance. I enjoyed an excellent dinner, carefully cooked and well presented, with many of the fruits and vegetables being homegrown. A well stocked bar and specially chosen wines complement the delicious food. The hotel is open all year round. Dinner, room and breakfast from £54.50 per day including VAT. No service charge.

HALMPSTONE MANOR

Bishops Tawton, Nr. Barnstaple, Devon EX32 0EA

Telephone. (0271) 830321 *Fax: 0271 830826*

Barnstaple 4, Bideford 8

R licence; 5 bedrooms, all with en suite bathroom, telephone and TV; last orders for dinner 9.30 p.m.; special diets; conferences up to 12; riding, shooting and fishing 1 mile; leisure centre, squash and tennis courts 5 miles; sailing and boating 6 miles; sea bathing and golf 8 miles; hotel open all year; Visa, Master Card and Amex accepted.

Halmpstone Manor, the family home of Jane and Charles Stanbury, is the English Country House Hotel at its very best. The Stanburys are never too busy to spend time with their guests, and their interest in their comfort is very evident. There are five bedrooms, two with four poster beds, and all are beautifully decorated with wonderfully luxurious bathrooms and magnificent views of the moors beyond. In winter, log fires blaze in the elegant peach and blue drawing room and the 16th century wood panelled dining room. Jane trained for a short time with the Roux brothers, and as a result her culinary skills are especially innovative and appetizing. The menu is extremely special. You could start with lightly poached oysters on a bed of spinach with a champagne sauce, and continue with noisettes of venison, with pears and cinnamon. As you would expect, there is an impressive and comprehensive wine list. There is much to do locally; perhaps a visit to the seal sanctuary on Lundy Island, or sightseeing at Buckland Abbey, Dartington glass, or a walk across lovely moorlands. Halmpstone is signposted off the A377 Barnstaple to Crediton road at the end of the village of Bishops Tawton. Room and breakfast from £60.00.

AUDLEYS WOOD COUNTRY HOUSE HOTEL

Basingstoke, Hampshire RG25 2JT

Telephone: (0256) 817555 *Telex: 858273* *Fax: 0256 817500*

F licence; 71 en suite bedrooms (34 ground floor) all with colour TV, telephone and full central heating; night service; last orders 10.00 p.m.; diets; children welcome, baby listening; dogs allowed; conferences up to 40; golf 3 miles; all major credit cards accepted.

A charming Victorian mansion, now a luxury Country House Hotel, Audleys Wood is set in 7 acres of lightly wooded parkland amidst the rolling Hampshire Downs. The hotel has beautifully furnished guest accommodation, elegant oak panelled reception rooms with large open fires and the restaurant, complete with Minstrels' gallery, is housed within the original Palm House Conservatory. Each of the principal meeting rooms has been carefully designed and decorated to suit intensive training courses, seminars and meetings, whilst the Simonds Room with its 17th Century oak panelled walls and magnificent oak table is ideal for boardroom meetings and private dinners. Leisure facilities include short croquet, putting green, golf driving net and petanque and a range of other activities can be organised either on site or locally such as archery, clay pigeon shooting, ballooning and fly fishing. The locality offers many places of historic interest; Chawton – home of Jane Austen, Stratfield Saye, the ancient city of Winchester and the delightful countryside of the New Forest and Watership Down to mention just a few. Whatever your reason for visiting the area, Audleys Wood is the perfect setting for both business and short breaks. Tariff on application.

BASINGSTOKE COUNTRY HOTEL

Nately Scures, Nr. Hook, Basingstoke
Hampshire RG27 9JS

Telephone: (0256) 764161 *Fax: 0256 768341*

London 40, Basingstoke 4, Winchester 18, Bournemouth 60

F licence; 70 en suite bedrooms (32 ground floor), all with colour TV, telephone and full central heating; lift; night service; last orders 9.45 p.m.; coffee shop; diets; children welcome, baby listening; dogs allowed; conferences up to 180; dancing monthly; indoor heated swimming pool; leisure centre; golf, tennis, squash, badminton, riding, shooting and fishing nearby; Amex, Visa, Diners and Mastercard accepted.

Set in 4½ acres of landscaped gardens, the Basingstoke Country Hotel is one of Hampshire's premier hotels. It is also a fine conference venue, for which it has a separate entrance and facilities that can cater superbly for up to 180 delegates. With air conditioning throughout, great care has been taken in furnishing and decorating the interior. The spacious bedrooms are very well appointed with everything the discerning guest could wish for, and there are six well thought out rooms available for the disabled. A beautifully designed conservatory has been added, with a very originally shaped ozone swimming pool. Included in this exciting complex is a fitness room and delightful garden restaurant, where the emphasis is on healthy eating, with salads and vegetarian dishes available all day. The Winchester Restaurant, named after the fifth Marquis of Winchester, who lived nearby at Basing House, serves excellent food from an exciting à la carte menu. The chef creates three course table d'hôte menus for lunch and dinner, all beautifully presented. The wine list is specially selected by Andrew Weir Vintners to complement the menus. Hotel open all year. Room and breakfast from £80.00 single, £90.00 double.

PHEASANT INN

Bassenthwaite Lake, Nr. Cockermouth,
Cumbria CA13 9YE

Telephone: (07687) 76234

London 295, Keswick 8, Cockermouth 5, Carlisle 25

F licence; 20 en suite bedrooms (3 ground floor); full central heating; late meals to 8.30 p.m.; diets; no smoking in dining room; children welcome; dogs in public rooms only; conferences up to 25; free golf locally; fishing; riding nearby; credit cards not accepted.

Dating from the 16th century, the Pheasant Inn has kept abreast of modern standards of comfort without losing any of its character and charm. Guests can enjoy bar snacks and real ale in the inn's original bar, which is traditionally furnished, or fine English food in the dining room, which retains its oak beams. You may be sure of finding a quiet corner in one of the three lounges, and the bedrooms are pleasantly furnished. It is heartwarming to return from any of the outdoor activities that may have brought you to this part of the Lake District and find the welcome of log fires and wholesome food, carefully prepared. The inn stands in a pleasant natural garden at the foot of Thornthwaite Forest and near to Bassenthwaite Lake. It would be hard to end a holiday in this peaceful setting without leaving for home completely relaxed and refreshed. For guests who want extra seclusion, there is a bungalow nearby. Room and breakfast from £45.00 single, £76.00 double. Inclusive terms for three days and over. Winter breaks available November to March. Closed on Christmas Day.

OVERWATER HALL

Ireby, Nr. Bassenthwaite Lake, Cumbria CA4 1HH

Telephone: (059 681) 566

London 310, Carlisle 22, Keswick 8

R and R licence; 13 en suite bedrooms, all rooms with radio, TV, hairdryers; telephone by arrangement; full central heating; late meals to 8.30 p.m.; children welcome; baby listening; dogs welcome; games room including billiards/snooker table; golf, riding, fishing, sailing all nearby; Access and Visa credit cards accepted.

To call Overwater Hall an hotel does not really do it justice. For here there is no cool receptionist to register you, hand you your key and then leave you to your own devices. No, here you are a guest in the beautiful Georgian mansion, and you are welcomed by Mrs. Kent herself, a lady to whom nothing seems too much trouble. This is also reflected in the furnishings and décor, for these have been carefully chosen to give the comfort of the modern era while preserving the atmosphere of the gracious old building. The colour schemes are restful and blend in to add to the air of tranquillity. What more can one ask for after a hard day's motoring or a strenuous day in the Lake District? The Hall is set in eighteen acres of beautiful mature woodlands and gardens, and, further afield lie Bassenthwaite, Keswick, Caldbeck and the surrounding lakes and fells. An ideal venue for any *Signposter* who, if he doesn't mind travelling, also has the Solway coast, the Pennines and the Scottish border country all within easy reach. Room and breakfast from £26.00 per person. Two day breaks from £66.00. Reduction for weekly terms. Closed January to mid-February.

COMBE GROVE MANOR HOTEL & COUNTRY CLUB

Brassknocker Hill, Monkton Combe,
Bath, Avon BA2 7HS

Telephone: (0225) 834644 *Fax: 0225 834961*

Bath 2, Exit 18 M4 Motorway 12

F licence; 10 bedrooms in hotel, 35 in Garden Lodge, all with en suite bathroom; telephone, TV, room and night service; last orders for dinner 9.30 p.m.; bar meals; conferences up to 40 in theatre; outdoor/indoor heated swimming pool; Country Club; sauna and solarium; 5-bed hydrospa; gymnasium; 3 squash courts; aerobics studio; steam room; 5-hole par three golf course, 17 station 2 tiered driving range, 9 hole mini putting course; 4 tennis courts; hotel open all year; all major credit cards accepted.

Over the past few years, I have been watching with interest the refurbishment of this Manor House and the creation of the Country Club. The Manor House is set on a hillside in sixty eight acres of gardens and woodland and has stunning views over the Limpley Stoke valley and yet is only two miles from the lovely Georgian town of Bath. The newly created Garden Lodge, adjacent to the Manor House, also has wonderful views and each bedroom has its own terrace. Within the Garden Lodge lies the Tapestry Room with superb conference facilities for up to 40 delegates. The Hotel has been tastefully decorated, all the bedrooms are most luxurious, each furnished in its own individual style. There is a beautiful drawing room and library enhanced by lots of fresh flowers and the dining room is equally attractive. Combe Grove Manor Hotel is personally supervised by its Manager, Mr. A. Parrilla who gave me a very warm welcome and is justifiably very proud of his establishment. For those who wish to have total relaxation with the opportunity of enjoying some of the finest country club sports and leisure facilities in the West Country whilst visiting this most interesting and beautiful part of England, I highly recommend a visit to Combe Grove Manor Hotel and Country Club. Room and Breakfast from £75.00 in the Garden Lodge and from £85.00 in the Manor House.

FOUNTAIN HOUSE

Lansdown Road, Bath, Avon BA1 5DV

Telephone: (0225) 338622 *Fax: 0225 445855*

London 105, Heathrow 75, Bristol 12

14 suites (one on ground floor), all have a sitting room with telephone and colour TV; 1, 2 or 3 bedrooms; 1 or 2 bathrooms; full central heating; lift; laundry/valet service; resident concierge; children welcome (baby sitting); dogs and cats accepted; garages; golf and tennis within two miles; squash, badminton, riding and shooting nearby; all credit cards accepted.

Bath is a beautiful and historic city, with many fascinating places to explore, both in the city centre and the surrounding area, and Fountain House offers a perfect base for any visitor. It is not, in fact, a hotel in the usual sense of the word, but a lovely Palladian Mansion which has been recently refurbished to enable the discerning traveller to enjoy all available luxuries yet maintain total independence. I was most impressed with the charming welcome I received from the staff and the owner of Fountain House, Mr Robin Bryan, who takes a lot of pride in the 'personal touch' of his establishment. All kitchens are well equipped and fully stocked with the necessary breakfast requirements, minibar and a basket of 'gourmet goodies'. Hot rolls, fresh milk and a newspaper are delivered to your suite each morning. Fountain House can make dinner reservations for you at any of Bath's superb restaurants, or arrange for groceries to be delivered, should you wish to entertain 'at home'. Room and breakfast start at £108.00 per couple per night. Open all year.

THE LANSDOWN GROVE HOTEL

Bath, Avon BA1 5EH

Telephone: (0225) 315891 *Telex: 444 850* *Fax: 0225 448092*

Bath 1

F licence; 46 en suite bedrooms; all with telephone, colour TV and full central heating; one lift; night service; last orders 9.30 p.m.; bar meals; diets; children welcome, baby listening; dogs allowed; conferences up to 100; sailing and boating, golf, tennis, squash and badminton, riding, shooting and fishing by arrangement; Master Card, Visa, Amex and Diners cards welcome.

Mr. and Mrs. Aubrey Jackman have owned this delightful hotel for many years. One of my greatest pleasures when visiting this splendid city of Bath is to be able to park my car when I arrive in Lansdown Grove! The hotel is a charming building, near the top of Lansdown Road, overlooking the town and set amidst a very pretty garden. Being a privately owned hotel, personally run by the Jackmans, with many longstanding members of staff, there is always a warm welcome and friendly service. The bedrooms are cheerful and comfortable with private bathrooms or shower, colour TV, telephone, radio and tea/coffee making facilities. The large and attractive restaurant offers excellent cuisine and a splendid wine list. As well as Bath itself, there are many places of interest in the vicinity, Glastonbury Abbey, Wookey Hole and Castle Combe to name but a few. Room and breakfast from £58.00, hotel open all year.

ROYAL CRESCENT HOTEL

Bath, Avon BA1 2LS

Telephone: (0225) 319090 *Telex: 444251* *Fax: 0225 339401*

Train Station 1, Heathrow 120, London 105, Bristol 12, Cheltenham 42, Gloucester 38, Wells 20

F licence; 44 en suite bedrooms (6 ground floor), all with telephone, colour TV; lift; night service; last orders 2.00 p.m. (lunch), 9.30 p.m. (dinner); children welcome; baby sitting; conferences max. 40; plunge pool, jacuzzis at the hotel; boating, golf, tennis, squash, shooting all nearby; Amex, Diners, Visa, Barclaycard, Access credit cards accepted.

The Royal Crescent Hotel, set within the central two houses of one of Europe's architectural masterpieces, offers facilities and service of the very highest quality within a most tranquil setting. I have dined here many times and always found the cuisine served in the Dower House restaurant to be worthy of the many honours it has received. Each of the bedrooms and suites is individually decorated and furnished to suit every taste, whether you prefer the intimate bedrooms or the grand suites with their elaborate plasterwork ceilings. The Royal Crescent Mews, which is situated overlooking the splendid gardens, is self-contained luxury, ideal for board meetings, private entertaining or simply that special occasion. Simon Combe and his staff will offer you a most warm and friendly welcome. Rooms from £90.00, suites from £240.00.

THE OLD SCHOOL HOUSE

Church Street, Bathford, Bath, Avon BA1 7RR

Telephone: (0225) 859593

Bath 3, London 110, Bristol 15, Oxford 50

R licence; 4 bedrooms all with en suite bathroom (1 suitable for disabled), telephone and television; last orders for dinner 9.00 p.m.; special diets; no pets; swimming pool, leisure centre and gymnasium, sauna and solarium, spa pool, squash – facilities all within 4 miles; golf 1½ miles; tennis 3 miles; riding 5 miles; credit cards accepted; hotel open all year.

This is a no-smoking house.

This pretty house is located in the lovely village of Bathford, and is a wonderful discovery, if you are looking for value for money, and the charm and welcome of a private home. Built in 1837, it stands on the site of the Old Manor Court Barn, and served for 140 years as the local village school until 1970 when it was converted to a private residence. Today, it is the home of Rodney and Sonia Stone, who take a great deal of pride in the services they offer. The four bedrooms are bright and cheerful, and cater for every possible need. One is made to feel like a welcome house-guest. With prior notice, Mrs. Stone can provide you with a romantic candle-lit dinner in the cosy dining room or in the garden conservatory. Of course, Bath is very near, and offers one of the prettiest theatres in the country and many restaurants and bistros for a night out. There are many historic places of interest to visit. The Old School House is located within a Conservation area, and is ideal for nature-lovers, who can wander through the wooded slopes, or gaze over the beautiful Avon Valley. If you are looking for something other than an ordinary hotel in this lovely part of England, I do recommend a stay in this lovely, friendly home. Room and breakfast from £35.00 single, £48.00 double. Weekly rates, £200.00 single, £270.00, double.

THE BEDFORD SWAN HOTEL

The Embankment, Bedford MK40 1RW

Telephone: (0234) 46565 *Fax: 0234 212009*

London 50, Cambridge 25, Oxford 50, Birmingham 65, Luton Airport 20, M1 (Junc. 13) 10, Woburn Abbey 15, Althorp 22

F licence; 122 bedrooms, all with en suite bathroom, TV and telephone; room and night service; lift; last orders for dinner Sun.–Fri. 9.30 p.m., Sat. 10.00 p.m.; sandwiches in bar; diets; children welcome; dogs by arrangement; conferences max. 300; indoor heated swimming pool; spa pool; tennis 1 and 3 miles; golf 3 miles; hotel open all year; credit cards accepted.

Recently, The Swan has undergone extensive restoration. It has an impressive new entrance, leading from a large car park, itself important to a town house hotel. I was amazed at the standard of the refurbishment; around every corner there was something to fascinate – the wonderful antiques, pictures and many other objets d'art. There are many places where you can sit and relax; my favourite was the old kitchen, with its original bread oven, now an open fireplace. In the other lounge, you can enjoy home made afternoon tea, a speciality of the hotel. The hotel's swimming pool is most impressive, decorated after the style of a Roman Bath, and is complete with heated floors. The centre piece of the restaurant is the original clock used to time the coaches, back in The Middle Ages. The first 'Swann Inn' was demolished in 1794, and rebuilt as a town house for the Duke of Bedford. There is an impressive, sweeping staircase which leads up to one of the Banqueting Halls, which like many of the rooms has lovely views over the River Ouse. The bedrooms are all very different, and extremely comfortable, leading off grand corridors lined with pictures and beautiful curtains. One corridor even retains the original Medieval stone wall. There are excellent table d'hôte and à la carte menus, changed daily. As there are no bar meals, you can eat as much as you wish in the Restaurant. Room and breakfast from £66.00 single, £72.00 double.

BOVEY HOUSE

Beer, Nr. Seaton, Devon EX12 3AD

Telephone: (029780) 241

London 153, Exeter 19, Lyme Regis 9, Seaton 3

R and R licence; 12 bedrooms (8 with private bath), all with colour TV, radio and telephone, tea/coffee making facilities; laundry room; late meals to 9 p.m.; salad/ wine bar; diets available; children welcome, baby listening service; dogs by arrangement; riding nearby, sea bathing, boating.

This historic 16th century manor house is situated in rolling farm and parkland between the seaside villages of Beer and Branscombe, only 2 miles from the sea and readily accessible to many places of interest. Bovey House is now owned and personally cared for by Mr. and Mrs. G. Cole and their daughter and son-in-law – Mr. and Mrs. L. Gosden. Much refurbishing has been done, but this lovely old country house, its historic surroundings and atmosphere have retained their charm. Bovey House once belonged to Catherine Parr, presented to her by Henry VIII as part of her dowry. Rumour has it that Charles II slept in the room named after him, it possessing one of the most flawless plaster ceilings I have ever seen. All bedrooms are comfortable and well appointed. The drawing room, with its beautiful Adam ceiling is spacious and elegant. In contrast, the dining room with its Tudor linen fold panelling and heavy beamed ceilings provides interesting table d'hôte and à la carte menus. There is a good choice and good presentation with much of the produce coming from the kitchen garden. Another attractive room is the Inglenooks Bar which is in the old part of the house; extremely good light lunches and evening fare, with fine wines are available. You feel that you can rest, relax and enjoy your stay as you would when visiting friends. Outside is an attractive walled garden. Room and breakfast from £28.00 (single), £41.00 (twin) inclusive of VAT. Open all year except January.

THE WILD BOAR HOTEL AND RESTAURANT

Beeston, Nr. Tarporley, Cheshire CW6 9NW

Telephone: (0829) 260 309 *Fax: 0829 261 081*

London 180, Birmingham 70

F licence; 37 en suite bedrooms (11 ground floor), all with colour TV, telephone and full central heating; night service; last orders 10.00 p.m.; bar meals, diets; children welcome, baby listening; dogs allowed; conferences up to 50; sailing, boating and golf nearby; riding, shooting and fishing by arrangement in the locality; credit cards accepted.

"The House That Jack Built"; thus my family dubbed the fascinating Wild Boar Hotel, as we travelled to and fro into Wales. So it was with much interest that I eventually paid it a visit. I found that the charming and witty old edifice with its many extensions, each different, but balancing and enhancing the whole, contained a modern and very comfortable hotel. It is run with commendable efficiency and hospitality by the manager, Miguel Hidalgo and his courteous staff. The bedrooms, housed in the latest extension, are very well appointed, extremely comfortable, have most pleasing colour schemes, and joy, instead of the ubiquitous duvets, the beds are furnished with crisp sheets, and blankets. In the earlier buildings, you will find an attractive and comfortable cocktail bar and the dining room where I enjoyed an excellent dinner. The menu offered traditional English and Continental cuisine, presented with imagination and style; the hotel is also justly proud of its wine list. Light lunches are served in the bar. There is plenty to see and do in the area, historic Chester is nearby and the old fortress of Beeston Castle is visible in the distance. The countryside is pleasant to wander through, and the Shropshire Union Canal flows gently nearby. The hotel offers weekends of special interest during the year, when it arranges such diversions as a voyage on the canal. Details of these, and the tariff can be obtained on application. Always open.

BIBURY COURT

Bibury, Gloucestershire GL7 5NT

Telephone: (028 574) 337 *Fax: 028 574 660*

London 86, Burford 10, Cheltenham 17, Cirencester 7, Kemble Station 10, Stow-on-the-Wold 14

F licence; 18 en suite bedrooms (3 single, 15 double/twin); 10 have four poster beds, and all have telephone, colour TV, razor socket; dogs welcome; small conferences; children welcome; river fishing; golf 8 miles.

This gracious mansion started life in 1633, and it has preserved its lovely appearance and peaceful, charming setting in an 8½ acre park, bordered by the River Coln, to this day. The hotel is run by Anne and Andrew Johnston, and Anne's sister Jane who give it a welcoming and friendly atmosphere. A most lovely panelled lounge with stone mullion windows leads from the flagstoned hall and the abundant fresh flowers and the attractive and comfortable furnishings make one feel really at home. The menus are very tempting. Chefs, Howard Morris and Andrew Seaton are in charge of the kitchen and Coach House restaurant. At lunchtime light snacks are available and in the evening you can choose from a wide range of dishes made from only the finest ingredients. Bibury is such a pretty village and there are many beautiful walks from the hotel itself. You can walk down the River Coln to Coln St Aldwyn, another charming village, in about 45 minutes and of course there are many other places of interest nearby — Bath, Oxford, Cirencester and Stratford-upon-Avon. If you are looking for good food, relaxation in a friendly home, and a warm welcome in a most beautiful part of the Cotswolds, then I highly recommend Bibury Court. Room and breakfast from £45.00–£50.00 single, £60.00–£66.00 double. Closed 23rd December–30th December.

THE ROYAL HOTEL

Barnstaple Street, Bideford, Devon EX39 4AE

Telephone: (0237) 472005 Telex: 42551 EXONIA G Fax: 0271 78558

London 203, Barnstaple 8, Exeter 48

F licence; 30 en suite bedrooms (2 ground floor), all with colour TV, telephone and full central heating; night service; last orders 9.00 p.m.; bar meals, diets; children welcome, baby listening; dogs allowed; conferences up to 60; dancing weekly; golf 1½ miles; sea bathing, sailing and boating 2 miles; leisure centre 8 miles; Access, Visa, Amex and Diners cards welcome.

The Royal Hotel overlooks the historic Bideford Bridge and picturesque Torridge Estuary, and combines four hundred years of history with every modern comfort. The Royal was transformed into a hotel 150 years ago, its most famous guest being Charles Kingsley, who penned *Westward Ho* here. The building is owned by the Brend family and is looked after personally by Richard Brend Jnr. Recently refurbished, you can now fully enjoy the historic and luxurious atmosphere of Bideford's leading hotel. From the reception area, you enter a fascinating lounge, the décor and furnishings of which give an air both of comfort and quality. The main bar is equally attractive, where you can enjoy a lunch time meal or an aperitif. There is a superb ballroom which can accommodate up to 250 people for dancing or special functions. As in all Brend Hotels, you can be assured of attentive service from a cheerful and obliging staff. The Royal has always enjoyed an excellent reputation for first class cuisine, complemented by a very fine wine list, selected from a well stocked cellar, which did service as a prison in the days of Judge Jeffries! Spacious, well-appointed bedrooms, are comfortable and restful. The Kingsley Room with its pine panelling and beautiful sculptured Venetian ceiling, and the Grenville Room are available for small functions. There are many lovely places to visit or discover in the area. Room and breakfast from £44.00 single, £33.00 (per person) twin, or weekly rates at £182.00. Other terms, including short breaks available on application. Open all year.

THE DRAGON HOUSE

Bilbrook, Nr. Minehead, Somerset TA24 6HQ

Telephone: (0984) 40215

London 162, Minehead 6, Dunster 3, Bridgwater 18, Taunton 18

R & R licence; 10 en suite bedrooms (1 ground floor) all with telephone and colour TV; full central heating; last orders 9 p.m.; light meals; diets; children welcome; baby listening; dogs accepted; conferences max. 45; sea bathing 1½ miles; fishing 1½ miles; sailing, boating, golf, riding 6 miles; shooting 10 miles; most credit cards accepted.

This delightful 17th century house is located on the south side of the A39 half a mile west of Washford. It is jointly owned by Dennis and Yvonne Munden and Joan Saw (sister of Dennis) who give careful attention and personal supervision to the needs and comfort of their guests — the hotel has a real family atmosphere. Set in 2½ acres of beautiful gardens, the Dragon House was originally a smugglers' drinking den but, in marked contrast, it later became a Methodist preaching house. Now it is a most attractive and comfortable hotel with a suntrap courtyard in summer and log fires in winter. The bedrooms are tastefully decorated and furnished and there is a very pleasant dining room with an extensive menu, excellent food including interesting vegetarian dishes, and a good wine list with wide choice. Service is both efficient and friendly. Light lunches and cream teas are served in the Garden Room all year. This is a very good centre for Exmoor National Park, the Quantocks, Dunster Castle and much lovely countryside. Room and full English breakfast from £35.00 single, £65.00 double, inclusive of VAT. Open all year including Christmas and New Year. See Bargain Break section.

OAKWOOD HALL HOTEL

Bingley, West Yorkshire BD16 4AW

Telephone: (0274) 564123/563569

Bradford 6, Keighley 4, Leeds 15, London 206

F licence; 16 en suite bedrooms (1 ground floor), all with telephone, col. TV, full central heating; night porter; late meals to 9.30 p.m.; diets; children welcome; conferences up to 20; Access, Amex, Barclaycard, Diners credit cards accepted.

Situated on the outskirts of the pretty market town of Bingley, in wooded surroundings, Oakwood Hall is a large Victorian listed building which has been most tastefully and comfortably decorated and furnished to provide all that the tourist or business person expects of a modern hotel, without detracting from the splendour that our forebears admired. A full à la carte menu of English and Continental cuisine is available, as are bar meals. It is perhaps superfluous to say that the food is exceptional, as is witnessed by the fact that many people from a wide area choose either to dine here or to hold private functions. The restaurant is open for lunches every day except Saturday. The Hotel is as much a perfect venue from which to conduct a business visit as it is an excellent centre from which to tour this lovely part of Yorkshire. Leeds, Bradford, Halifax and Harrogate are only a short drive from the hotel and within walking distance are the delights of the Aire Valley. The Leeds–Liverpool canal with the famous Bingley Five Rise Locks is a must for any tourist. Ilkley Moor, the Brontë country and the superb scenery around Skipton are also within easy motoring distance. Room rates – from £45.00 single, £80.00 double, inclusive of full English breakfast and VAT. Open all year, except for one week at Christmas.

NORTON PLACE HOTEL

180 Lifford Place, Kings Norton, Birmingham B30 3NT

Telephone: (021) 433 5656 *Fax: 021 433 3048*

Birmingham 5, Oxford 65, Cheltenham 35, Stratford upon Avon 20

R & R licence; 10 en suite ground floor bedrooms, 1 especially suited for disabled guests, 1 four poster suite; all with telephone, television with video and video library, trouser press & iron, wall safe; ceiling fans in most rooms; room and night service; last orders for dinner 10.00 p.m.; helicopter landing pad; light lunches; special diets; no children; no dogs allowed; 6 conference rooms for up to 100 delegates; fitness centre; laser and clay pigeon shooting; hotel open all year; credit cards accepted.

You would not expect to find an oasis of such luxury in the middle of Kings Norton, a suburb of busy Birmingham. Situated in secluded gardens, where flowers and trees abound among the fountains, is the Norton Place Hotel. The hotel has ten bedrooms of exceptional quality, with mini bars, home-made biscuits by the bed, fresh fruit and daily papers all provided for the added comfort of the guests. The bathrooms are spectacular, each having its own mural, and some have stained glass windows. Bathrobes and a wealth of Crabtree & Evelyn toiletries are provided. The Lombard Room has a high reputation for its cuisine, and the conservatory, where we relaxed before dinner was light and elegant. Dinner itself was superb; I chose poached paupiette of Dover sole in a chive butter sauce, with a ragout of shellfish. The chef, Paul Bingham, is becoming very well known for his original dishes and top presentation. I was impressed with the crystal and claret glasses, and I loved the marble plates. Within the hotel grounds are the Alexick Hall and The Patrick Collection of classic cars. Should it be conference facilities you require, then look no further. Everything is provided to ensure your day runs smoothly. From the moment you enter Norton Place, the staff do their utmost to look after you. Prices from £135.00 single, £155.00 double, including Continental breakfast.

THE PLOUGH AND HARROW HOTEL
Hagley Road, Edgbaston, Birmingham B16 8LS

Telephone: 021-454 4111 *Telex: 338074* *Fax: 021 454 1868*

London 112, Coventry 18, Stratford-upon-Avon 24, Wolverhampton 13, Bristol 88, Manchester 84
1 mile west of city centre on A456 leading to Junction 3 of M5

F licence; 44 en suite bedrooms including 3 suites, all with colour TV and radio; children welcome; night service; meals to 10.15 p.m. (last orders); conferences taken; diets available.

For more years than I care to remember, I have been a regular visitor to the Plough and Harrow and my parents were before me. The hotel has always been first class and yet has got better still as time has gone on in the care of the General Manager, Mr. Stuart Smith, and the Chef who was previously at the Ritz Hotel in London. The Restaurant now concentrates on seasonal specialities and a four course gourmet menu supplements a variety of dishes that are available à la carte. It is no wonder that many local businessmen have lunch at the hotel. The décor and furnishings throughout the hotel are in the very best of taste and I have yet to see any bedroom in which I would not be very happy to spend a night myself and have any hesitation in recommending to friends. Whether you are visiting Birmingham on business or for some social occasion, you will be extremely comfortable and well looked after at the Plough and Harrow. Single room from £98.00, double/twin from £112.00. Always open.

SWALLOW HOTEL

12 Hagley Road, Five Ways, Birmingham B16 8SJ

Telephone: (021) 452 1144 *Fax: 021 456 3442*

Stratford-upon-Avon 24, London 112, N.E.C. 8, Manchester 84

F licence; 98 bedrooms (1 for disabled) all with en suite bathroom; air conditioning; telephone, television including 13 satellite channels; 24 hour room and night service; baby listening by arrangement; lift; last orders for dinner 10.30 p.m.; light lunches; Langtry's Restaurant; vegetarian menu; children welcome; dogs allowed; conferences, 5 rooms for up to 20 delegates; valet service; indoor heated swimming pool; steam room and 2 solaria; spa pool; gymnasium and leisure centre; hairdresser and barber; beauty salon; hotel open all year; credit cards accepted.

The Swallow Hotel was completely reconstructed out of a well-known Birmingham landmark. As you enter the foyer and step onto the Italian marble flooring, you are immediately caught up in the atmosphere of sophistication. The elegant Drawing Room, with its crystal chandeliers, antiques and fresh flowers, presents an inviting place in which to relax. The Cocktail Bar and the adjoining Edward Elgar Restaurant have a distinct Edwardian feel about them. An à la carte menu is always available, and the table d'hôte offers an excellent choice at sensible prices. For a more informal meal, Langtry's is next door, furnished after the style of an Edwardian conservatory. There is traditional British cooking, and also a different Regional speciality daily. On my visit I chose salmon cooked in cider. The bedrooms are all double-glazed to ensure a peaceful night. I liked the extra touches like bonbon dishes and giant-size bathtowels, and the bathroom furnishings continuing the Edwardian motif. The pool area has been designed on an Ancient Egyptian theme and is wonderful to relax in after a hard day. The Swallow Hotel is indeed a Town House Hotel with every convenience nearby. Under the keen eye of Hugh Patton, the staff are all pleasant and attentive, to make your stay a happy one. Prices from £80.00 to £97.50 single, £97.50 to £120.00 double, including full English breakfast and VAT.

FOXLEY HOTEL

Bishop's Stortford, Hertfordshire CM23 2EB

Telephone: (0279) 653977/654679 *Fax: 0279 507176*

London 33, Cambridge 26, Colchester 33, Newmarket 31, Stansted 4, M11 2

R and R licence; 14 en suite bedrooms (2 annexe ground floor); dogs welcome; TV, radio; conferences; diets; children welcome; late meals to order.

The Foxley Hotel, once a private house, is situated in a quiet residential area close to the centre of the market town of Bishop's Stortford, and is only 5 minutes away from the motorway and Stansted Airport. The hotel is now run by Mr. Barrett who personally supervised the building of two cottages with kitchen, sitting rooms and en suite bedrooms, which can function as holiday lets, apartments or just double rooms, providing all looked-for comforts. The bedrooms in the main house are all very different; some are just being refurbished and one of these is the lovely bridal suite with a double jacuzzi. All the rooms have en suite facilities with direct dialling telephones. The restaurant is renowned for its fine French and English cuisine, prepared by Chefs who have been at the hotel for over 20 years – always a good recommendation. I have eaten here many times and have always had a good meal. The menu is very extensive with a wide selection of wines, from the house wine to a more superior vintage. Open all year. Tariff on application.

DOWN HALL COUNTRY HOUSE HOTEL

Hatfield Heath, Nr. Bishops Stortford, Hertfordshire CM22 7AS

Telephone: (0279) 731 441 *Fax: 0279 730 416*

Stansted Airport 7, M11 8, London 35, M25 15, Cambridge 35

F licence; 103 en suite bedrooms (including some suitable for disabled) all with colour TV, telephone and night service; last orders 9.30 p.m.; diets; children welcome; baby listening; dogs accepted on request; conferences up to 200, games room; dancing by arrangement; indoor heated swimming pool; sauna; 2 tennis courts (hard); riding 2 miles; golf, squash, badminton and fishing 8 miles; Amex, Diners, Visa and Master Card accepted.

It is lovely to see our English Heritage restored to its former glory, as it is at Down Hall Country House Hotel. Its name has existed for 900 years, being recorded in the Domesday Book. The current house was built in the Italian style in 1873 by Henry, Lord Rookwood, and it has been a war hospital, a private girls' school and a residential conference centre. It is now owned by Veladail Hotels who invested over £2½m in restoring the building to its original splendour. The Main Hall is sumptuous with its original high ceilings, columns and massive chandeliers, leading into grand, spacious rooms, suitable for all occasions. The newly opened West Wing is very much in keeping with the rest of this beautiful house, containing the Downham Restaurant, and banqueting/conference facilities for 200 people. There is an excellent daily and à la carte menu, the accent being on good food, beautifully served by Mark Nolan, the Chef de Cuisine. The Picture Gallery is reached by a magnificent sweeping staircase, off which are many of the bedrooms. These have been totally refurbished and offer luxurious accommodation, with soft colours and marble bathrooms including all modern conveniences. The sporting facilities are excellent, with a games room offering chess, backgammon and snooker. This room is situated in the original Adam conservatory, it leads to the indoor pool. In the 110 acres of grounds you have a jogging trail, 9-hole putting green, croquet lawn and giant chess board, so you are free to be energetic, or you can just relax in the beautifully peaceful setting. Open all year, except for Christmas and New Year. Tariff on application.

THE BLAKENEY HOTEL

Nr. Holt, Blakeney, Norfolk NR25 7NE

Telephone: (0263) 740797 *Fax: 0263 740795*

London 127, Cambridge 60, Norwich 25, King's Lynn 30, Brancaster 15, Cromer 15

F licence; 50 en suite bedrooms (6 ground floor), all with telephone, radio, TV; full central heating; night service; meals 24 hours; diets; children welcome, baby listening; dogs welcome; conferences; sauna; games room; bar billiards; indoor heated swimming pool; sea bathing nearby; sailing and boating; golf, tennis, squash, badminton, riding, shooting, fishing all nearby; most credit cards accepted.

The first impression of the hotel is its magnificent position overlooking the picturesque harbour. Blakeney, a paradise for yachtsmen, ornithologists and naturalists, has a certain tranquillity which is also felt in this superb hotel, run by Michael Stannard. The tremendous improvements have made it into one of the premier hotels in Norfolk. Of the two lounges, the one on the first floor gives panoramic views over the harbour and towards the point, the other has a very comforting fire. The restaurant, again with views over the harbour, is famous for its fresh local fish and game, accompanied by an excellent choice of wines. The Bar is elegant, stands next to the Restaurant and serves real ale. There is a lovely well kept garden. The 'Granary' holds ten bedrooms, all en suite, those on the ground floor having their own private patio and garden. The ballroom has a fine dance floor and is ideal for private parties and conferences. Two other banqueting rooms are available. The hotel bedrooms have been refurbished and include a four poster bedroom, and a jacuzzi bathroom. Room and breakfast from £43.00. Two day breaks from £44.00 per person, per night. Special 4-day mid-week holiday from £160.00. Open all year.

THE LORD CREWE ARMS HOTEL
Blanchland, Co. Durham DH8 9SP

Telephone: (0434) 675251 *Fax: 0434 675337*

London 274, Edinburgh 110, York 80, Newcastle upon Tyne 24, Durham 24, Hexham 10

F licence; 18 bedrooms, all with en suite bathroom, telephone, TV and room service; last orders for dinner 9.15 p.m.; Bar lunches; special diets; dogs accepted; golf, riding, fishing, sailing and boating locally; tennis in village; hotel open all year; all major credit cards accepted.

What a delightful hotel! Built in the mid 13th century, it was once the house of the Abbot of Blanchland. You could be forgiven for thinking that he still lives here for the ambience is full of the cosiness and good living of those years long ago. The present proprietors, however, have improved on the comforts of those times by discreetly incorporating such essentials as superbly comfortable beds, modern bathrooms, and so on, without detracting from the warmth that the antiques and well chosen décor impart to the atmosphere. A pretty well-tended garden and the most enchanting village add to the flavour of this hotel, and the food, together with the well chosen wine list, is excellent. This is a perfect base from which to explore the many and varied sites and scenes of this very historic district. To stay here is a must for any *Signpost* reader visiting this area, but I should add a word of warning. You could find it hard to tear yourself away, as did one Dorothy Foster who has been here since 1715 and who reputedly haunts one of the rooms! I leave you to find out which room for yourself. Room and full English breakfast from £60.00–£72.00, double £84.00–£96.00. Dinner, bed and breakfast for a minimum of any 2 nights £102.00 per person.

THE CROWN INN AND HOTEL

Blockley, Gloucestershire GL56 9EX

Telephone: (0386700) 245 *Fax: 0386700 247*

London 87, Oxford 32, Chipping Norton 12, Stow on the Wold 7

F licence; 21 en suite bedrooms, 2 four-poster rooms, 2 four poster suites and 2 standard suites; 11 ground floor rooms, suitable for disabled guests; telephone and TV; full central heating; Coach House Restaurant (last orders 9.30 p.m.) and Fish Restaurant; bar meals; diets; children welcome; baby listening; dogs accepted; small conferences; garden; golf 4 miles; credit cards accepted.

Blockley is a small Cotswold village, just four miles out of Moreton in Marsh. Here in this picturesque, peaceful place, you will find The Crown Inn. Parts of this hotel date back to the 16th century, and the old Baker's Oven can be found in the bar. The Champion family own and run the Crown and have recently bought the Bakery next door, and converted the ground floor into an excellent Fish and Grill Restaurant. There are at least 25 different fish dishes on the menu. These range from devilled whitebait and grilled sardines, to lobster or turbot. It is open for lunch and dinner and you are well advised to book first to avoid disappointment. The Coach House Restaurant combines elegance and taste, serving the best in English and French cuisine. It is only open in the evening, for dinner, but lunches can be served by prior arrangement. There is a good wine list, with variety enough for everyone's palate. The conversion has also provided a further six bedrooms, all en suite. They are all bright and full of character, and reminiscent of bygone days. The new rooms have been built round a compact and well-kept garden. The village of Blockley is pretty with narrow streets, and window boxes full of flowers. The Crown is in the middle of the High Street and an ideal venue for a stay in The Cotswolds. Room and breakfast from £49.50 single, and £33.25 double, inclusive of VAT.

DEVONSHIRE ARMS COUNTRY HOUSE HOTEL

Bolton Abbey, North Yorkshire BD23 6AJ

Telephone: (075671) 441 *Telex: 51218* *Fax: 075671 564*

Leeds 20, York 40, Ilkley 6, Harrogate 20

F licence; 40 en suite bedrooms (18 ground floor), all with telephone, colour TV; full central heating; night service; last orders 10.00 p.m.; bar meals; vegetarian diets; children welcome; baby listening; dogs accepted; conferences max. 150; golf, tennis, squash, badminton, riding and hot air ballooning can all be arranged; shooting; fishing; Access, Amex, Diners, Visa credit cards accepted.

The Devonshire Arms at Bolton Abbey, for many years renowned as one of the best hotels in Yorkshire, is a contrast in styles. On the one hand there is the original coaching inn with the warmth and atmosphere of days gone by and on the other is the new extension with all the light and space created by a modern building. The superb furnishings and décor have been most tastefully chosen by the Duchess of Devonshire herself using many paintings and antiques from her home at Chatsworth. But this is no old-fashioned hotel, for the modern conveniences that we all expect, and so often do not find, are discreetly at hand and the service is impeccable. The food, acclaimed by all in a county where an appreciation of the culinary art is paramount, is delicious, well presented and served by willing and attentive staff. It need hardly be added that the hotel is situated in one of the most enviable of positions. Set in the heart of Wharfedale, it is close to Bolton Abbey and the river with its romantic chasm known as the Strid and within easy motoring distance of all the famous historic and beautiful buildings with which Yorkshire is so richly endowed. It could perhaps be suggested that, in this rural setting, here is the ideal venue for a business meeting or conference. As in most things, The Devonshire Arms can cater for this providing all the visual aids, secretarial services, telex. etc. necessary. To sum up, here is an hotel of warmth, charm and style, yet thoroughly modern in its approach to comfort and efficiency. Room and breakfast from £75.00 single, £95.00 double. Open all year.

THE CARLTON HOTEL

East Overcliff, Bournemouth,
Dorset BH1 3DN

Telephone: (0202) 552011 *Telex: 41244* *Fax: 0202 299573*

Heathrow 88, Gatwick 102, London 104, Southampton 34, Manchester 230, Plymouth 126

F licence; 65 en suite bedrooms all with telephone and colour TV; full central heating; lift; night service; bar meals; diets; children welcome; baby listening; no dogs; conferences max. 120; games room; dancing once weekly; billiards; outdoor heated swimming pool; sauna; solarium; leisure centre; sea bathing; sailing and boating; golf, tennis, squash, badminton 2 miles; riding and shooting 10 miles; fishing on the coast; credit cards accepted. A five star hotel.

The Carlton Hotel is superbly situated on the East Cliff of Bournemouth with magnificent views over the sea. I thoroughly enjoyed my stay in this fine Edwardian hotel with its spacious elegantly furnished bedrooms. I felt positively pampered by the charming and efficient staff. This really is a first class hotel and must rank amongst the finest on the South coast. The restaurant and bar are gracious and most attractively furnished and I recommend an aperitif in the bar, before dinner, listening to the resident pianist. The elegant restaurant offers imaginative menus superbly cooked and presented, complemented by an extensive wine list. The Carlton has a comprehensive Health and Beauty Spa Club attended by professional therapists and the extensive gardens and swimming pool are perfect for relaxation. Excellent conference and business facilities are available with full secretarial services. There is lots to do and see in the vicinity and the town centre and famous sandy beaches are only a few minutes walk away. Tariff £135.00 for a double room including full English breakfast. Open all year.

THE CHINE HOTEL

Boscombe Spa Road, Bournemouth, Dorset BH5 1AX

Telephone: (0202) 396234 *Fax: 0202 391737*

London 100, New Forest 8

F licence; 98 bedrooms, all with en suite bathroom; telephone and TV; room and night service; baby listening; lift; last orders for dinner 8.30 p.m.; special diets on request; children welcome; no dogs; conferences up to 150; outdoor/indoor heated swimming pools; sauna and solarium; sea bathing, sailing and boating; tennis ½ mile; golf 3 miles; riding 8 miles; hotel open all year; major credit cards accepted.

A prime cliff top situation provides The Chine Hotel with a commanding sea view across Poole Bay. The hotel stands in the most beautiful and tranquil ornamental grounds. There is an attractive outdoor pool, extensive gardens and patio areas, and a chine side walk down to Boscombe Pier and the beach. All rooms are exceptionally well appointed, with light, attractive décor and thoughtful extras, such as tea/coffee making facilities. From tastefully furnished public lounges and bar, visitors can enjoy fine views over the delightful gardens, or the scenic cliff tops. The main restaurant too, is ideally located to take advantage of this glorious panorama. The carefully selected menus are all of a high standard, and there is a comprehensive wine list to accompany the excellent cuisine. Staff are both attentive and friendly, providing first class service. Conferences of up to 150 delegates can be expertly catered for. Business suites, meeting rooms, and so on, can be adapted for individual requirements. A lower lounge provides an excellent ballroom/bar, as well as an entertainment facility for larger functions. There is also a lovely, Romanesque indoor pool. The Chine Hotel is a first class establishment, and is well worth a visit. Room and breakfast from £35.00 per night, and from £360.00 per week, full board.

THE CUMBERLAND HOTEL

East Overcliff Drive, Bournemouth,
Dorset BH1 3AF

Telephone: (0202) 290722 *Fax: 0202 294810*

New Forest 10, London 106

R and R licence; 103 en suite bedrooms all with radio, telephone, TV; full central heating; lift; night service; late meals to 8.30 p.m.; diets; children welcome; baby listening; dogs welcome; conferences; solarium; pool table; games room; dancing 3–4 days a week in season, twice weekly out of season; outdoor heated swimming pool high season only; sea bathing; sailing; golf 2 miles; tennis near; squash 100 yards; riding 5 miles; fishing by arrangement; most credit cards accepted.

The Cumberland Hotel is situated on East Overcliff Drive at Bournemouth with magnificent sea views. The hotel is now under the ownership of the Young family, who also own and run the Queen's Hotel (see page 57). The bedrooms have all been refurbished and the new decoration and furnishings make them even more relaxing and comfortable. They are all equipped with all the latest modern amenities. There are admirable facilities for small in-house conferences, also a separate ballroom for dancing. I found the table d'hôte menus imaginative and well presented, coupled with a carefully chosen selection of good wines to suit even the most discerning guest. You can relax in the elegantly furnished, comfortable lounges, or sit on the large sun terrace by the 60 foot swimming pool with a cooling drink. All in all, the Cumberland Hotel offers the utmost in personal service, entertainments and amenities to both the business man and the holiday maker. Room and breakfast from £34.00 (single). Other terms on application. Open all year.

LANGTRY MANOR HOTEL

Derby Road, East Cliff, Bournemouth, Dorset BH1 3QB

Telephone: (0202) 553887

R licence; 27 bedrooms all with en suite bathroom, telephone, television; room and limited night service; baby listening; last orders for dinner 9.30 p.m.; bar luncheons; special diets; children welcome; dogs accepted; conferences up to 50; sea bathing, sailing and boating nearby; tennis, riding, shooting and fishing nearby; hotel open all year; all major credit cards accepted.

Edwardian intrigue and important historic connections make the Langtry Manor something very special. The hotel was built by Edward VII in 1877, for his favourite mistress, Lillie Langtry. An Edwardian theme has been sympathetically re-created throughout the hotel and its bedrooms by the Howard family, who own and operate this regal establishment. On Saturday evenings, guests can enjoy the famous Edwardian Dinner Party six course dinner, which is quite breathtaking, set in the lofty galleried dining room. A choice of a variety of courses is always offered and the Langtry Manor à la carte menu also provides a good selection of dishes. A varied and well chosen wine list ensures that dining in the Lillie Langtry Dining Hall is a memorable event. Staff dressed in Edwardian costume do make the service, setting and atmosphere so complete. Retiring at leisure to your guest bedroom is another treat to savour. All the bedrooms have been individually designed, enhancing the Edwardian theme, and each one is full of charm, elegance and comfort. Attention to detail is paramount. Lace, floral drapes, carved oak fireplaces and four poster beds are some of the features that grace this Edwardian hotel. The finery of Langtry manor is quite unique. A stay here of any duration, would certainly prove to be quite memorable. Room and breakfast nightly from £37.50, or £262.50 weekly.

QUEEN'S HOTEL

Meyrick Rd., East Cliff, Bournemouth,
Dorset BH1 3DL

Telephone: (0202) 554415 *Fax: 0202 294810*

London 100, New Forest 10, Southampton 35

R and R licence; 114 en suite bedrooms, with radio, TV, direct dial telephone, tea and coffee making facilities; full central heating; lift; night service; meals to 9.00 p.m.; diets; children welcome; baby listening; dogs accepted; conferences; games room; dancing; sea and sailing. Access and Visa credit cards accepted.

Beautiful Bournemouth has many good hotels; but few are better than The Queen's Hotel which stands in a prime position 100 yards from the cliff lift and the zig zag path leading to the golden sands, pleasure gardens and the town centre. Queen's is owned by the Young family, who also own the Cumberland (see page 55), and they are experienced and highly professional hoteliers. They have injected new life into the hotel, creating a fresh and welcoming atmosphere and the caring and dedicated staff provide excellent support. Many of the luxurious rooms have views of Poole Bay, the Isle of Wight and Studland and some have private balconies. Our Inspector was additionally impressed by the excellent cuisine which has broken the mould of the traditional British resort hotel. In a spacious, airy dining room the menu offers a wide but sensible choice of appetising dishes, expertly cooked and complemented by a carefully chosen wine list. Regular entertainment is provided in the ballroom throughout the season; facilities for guests' leisure and relaxation include a games room, snooker and pool table. For the ladies, there is Clare's Beauty Salon, which offers a wide range of beauty and body treatments. Under the same family, only a few hundred yards away, is the Cliffeside Hotel which commands a dazzling, panoramic view over Bournemouth Bay. Room and breakfast from £34.00. Open all year.

THE TROUVILLE HOTEL

Priory Road, Bournemouth, Dorset BH2 5DH

Telephone: (0202) 552262 *Fax: 0202 294810*

London 102, New Forest 10

R & R licence; 80 bedrooms, all with en suite bathroom; telephone and TV; room and night service; baby listening; lift; last orders for dinner 8.30 p.m.; bar meals; special diets; children welcome; dogs accepted; conferences up to 60; games room; sauna, solarium and spa pool; gymnasium; nearby squash court; sea bathing, sailing and boating; golf, tennis 1 mile; shooting and fishing 4 miles; riding 15 miles; seasonal in-house entertainment; adjacent to Bournemouth International Centre; Hotel open all year; Access and Visa cards accepted.

The Trouville Hotel is situated on Priory Road, in the centre of Bournemouth, and is a recent acquisition for the local Arthur Young Hotel Group. Having been fully refurbished, rooms are now fitted to an extremely high standard, with all comforts provided. All rooms have en suite amenities, TV, telephone, hair dryer, tea/coffee making facilities. The décor is attractively colour co-ordinated. There are excellent individual suites fully equipped for business and conference meetings, which are in great demand. For relaxation, the hotel has the advantage of its own trymnasium, sauna, jacuzzi and solarium. A panoramic open aspect of Bournemouth town centre and the gardens is enjoyed from the hotel's spacious restaurant. A very well chosen table d'hôte menu, and a wine list to match, are offered nightly, by friendly and attentive staff. The hotel meeting rooms, lounges and cocktail bar are all decorated to new standards of excellence, and contribute to the wonderful atmosphere. The location of The Trouville Hotel is ideal for delegates attending conferences at the new Bournemouth International Centre, and it is also perfect for individual or family holidays. It is only a few minutes' walk to the prestigious shopping centre and the beautiful, sandy beaches of Poole Bay. Room and breakfast from £34.00, or £210 weekly.

THE WINTER GARDENS HOTEL

Tregonwell Road, Bournemouth, Dorset BH2 5NU

Telephone: (0202) 555769 *Fax: 0202 551330*

London 100, Christchurch 4, New Forest 10, Poole 5

R & R licence; 83 bedrooms (73 en suite); telephone, colour TV; tea/coffee making facility; room service; baby listening on request; porterage; lifts; last orders for dinner 7.30 p.m.; bar snacks; diets on request; children welcome; dogs allowed; conferences suite max 150; leisure centre with 30′ indoor heated pool, 2 fitness rooms with top grade exercise equipment, including the unique Ski Master skiing & windsurfing simulator/trainer, sauna & solarium, pool & table tennis; tennis, seabathing and boating ½ mile; golf 1 mile; riding, shooting & fishing within 5 miles; all major credit cards accepted; open all year.

The 1811 luxury home of the daughter of Lord Tregonwell (Bournemouth's founder), with its original sunken gardens and patios, for guests' relaxation, and the old Wyche Hotel, combined into a fine complex, are truly only a few minutes walk to the main shops, theatres and sea front. All bedrooms are well appointed, and the décor of the spacious public rooms and bars is tastefully pleasing, enhancing the hotel's warm and friendly atmosphere. Splendid food is served in a very attractive refurbished restaurant, and the specially chosen wine list complements the 6 course table d'hôte dinners, which are thoughtfully prepared by the Head Chef. A major attraction is the new leisure centre, which Diana Moran (The Green Goddess) stated as being one of the best she had ever seen. The Winter Gardens, with its sister hotel the Melford Hall, offers varied, well equipped conference suites, plus the choice of staying in three or four crown hotels, each with ample parking and their own leisure facilities, good 'live' seasonal entertainment, and a total of 145 bedrooms. Colour brochure/tariff on request.

THE OLD VICARAGE HOTEL

Worfield, Bridgnorth, Shropshire WV15 5JZ

Telephone: (07464) 497 *Telex: 35438 Telcom G.* *Fax: 07464 552*

Bridgnorth 4, Telford 8, Kidderminster 12, Birmingham 25

R & R licence; 15 en suite bedrooms (1 for disabled) all with direct dial telephone, TV; baby listening; last orders for dinner 9.00 p.m.; special diets; children welcome; dogs accepted; conferences max 30; Visa, Access, Amex and Diners cards accepted.

Situated in the pretty conservation village of Worfield, the Old Vicarage hotel is a peaceful retreat for travellers whether on business or pleasure. The style of this old parsonage has been preserved with subtle refurbishment in keeping with modern comfort. Pretty watercolours add an intimate and homely touch. An attractive Edwardian conservatory, with views of the gardens, has been recreated and provides a comfortable and pleasant sitting room at any time of the day. The small restaurant is renowned for its first-class cuisine, excellent wines and pleasant service. People travel from as far afield as Birmingham, just to enjoy an excellent dinner. The bar is a comfortable lounge with cosy chairs and settees. I was very impressed with the bedrooms; those in the main house retain their Victorian charm with huge antique beds and wardrobes, comfortable chairs and lovely views over the quiet Shropshire countryside. Recently the old stables have been converted into beautiful large bedrooms, all furnished to a very high standard and exquisitely decorated using splendid colour schemes. Peter and Christine Iles, the resident proprietors are attentive and welcoming hosts who endeavour to make your stay memorable. Room and breakfast from £60.00 (single), £74.50 (double). Weekly – dinner, bed and breakfast for two persons £595.00. Open all year.

THE CASTLEMERE HOTEL

Western Esplanade, Broadstairs, Kent CT10 1TD

Telephone: Thanet (0843) 61566

Canterbury 19, Dover 20, Deal 15, Sandwich 9, London 76

F licence; 41 bedrooms (5 ground floor), 31 with private bath, 2 four posters and 2 twin canopy rooms; all rooms have colour TV, direct dial telephones, tea/coffee making facilities, hairdryers; golf and tennis nearby; sea bathing; boating; fishing; children welcome; late meals by order; diets; dogs accepted; conferences taken; large garden; sandy beach at Dumpton Gap; Dickens Festival.

On the Western Esplanade, overlooking the sea, and away from the noise of traffic – yet within easy walking distance of Broadstairs, stands the Castlemere Hotel. Mr. W. Hyde FCHI, the proprietor since 1960, maintains his hotel to a high standard of cleanliness, and you will always be greeted and looked after with quiet courtesy. The rooms are bright and tastefully furnished. Most have en suite bathrooms and all have amenities such as tea-making facilities, hairdryer, TV, radio and so on, provided. The menu, whilst small, is selective and carefully prepared, and there is a large choice of wines. For warm days, the beach is conveniently nearby, or you may prefer the well kept gardens, which are a pleasure to sit in on cooler days. There is much to see and do in Kent, many castles, gardens and churches to visit, and of course, golf courses for the more energetic. Bed and breakfast from £35.25 single, £66.50 twin, according to season. Special weekly rate for senior citizens

BROADWAY HOTEL

Broadway, Worcestershire WR12 7AA

Telephone: (0386) 852401

London 95, Cheltenham 15, Evesham 5, Moreton-in-Marsh 8, Oxford 37, Stow-on-the-Wold 10, Stratford-upon-Avon 15, Worcester 22

F licence; 24 bedrooms, mostly en suite, all with radio, colour TV, telephone; golf, tennis, pony trekking nearby; Access, Amex, Barclaycard, Diners, Eurocard credit cards accepted.

This picturesque and valued old friend has featured in over 50 editions of *Signpost*. The hotel is half-timbered, half Cotswold stone and was converted from a 16th century house formerly used by the Abbots of Pershore. It rests peacefully well back from the main road on the village green. Some years ago it was artistically redesigned and enlarged with most gratifying results, as you will discover when you see the lofty timbered lounge, an attractive restaurant, the sun lounge, small paved and sheltered courtyard and a new wing of welcoming bedrooms. A conference room and garden suite of bedrooms are also available. You will notice how well colour, comfort and convenience have been combined to produce a homely and civilised result. The bedrooms are well away from traffic noise, and are quiet and peaceful. The cuisine is excellent, country cooking at its best, using only top quality ingredients and all at a very reasonable price. I was pleased to find competent and courteous reception at the office, it makes such a difference to one's stay. The hotel is owned by Ian Allan Hotels Ltd. Enlarged car parking space. Room and full English breakfast from £48.50 single, £37.00 twin or double room per person per day. Bargain Breaks available during the winter months. Always open.

THE LYGON ARMS

Broadway, Worcestershire WR12 7DU

Telephone: (0386) 852255 *Telex: 338260* *Fax: 0386 858611*

London 95, Oxford 37, Worcester 22, Stratford-upon-Avon 15

F licence; 63 en suite bedrooms (9 ground floor), including 5 suites, all with telephone, colour TV, hairdryer; children welcome; night service; late meals; special diets; conferences; wine bar; dogs allowed; antiques; Leisure Centre including swimming pool, spa bath, sauna, gymnasium, steam room, billiards, and beauty therapy; golf 2 miles; tennis; hunting; riding, clay pigeon shooting, hot air ballooning, archery and squash by arrangement.

Standing at the centre of this beautiful Cotswold village, the Lygon Arms has been offering hospitality as an Inn for over 400 years. Owned by the well-known Savoy Group, the hotel's aim is to provide today's luxuries with the style and courtesy of yesterday. Kirk Ritchie, the Managing Director, and his staff give you a warm and friendly welcome to this historic house. Throughout this beautiful Elizabethan building, you will find reminders of its long history. The old kitchen is now the Inglenook Lounge with the original cooking utensils displayed around a huge fireplace. There are also delightful period bedrooms such as the Great Bedchamber and the Charles I suite, both with four-poster beds, or there are more modern guest rooms in the Garden and Orchard wings. Traditional dishes and modern favourites are offered in the magnificent Great Hall Restaurant, with its minstrel's gallery, and in summer, more informal meals can be taken in the Patio Restaurant, set in the garden courtyard. The hotel has just opened a new leisure centre, The Lygon Arms Country Club, which includes a most luxurious swimming pool and a beauty therapy centre. A balcony running round the perimeter and reached by a Spiral Staircase leads to the upper lounge where drinks and light eats are served. As a guest, one is an automatic member of this beautiful new club. Tariff on application.

DORMY HOUSE HOTEL

Willersey Hill, Broadway, Worcestershire WR12 7LF

Telephone: (0386) 852711 Telex: 338275 DORMY G Fax: 0386 858636

London 95, Stratford-upon-Avon 15, Cheltenham 15, Birmingham Airport 40, Oxford 40

F licence; 49 en suite bedrooms (22 ground floor rooms and 3 suites) all with telephone, colour TV; tea/coffee making facilities; full central heating; night service; last orders 9.30 p.m.; bar meals; diets on request; children welcome; baby listening; dogs accepted; conferences up to 74 residential/daily; adjacent golf course; tennis, squash, badminton, riding, shooting all nearby; major credit cards accepted.

To write about the Dormy House is easy for me, for it is one of my favourite hotels, tucked away high above Broadway and next to the golf course. The high standard of this superb hotel has only improved over the years. The original part of the building is a 17th century cotswold stone farmhouse with a charming drawing room, warmed by log fires in winter and enhanced by fresh flowers in summer. The exciting news about this lovely hotel is the addition of a wonderful new restaurant, which is completely in keeping with the character of the building, and as always, provides food of a truly international standard – fresh ingredients of the highest quality ensure an unforgettable gastronomic experience. A pretty bar serves lunch time snacks. Each of the forty nine bedrooms are individually and beautifully decorated. The Dormy House is now under the personal supervision of its Managing Director, Mrs. Ingrid Philip-Sorensen, whose charming personality, together with her skilled team, give one the warmest welcome to a most memorable hotel. Whether you just eat in the restaurant, or visit on Sunday for lunch, stay for the Cheltenham Races or even sample a Champagne Weekend, The Dormy House will be an experience you will wish to repeat. Room and full English breakfast from £54.00 per person. Hotel closed at Christmas.

CAREY'S MANOR HOTEL

Brockenhurst, New Forest, Hampshire SO42 7RH

Telephone: (0590) 23551 *Fax: 0590 22799*

London 90, Southampton 13, Bournemouth 18, Lymington 5

F licence; 80 en suite bedrooms (30 ground floor), four-poster beds, all with radio, bathrobes, hairdryer, trouser press, books, hospitality tray, satellite channels, colour TV and telephone; central heating; night service; meals until 10 p.m.; diets; children welcome; dogs welcome; small conferences; new leisure complex featuring large indoor pool, jacuzzi, sauna, solarium, steam room, impulse shower and gym; sea bathing, squash, riding, shooting and fishing all nearby; sailing and boating at Lymington; most credit cards accepted.

In Brockenhurst, set deep in the New Forest, you will find an elegant country mansion originating from the time of Charles II when the king is said to have used the old manor house as a hunting lodge. In 1888 the present house was built on the same site and a garden wing has been added where each room has its own patio or balcony and chairs. A superb new lounge was recently added, offering a peaceful place to relax. Forty of the rooms have also just been refurbished to de-luxe standards, and also include personal safes and mini bars. A new leisure complex (see above) means the emphasis is now on health care and keep fit with qualified instruction on exercises and diets. Massage, beauty treatment and physiotherapy can also be arranged. Dinner dances are held most winter weekends. A hundred yards from the Hotel, under the same management, "Le Blaireau" is open for meals, drinks and snacks. Brockenhurst is a fine centre for the New Forest area and most kinds of sporting activities are readily available close by. Bargain breaks throughout the year. Tariff on application. Always open.

THE GOLDEN PHEASANT INN

The High Street, Burford, Oxfordshire OX8 4RJ

Telephone: (099382) 3223 or 3417 *Fax: 099382 2621*

Oxford 15, Cheltenham 20, Stratford upon Avon 30, Banbury 25

F licence; 12 bedrooms (2 for disabled), 11 with en suite bathroom; telephone and television; room service; baby listening; last orders 9.30 p.m.; light lunches; special diets; children welcome; dogs by arrangement; conferences up to 12; car valeting available; golf 1 mile; shooting and fishing nearby; hotel open all year; Visa and Mastercard accepted.

The Golden Pheasant is found in the middle of Burford, one of the prettiest Cotswold villages. The hotel is steeped in history, as parts of the building date back to the fourteenth and fifteenth centuries. The first connection with food and drink came when a Burford maltster acquired the property in 1737. Recently the hotel has been bought by a small hotel group, and is now run by the competent young manager, Paul Brown. The bedrooms are all well furnished and comfortable, and two have four poster beds. There is an exceptionally large room in the roof space which has all the original trusses and beams. The restaurant has a large open fireplace and provides a friendly and warm atmosphere. Menus are well priced and provide a wide choice. There is also a separate and unusual vegetarian menu, with which it is well worth experimenting. To complement your meal there is an extensive wine list, comprising nearly 150 bins, so it is a good idea to spend some time making your choice! On warmer days, drinks can be had in the pretty courtyard, which has been well planted and is filled with beautiful tubs of flowers. The Golden Pheasant is ideal for relaxing, or as a base from which to visit the Cotswolds. You can be sure of being well cared for. Room and breakfast from £50.00 single, £69.00 double. Four poster rooms £88.00.

BOSKERRIS HOTEL

Carbis Bay, Nr. St. Ives, Cornwall TR26 2NQ

Telephone: St. Ives (0736) 795295

London 277, Helston 13, Penzance 8½, Redruth 14, St. Ives 1

R and R licence; 18 bedrooms (some ground floor), one self catering apartment or suite, 16 private bathrooms, remote control colour TV, direct dial telephone and tea/coffee making facilities; diets available; children welcome; drying and games rooms; heated outdoor swimming pool; putting green; golfing packages available; sea bathing, boating, surfing, rock climbing and tennis all nearby, ample car parking facilities.

Boskerris stands in attractive gardens above the safe golden sands of Carbis Bay, with fine views across St. Ives Bay. This delightful hotel is owned and personally cared for by the Monk Family, who have created a friendly happy atmosphere. The public rooms are attractive and furnished to a high standard and together with the Cocktail Bar have extensive views over the Bay. In the Dining Room a carefully chosen menu is offered. The dishes are interesting, well presented and nicely served. Similar care is given in the selection of wines, which is excellent. The majority of the comfortable and well appointed bedrooms, most with private bathrooms, enjoy sea views and overlook the well-kept gardens. Boskerris is an ideal centre for a wide range of activities, including a golfing package which enables you to play at ten major golf courses in Cornwall, all within easy distances, plus the many beautiful moorland and coastal walks. Room and breakfast from £24.50 per person including VAT. Other terms on application. Off season bargain breaks from two to four days. Open Easter till November, and opening over Christmas for the first time.

CUMBRIA PARK HOTEL

Scotland Road, Carlisle, Cumbria CA3 9DG

Telephone: (0228) 22887 *Fax: 0228 514796*

London 307, Hexham 38, Keswick 31, Penrith 19

F licence; 51 en suite bedrooms (9 ground floor), all with colour TV, telephone and full central heating; lift; night service; last orders 9.00 p.m.; bar meals; diets; children welcome; baby listening; no dogs; conferences up to 170; tennis, squash, badminton within ½ mile; golf and fishing 1 mile; Visa, Access and Amex welcome.

What a delightful hotel! On the road to Scotland, only minutes from Carlisle city centre, it must be the ideal centre for the businessman or for the tourist. For the former there are conference rooms in which to meet colleagues from both North and South, and beautifully appointed bedrooms in which to house them. For the latter the historic castle, cathedral and Roman remains of the city are within walking distance and the Roman Wall, The Lake District and border towns such as Gretna, Dumfries, Langholm and Hawick are all within an hour's car drive. Rarely does an hotel offer so much history, natural history and open air activity within so short a distance. But enough! The hotel is worth a visit purely on its own merits. For here are magnificent award winning gardens, comfortable and tastefully decorated public rooms, super bedrooms and excellent food. The hotel is family owned and run so you can be assured that the service is friendly and efficient, and that, although it is a fairly large hotel, the personal touch is always evident. Hotel open all year. Room and breakfast from £50.00 per night.

THE STRING OF HORSES INN & RESTAURANT

Faugh, Heads Nook, Nr. Carlisle, Cumbria CA4 9EG

Telephone: (0228) 70297 *Fax: 0228 70675*

Carlisle 7½, Newcastle 50, London 310

F licence; 14 en suite bedrooms all with telephone, TV; late meals until 10.30 p.m.; coffee shop; diets; children welcome; baby listening; dogs by arrangement; conferences up to 25; sauna and solarium; whirlpool spa; in-house movies; heated outdoor swimming pool; golf, sailing, squash, badminton, riding, fishing nearby; credit cards accepted.

Anyone who a few years ago, said that Cumbria was an hotel seeker's nightmare was probably right. These days, however, the hotels equal almost any in the country. One of the best is the String of Horses Inn at Faugh. It was originally built in the 17th century, and it still retains in its public rooms, the beams, panelling and the atmosphere of those days. But upstairs, the bedrooms are decorated with the finest furniture and materials. Some have four poster beds and most have a bathroom with either a round or a double bath, all of which have gold fittings. Fresh fruit, complementary sherry, colour TV, in-house movies and even dressing gowns are all provided. In short, this is the very best in unashamed, romantic luxury. But it doesn't end there; the hotel also has a sauna, solarium and spa pool. There is also a separate cottage next to the hotel, which is let as a unit, with two double bedrooms and two sitting rooms. The food is excellent, and unusually for this area, lunch can be taken in the restaurant, or as a hot/cold meal in the bar, or there is a delicious cold buffet. If you are visiting Carlisle, or the Border area, to stay at this extraordinary inn is an experience well worth trying. Room and breakfast from £55.00 single, £62.00 double. Open all year.

BROCKENCOTE HALL

Chaddesley Corbett, Kidderminster, Worcestershire DY10 4PY

Telephone: (0562) 777876 *Telex: 333431*

Birmingham 17, Kidderminster 3, Worcester 10, Exit 4 M5 7, Birmingham Airport and N.E.C. 20

F licence; 8 en suite bedrooms, all with telephone, col. TV, full central heating; last orders 9.30 p.m.; children welcome; baby listening; no dogs; conferences max. 15 non-residential; Mastercard, Amex, Diners, Visa credit cards accepted.

This classically built hall is situated on the A448 Bromsgrove to Kidderminster road. Recently transformed into a luxury country house hotel, the outside setting where rare trees loftily survey the surrounding 70 acres of landscaped grounds and lake cannot fail to impress you, and inside it is just as attractive and inviting. The atmosphere suggests comfortable and relaxed country living. All the bedrooms are individually designed and charmingly decorated, each with a character of its own. I enjoyed an excellent dinner for the dishes combine a delicacy of flavour with artistry of presentation. This is complemented by a very good wine list. The central geographical position of Brockencote means that many places are only a short distance away. For example, the Vale of Evesham, the Malvern Hills and the Cathedral and Royal Porcelain Company at Worcester are within easy reach. My memory of Brockencote Hall is the delightful décor and fine cuisine combined with countryside comfort. The owners, Alison and Joseph Petitjean, are supported by a young and attentive staff. Room and full breakfast from £57.00 single, £90.00 double. Restaurant closed on Sunday evenings. Hotel closed 26th December to 20th January.

EASTON COURT HOTEL

Easton Cross, Chagford, Devon TQ13 8JL

Telephone: (0647) 433469

Exeter18, Chagford 1½, Plymouth 30, Moretonhampstead 4, London 190

R & R licence; 8 en suite bedrooms, 2 for disabled; all with direct dial telephone & TV; last orders 9.00 p.m.; special diets; children over 14 years welcome; dogs accepted; golf, riding, shooting & fishing nearby; hotel closed in January; all credit cards accepted.

Easton Court, featured in the first edition of *Signpost*, was established in the 1920's by the distinguished American Carolyn Cobb when she purchased the Tudor house and added the dining room and extra bedroom wing. Mr. and Mrs. Graham Kidson have recently acquired the hotel and intend to retain its charm and character. This delightful stone house is situated in the heart of Devon's unspoilt countryside and great care has been taken to preserve the original structure with its thatched roof, oak beams, quaint corners, ancient doorways and great stone fireplaces. It is no wonder that Alec and Evelyn Waugh and other literary personalities have found its ambience so attractive and conducive to their work. The public rooms include a comfortable and well furnished drawing room, complete with log fire, the Evelyn Waugh bar and a library where solitude with a book can be enjoyed or a family party held. The Dining Room is particularly attractive for guests who enjoy a romantic candlelit dinner. The food is excellent, with a wide choice offered together with a well chosen wine list. All the bedrooms are comfortable and attractive and you can be sure that your visit to Easton Court will be a memorable one that you wish to repeat. Tariff on application.

MILL END HOTEL

Sandy Park, Chagford, Mid Devon TQ13 8JN

Telephone: (0647) 432282 *Fax: 0647 433106*

Exeter 20, Chagford 2½, London 190, Plymouth 30, Okehampton 11

R and R licence; 15 en suite bedrooms 2 single rooms with adjacent bathroom; 3 ground floor, all with telephone, colour TV, radio and baby listening; full central heating; late meals, cold supper by arrangement; diets (special Breakfast Menu and main dish at Dinner offered for vegetarians); children welcome; dogs welcome; fishing; swimming pool; golf and tennis nearby; bird watching; an ideal area for walking; Amex, Visa, Diners and Access cards accepted.

This really comfortable hotel was converted from an old flour mill about 75 years ago – the mill wheel and sluices can still be seen – it rests peacefully on the banks of the trout river Teign. It can be easily reached from the Exeter to Okehampton A30 at Whiddon Down, or is only two miles from the small moorland town Chagford on the main A382, ideally placed for exploring Dartmoor. The owners Nicholas and Hazel Craddock, run this lovely house, making their guests feel very much at home. All the public rooms and bedrooms are delightfully furnished, colour schemes are soft and restful, giving an air of comfort and quality. A great feature of Mill End is the French/English cooking – they take a special pride in their food, believing that quality and attention to detail are of paramount importance. I really enjoyed a delicious dinner from a choice table d'hôte menu, that is changed each evening, dishes were interesting and adventurous. The chef cooks with imagination, individuality and artistry, ably abetted by a cellar stocked with carefully chosen wines. Their sweet trolley is another speciality, quite outstanding in its choice and quality. Mill End is a great favourite of mine, well worth a visit, and you won't be disappointed. Dinner, room and breakfast from £60.00 (single), £115.00 (double), including VAT. Discounts available for stays over four days. Special fishing packages with tuition. Open all year except 12th–22nd December and 10th–20th January.

GREAT TREE HOTEL

Sandy Park, Nr. Chagford, Devon TQ13 8JS

Telephone: (0467) 432491 *Telex: 9312132116*

Chagford 1½, Exeter 17, Okehampton 8, Plymouth 35, Torquay 30
Situated on the main A389 – 1½ miles north of Chagford

F licence; 12 en suite bedrooms (10 ground floor) all with direct dial telephone, colour TV, tea/coffee making facilities, radio & child listening facilities; full central heating; last order 8.45 p.m.; bar meals available; diets; well behaved children welcome; dogs accepted; conferences max. 25; sailing & boating; golf, riding, shooting, fishing all nearby; nature rambles; lovely walks; Visa, Access, Amex, Diners cards accepted.

Set amidst the splendour of Dartmoor National Park, the Great Tree Hotel, once a hunting lodge, stands in 18 acres of woodland, forming part of Rushford Wood, listed as a site of special interest by the Nature Conservancy Council. It offers all that is best in the country house tradition with a relaxed and homely atmosphere, thanks to the owners, Bev and Nigel Eaton-Gray, who personally care for this pleasant and comfortable haven. The large lounge is most attractive with a welcome log fire in colder weather. You will like the convivial surroundings of the cocktail bar, before enjoying an excellent dinner in the Whitewater restaurant. There is plenty of choice and the dishes are imaginative and beautifully cooked – no small portions here! The majority of bedrooms are at garden level and are very comfortable and well appointed. This is a lovely area and there are plenty of local beauty spots and places of interest to visit. Room and breakfast from £34.00 per person per night inclusive of VAT. Weekly from £310.00 per person, half board. Other terms on application, see Bargain Break section. Open all year.

MOLLINGTON BANASTRE HOTEL

Parkgate Road, Chester, Cheshire CH1 6NN

Telephone: (0244) 851471 *Fax: 0244 851165*

London 188, Manchester 24, Liverpool 25, North Wales Coast 20

F licence; 70 en suite bedrooms (15 ground floor), all with direct dial telephone, radio, colour TV; lift; night service; late meals to 10.30 p.m.; Grill Room; special diets; children welcome, baby listening; dogs allowed; conferences; sauna, solarium; indoor heated swimming pool; squash, riding, shooting; Access, Amex, Diners, Visa accepted.

As there is no space here for rhetoric, let me just list some of the superb attributes of this magnificent RAC four star hotel; wonderfully comfortable public rooms and bedrooms; service second to none; a fantastic sporting and health centre; three restaurants, all delightfully different and all serving delicious food. There are fine banqueting rooms, conference facilities with the best of audio-visual equipment, and arrangements for outdoor activities from shooting to flying lessons. I could go on, but if you try Mollington Banastre on business or as a tourist you will find that I do not exaggerate. There are brochures available about all their special breaks; "Spend, Spend, Spend", "Totally Whacked", "Molly Bear" or "Gourmet" weekends. Pamper yourself today. The thought that has been put into this hotel shows in the provision made for disabled guests. Accommodation for children sharing with their parents is free, and there are also special menus for them. The historic and beautiful city of Chester is nearby, as are many of the business centres of the North West. Room and breakfast from £73.00 single, £90.00 twin. Special weekend breaks available from £51.00 per person, per night. A sister hotel to Solberge Hall at Northallerton (see page 193). Open all year.

ROWTON HALL HOTEL

Whitchurch Road, Chester, Cheshire CH3 6AD

Telephone: (0244) 335262 *Fax: 0244 335464*

Chester 2, Liverpool 30, Manchester 40, Birmingham 80, London 200

F licence; 42 en suite bedrooms, 8 ground floor, all with radio, telephone and TV; full central heating; night service; meals to 9.30 p.m.; diets; children welcome; conferences and private parties; helicopter pad; leisure centre; heated indoor swimming pool, sauna-steam room; gym; sea bathing and sailing 15 miles; tennis, squash, badminton, riding and fishing 1 mile. Master Card, American Express, Diners Club, Visa cards accepted.

Rowton Hall, originally a country manor house standing on the site of the Battle of Rowton Moor 1649, in eight acres of gardens, is two miles from the historic city of Chester, just off the A41 Chester to Whitchurch road. The hotel is now owned by Stuart and Diana Begbie. The public rooms are comfortable and distinctive, particularly the Cavalier Bar, where light lunches are served, and the attractive oak-panelled dining room. The bedrooms are decorated, furnished and appointed to a high standard. Private rooms are available for conferences and private parties. For those seeking healthy relaxation, or indeed, for those of a sporting nature, the new leisure centre offers ample opportunity, with its gymnasium, solarium, steam room and swimming pool. It should be noted, however, that children under six are not allowed in the leisure centre, and those aged 6–16 have their own special hours. An ideal centre for touring and there are many sporting activities in the area. Room and breakfast from £68.00 single, £78.00 double including VAT. Other terms on application. Always open.

THE COTSWOLD HOUSE

Chipping Campden, Gloucestershire GL55 6AN

Telephone: (0386) 840330 *Fax: 0386 840310*

London 90, Stratford-on-Avon 11, Cheltenham 22, Oxford 32

F licence; 15 en suite bedrooms all with telephone, colour TV; last orders 9.30 p.m.; bar meals 9.30 a.m.–9.30 p.m.; children over 8 years welcome; conferences max. 20; golf 3 miles, tennis by arrangement; Amex, Diners, Visa and Master Card accepted.

The Cotswold House, with its mellow stone walls, stands in pride of place overlooking the old market square of Chipping Campden. The hotel has been lovingly restored to its original splendour by Robert and Gill Greenstock. As I entered I was immediately aware of the spectacular spiral staircase which wound its way upwards to the 15 luxurious and well-appointed bedrooms. Each is individually decorated and named accordingly. Whether you are allocated the Indian Room, Garden Room or Ribbons and Bows, each is impeccable. The Colonial Room has most recently been redecorated, with a turn of the century South American theme in mind; stencilled pineapples on the walls, a sign of friendship and hospitality, add to the unusual décor, as well as a high four poster bed. Greenstocks continental-style Cafe-Bar provides a wide choice of food available throughout the day. The Restaurant overlooks the pretty old world garden with clipped yew hedges and has a fine reputation for the quality of its à la carte. A pianist provides entertainment three nights a week. The hotel has an attractive room which is suitable for small private parties or meetings. The whole place has a cosy, yet luxurious, atmosphere and is an ideal place to stay after visiting the surrounding Cotswolds. Single room and breakfast from £44.00. Double from £37.50 per person including VAT.

CHARINGWORTH MANOR

Charingworth, Nr. Chipping Campden,
Gloucestershire GL55 6NS

Telephone: (0386) 78555 *Fax: 0386 78353*

Chipping Campden 3, Cheltenham 24, Stratford-upon-Avon 10, London 75, Moreton-in-Marsh (mainline station to London) 6

R & R licence; 25 bedrooms with en suite bathroom; telephone, TV with remote control; room and night service; last orders 10.30 p.m.; light lunches; diets; dogs allowed by arrangement; conferences up to 34 (2 rooms); golf 6 miles; hotel always open; credit cards accepted.

Charingworth Manor was first mentioned in the Domesday Book in 1086, and is a grand monument to English history. Today it is an impressive country hotel, decorated throughout to the highest standards, and featuring some lovely antique furniture. The library has a relaxed atmosphere, with an oak beam ceiling, log fire and mullion windows. As there is no bar, drinks are served in the various rooms which makes one feel as though one is staying in a private home. The dining room enjoys superb views over the Cotswolds and the cuisine, under talented Chef Tony Robson-Burrell, presents modern and exciting dishes using the very best ingredients. Many of the bedrooms are named after previous owners of the manor, an exception is the T. S. Eliot Suite, so-called in memory of the famous poet who was also a frequent guest. Eight rooms are contained in the house, and the remainder have recently been renovated from old stabling to provide a series of courtyard rooms, which are all linked to the hotel. Each room has its own character and degree of excellence. The Long Room is ideal for private parties or meetings. Simon Henty and his staff make staying at Charingworth an experience not to be missed. Double rooms with single occupancy from £80.00, double rooms from £95.00. Short breaks are available mid-week and at the weekend.

CHISELDON HOUSE

Chiseldon, Nr. Swindon, Wiltshire SN4 0LX

Telephone: (0793) 741010 *Fax: 0793 741088*

Swindon 6, M4 (Junction 15) ½ mile

F licence; 21 en suite bedrooms, all with telephone, colour TV and full central heating; last orders 9.30 p.m.; diets by arrangement; children welcome; dogs allowed; conferences up to 25; games room; dancing during winter months; outdoor heated swimming pool; golf 1 mile if requested; squash, badminton, riding, shooting and fishing by arrangement, 6 miles; all credit cards accepted.

This charming early Regency country House, set in 3 acres of mature gardens, is an ideal retreat in which to relax and enjoy luxurious comfort and a high standard of professional service. Proprietors, David Ball and Josephine Scott, also owners of Ivy House Hotel in Marlborough, have tastefully converted and restored this house, formerly the home of the Borelli family. The late Victorian rear wing has been remodelled and extended to provide luxury bedrooms and the Orangery Restaurant, which overlooks the grounds and heated swimming pool. Public rooms are elegant, with fine pictures, fresh flowers and antiques. The 21 bedrooms vary in size and style, and include suites as well as spacious executive rooms. Each is individually decorated, with all modern comforts. There are excellent custom built facilities for senior level management meetings and conferences which are discreetly sited for peacefulness. Imaginative English and French cuisine is served in the Orangery Restaurant, using fresh local produce. This is supported by a comprehensive wine cellar. Chiseldon is ideally situated to visit the Cotswolds, Bath, Salisbury and Blenheim. For the sports enthusiasts, squash, fishing, golf, croquet, swimming, walking and cycling are available by arrangement. Guests can be confident of receiving genuine hospitality, individual service and informal luxury, personally supervised by the proprietors. Room and breakfast from £80.00–£95.00 per night and £350 per week. Open all year.

THE HOOPS INN

Horns Cross, Nr. Clovelly, North Devon EX39 5DL

Telephone: (0237) 451222/451247

Clovelly 4, London 210, Bideford 5

F licence; 13 bedrooms, 8 with private bathroom, colour TV and full central heating; tea/coffee making facilities in en suite rooms; last orders 9.00 p.m.; cream teas served in coach house from Whitsuntide–30th September; bar meals; diets; well behaved dogs (bring own bedding); sea bathing, sailing and boating, golf, shooting and fishing nearby; all credit cards accepted.

Hoops Inn is a 13th century inn, one of the most notable ports of call in Devonshire, located on the A39 between Bideford and Clovelly, ¾ mile from the coast. It is now owned and personally run by Marjorie and Derek Sargent. The Hoops is one of Devon's oldest and most famous inns, notorious as a meeting place for smugglers, before it became a coaching inn. It was regularly used by Sir Richard Grenville (born only a few miles away), Raleigh, Drake and Hawkins, who sponsored the 1556 bill calling for the construction of Hartland Quay nearby, when potatoes and tobacco were first imported into this country. Despite the hotel's exciting past, its appearance today is immaculate, with its thick wheaton's-reed thatch, clean white walls and black painted wood-work, all testifying to the care and attention with which the present owners tend it. Inside, you will see quaint semi-circular brick fire places, baking ovens and piles of logs, ready to warm the comfortable lounges and dining room. The homely atmosphere is enhanced by the antique furnishings and pleasant décor. Behind the old house is a luxurious bedroom wing, where you will be able to rest in complete tranquillity. The Inn is surrounded by beautiful unspoilt countryside and close to the North Devon coast. Room and breakfast from £25.00 per person (low season), inclusive of VAT. Other terms on application. Open all year.

TREGLOS HOTEL

Constantine Bay, Nr. Padstow, Cornwall PL28 8JH

Telephone: (0841) 520727 *Fax: 0841 521163*
Telex: 45795 WSTTLX. GTGS

London 256, Newquay 10, Padstow 5, Falmouth 36, Truro 25

R and R licence; 44 en suite bedrooms, all with telephone, colour TV, hairdryers, 3 rooms with sitting rooms (one ground floor); lift; meals to 9.30 p.m.; night service; off season conferences; diets; log fires; full central heating; bridge room; snooker and pool table; indoor heated swimming pool; spa bath; sea bathing; sailing; boating; golf and tennis by arrangement with Trevose Golf Club; sea fishing; riding nearby; surfing; 4 self-contained luxury flats.

Treglos has been recommended by *Signpost* for many years. It is run as a Country House Hotel – the 'hotel' atmosphere being hardly apparent. It is a veritable model of elegance and luxury, standing in its own grounds overlooking the Atlantic. Personal consideration is the keynote to this splendid house, personally cared for by the owners, Ted and Barbara Barlow, who retain a loyal, cheerful and attentive staff. There are five lounges, all traditionally furnished to the highest of standards. The décor is pleasant and restful with freshly cut flowers and, in cooler weather, log fires. Upstairs is as sumptuous as down, with all the appointments expected here. In the dining room, Treglos has a great reputation for the excellence of the fare. A varied selection of interesting and carefully prepared dishes are offered, and local sea-food and vegetables are served whenever possible. All this good food is complemented by a wide selection of carefully chosen wines at moderate prices. The elegantly designed indoor swimming pool leads to open lawns and sunken gardens. Within a few hundred yards are the sandy beaches of Constantine, Treyarnon and Booby's Bay. The Barlows are also co-owners of the Budock Vean Hotel, Falmouth (see page 96). Dinner, room and breakfast from £49.00 (single), and £47.00 per person (twin). Demi-pension weekly from £265.00 per person including VAT. Closed mid November to early March; office open for enquiries.

RUDLOE PARK HOTEL & RESTAURANT

Leafy Lane, Corsham, Wiltshire SN13 0PA

Telephone: Bath (0225) 810555 *Fax: 0225 811412*

London 110, Bath 7, Chippenham 5, Castle Combe 8, Lacock 5, Bristol 20

F licence; 11 en suite bedrooms, all with telephone, radio, TV; 1 four poster and 2 tester beds; full central heating; service until midnight; late meals to 10.00 p.m.; diets; children over 10 welcome; small conferences; heated swimming pools, indoor 1 mile, outdoor 5 miles; boating 7 miles, golf 3 miles, tennis 5 miles, squash and badminton 1 mile, riding nearby, shooting 1 mile, fishing 5 miles, sports centre 1 mile; croquet lawn, 4 acres beautiful gardens; all credit cards accepted.

This Country House hotel and restaurant is located just off the A4, a mile west of Corsham, down Leafy Lane. Set in delightful grounds, the hotel and some bedrooms command magnificent views down Box Valley to the Georgian city of Bath. Marion and Ian Overend, the Resident Directors, give personal attention to the wants of their guests. The bedrooms are most comfortable, with charming décor and well furnished. I enjoyed an excellent lunch served efficiently and with courtesy in a relaxed atmosphere. There is a good menu choice, set meal or à la carte, and the china and table appointments are first class. A traditional Roast Beef luncheon is served on Sundays and all food is fresh and cooked to order. An extensive wine list is available including 600 wines and 600 whiskies, cognacs and liqueurs. The hotel has been awarded the Armagnac Restaurant of the Year (42 Armagnacs) and Best Hotel Cheese Trolley. The lounge bar carries a fine selection of draught beers and is a bar for all seasons – north facing, it is cool in spring and summer and, with a roaring fire, warm in autumn and winter. The hotel is ideally situated for Bath and Bristol, the lovely villages of Lacock and Castle Combe, Stonehenge, Cheddar Gorge, Avebury Circle, and many National Trust Properties – an excellent gateway to the West Country. Room and full English breakfast from £60.00 single, £80.00 double, inclusive of VAT and service. Open all year.

WINSTON MANOR HOTEL

Beacon Road, Crowborough, East Sussex TN6 1AD

Telephone: (0892) 652772 *Fax: 0892 665537*

Gatwick 23, Brighton 23, Tunbridge Wells 7

F licence; 54 en suite bedrooms, all with telephone, satellite TV and full central heating; lift; night service; last orders 9.45 p.m. (9.30 Sunday); coffee shop; bar meals; diets; children welcome, baby listening; dogs allowed; conferences up to 250; private dinners and meetings; dancing held frequently; indoor heated swimming pool; sauna; gymnasium; golf, squash, badminton and riding within 2 miles; Access, Visa, Amex and Diners' cards welcome.

This very comfortable hotel which has recently been refurbished and considerably extended, was once frequented by the Churchill family. It boasts 54 bedrooms all with en suite bathrooms or shower, plus every modern comfort. The Winston Manor has a wonderful reputation for its food; the dishes are original and well presented, and served by a cheerful and obliging staff. There is a coffee shop, and the new leisure centre includes a superb swimming pool with jet stream, gymnasium, sauna and jacuzzi. Locally, Ashdown Forest is a great beauty spot. There is golfing, riding, an adventure course and even a dry ski slope within a short distance of the hotel, and of course Tunbridge Wells, with its spa and attractive Pantiles is only 7 miles away. The hotel prides itself on its conference and banqueting facilities, and can cater for up to 250 people attending a dinner dance or wedding reception. Tariff on application. Open all year.

SELSDON PARK HOTEL

Sanderstead, Nr. Croydon, Surrey CR2 8YA

Telephone: 081-657 8811 *Telex: 945003* *Fax: 081-651 6171*

London 13, Croydon 3, Epsom 9, Reigate 10, Kingston 11, Heathrow 1 hour, Gatwick ½ hour, East Croydon to Victoria 17 mins, hotel car service

F licence; 170 en suite bedrooms-all with colour TV and phones; hospitality tray, room bar, trouser press, hairdryer; 3 lifts; dinner dance on Saturdays; night service; children welcome; children's play area; baby listening; conference suites; leisure complex with pool, squash, gymnasium and health suite; billiards; golf course; 2 grass and 2 floodlit, all-weather tennis courts; outdoor heated swimming pool; jogging trail; riding from nearby stables; boules, croquet, putting green; helipad; most credit cards.

This luxurious and highly commended hotel is outstanding for its amenities, personal service and efficiency, all largely due to the Sanderson family, who have owned Selsdon Park for over 60 years. It is now under the personal direction of Mr Basil Sanderson, a man with very high standards, who is well assisted by a first-class team. The hotel, originally one of England's finest country houses going back to 891 AD, is situated amid the Surrey hills in 200 acres of lovely parkland with an 18-hole Championship golf course designed by the famous J H Taylor. There is a country house feeling and friendly atmosphere at Selsdon Park. The public rooms are most comfortable and the bedrooms are decorated and furnished with care. I found both the à la carte and table d'hôte menus imaginative and perfectly cooked and there is a carefully chosen selection of excellent wines. There are admirable facilities for large or small conferences, including an exclusive Tropical Leisure Complex, and attractive terms for special weekends. Chauffeur-driven cars and helicopter are available by prior arrangement. Room and breakfast from £115.00 single, £138.00 double, including service and VAT. Always open.

HALL GARTH COUNTRY HOUSE HOTEL

Coatham Mundeville, Darlington,
County Durham DL1 3LU

Telephone: (0325) 300 400 *Fax: 0325 310 083*

Darlington 4, Durham 18, London 249, Middlesbrough 15

F licence; 43 en suite bedrooms (3 ground floor), all with telephone, colour TV with satellite channels and teletext and full central heating; night service; last orders in restaurant 10.00 p.m.; bar meals; diets; children welcome, baby listening; no dogs except guide dogs; conferences up to 250; outdoor heated swimming pool; sauna and solarium; golf and tennis; Visa, Access, Amex, Diners and Consort Club Card.

Hall Garth was until recently a small, old fashioned family run hotel noted for its service and its cuisine. After complete refurbishment and the conversion of the stable block, it is still small, it is still famed for its cuisine and personal service, but it now boasts a host of facilities which would put many a large group hotel to shame. Where else can you find a delightful English country house hotel, dating back to 1540, which has a swimming pool, tennis court, croquet lawn and a solarium, etc? What other hotel of this size can offer a choice of dining venues; the stable bar for a relaxed lunch or dinner, and the restaurant for a more intimate or formal meal? In either case, you can be sure of friendly service, excellent food and a most interesting and well chosen wine list. Coatham Mundeville is unusual in that it is well situated for communications (being close to Teesside Airport, the A1 and the main railway at Darlington) and it is central for many industrial towns and cities, yet is within easy driving distance of many rural and historic tourist attractions. The latter include Northumberland, Durham County and City, North Yorkshire, Beamish and Darlington Railway Museums. Hall Garth is thus an hotel ideal for both the hedonistic business man or tourist. To find Hall Garth, turn off the A1 on the A167 towards Darlington, take the first left and the hotel is ¼ mile down the road to Brafferton. Hotel open all year, tariff on application.

THE ROYAL CASTLE HOTEL

The Quay, Dartmouth, Devon TQ6 9PS

Telephone: (0803) 833033 *Fax: 0803 835445*

Torquay 10, Plymouth 23, Exeter 40, Dartmoor 20

F licence; 25 en suite bedrooms, all with colour TV, telephone and full central heating; night service; last orders 9.30 p.m.; restaurant; coffee shop; bar meals; vegetarian and other diets; children welcome, baby listening; dogs allowed; conferences up to 45; fishing, sailing and boating; Access and Visa cards welcome.

The Royal Castle Hotel stands in a wonderful position on the quayside in Dartmouth. A hostelry since 1594, the hotel was originally four Tudor merchants' houses, and notable guests include seven reigning monarchs. The Dartmouth ferries can take visitors to the steam railway and the ancient Dartmouth castle, or you can go up-river to Totnes in a pleasure boat. The unspoilt coastline is mainly National Trust and there are secret coves and lots of interesting and beautiful countryside to explore. The attractively decorated bedrooms, some with lovely river views, some with four poster beds, are comfortable and have all modern amenities. Leading to the bedrooms is a winding staircase displaying a fascinating collection of old bells. The original courtyard can still be seen in the centre of this lovely old building and antiquities and period furniture abound. A wide range of bar-meals and snacks are available in the Galleon Bar, and there is also the less formal Harbour Bar. The Adam Room, overlooking the river on the first floor is an elegant restaurant offering excellent food in picturesque surroundings. As you would expect, seafood and local fish are a speciality. The hotel is privately owned and managed by Mr. and Mrs. Nigel Way. Room and breakfast from £34.00. Hotel open all year.

FINGALS HOTEL & RESTAURANT

Dittisham, Nr. Dartmouth, South Devon TQ6 0JA

Telephone: (080 422) 398 *Fax: 080 422 401*

Dartmouth 7, Totnes 7, London 200

R & R licence; 10 bedrooms with private bathroom (1 ground floor), all with telephone and full central heating; TV lounge; diets; children welcome, baby listening; dogs permitted; conferences up to 25; games room; snooker; outdoor heated swimming pool; jacuzzi; tennis; fishing on the Dart, sailing and boating 1 mile; riding 3 miles; sea bathing 7 miles; golf 15 miles; all cards except Amex accepted.

Fingals Hotel and Restaurant, situated in Dittisham, Dartmouth, is a most original hotel, run by Richard Johnston, previously of Fingals in the Fulham Road. The building has been wonderfully updated without in any way losing the old world charm of the original manor house. It was built in the 17th century and still has a Queen Anne facade. Next door, the old barns have been converted into studio workshops and courses include pottery, painting and photography. Day rates can also be arranged. Visitors can bathe in the sea nearby, and windsurfing, canoeing and motor boats are available. Pony-trekking on Dartmoor, and river and deep sea fishing can be arranged. Golf too, can be organised nearby, and the hotel has its own grass court for tennis as well as an outdoor swimming pool. The bedrooms are charming, mostly en suite and attractively decorated. There is a new conference room for up to 25 delegates built with traditional heavy oak trusses. Downstairs, there is a bar, a sitting room, library and lovely panelled dining room. The friendliness of the staff and the other guests make for an evening which has the feel of a private dinner party. The wine list is comprehensive, and as you would expect, the food is superb, with only the freshest ingredients being used. This is a wonderfully relaxing corner of Devon in which to spend your holiday. Room and breakfast from £35.00, weekly rates from £200.00. Hotel closed from January to Easter except for conferences.

STAVERTON PARK HOTEL AND GOLFING COMPLEX

Staverton, Nr. Daventry, Northants NN11 6JT

Telephone: (0327) 705911 *Fax: 0327 300821*

London 75, Coventry 20, Birmingham 40, N.E.C. 30, Stratford 30, Silverstone 15, Oxford 40

F licence; 50 bedrooms, all with en suite bathroom, TV (with satellite channels) and telephone; baby listening; night service; last orders for dinner 9.30 p.m.; bar meals; special diets; children welcome; no dogs; conferences max. 300; games room; snooker; leisure centre planned; sauna and 2 solaria; gymnasium; golf; shooting and fishing; riding locally; open all year; major credit cards accepted.

Staverton Park is surrounded by an 18-hole tournament golf course, which has two golf professionals on hand. There is a well-stocked lounge bar and a comfortable restaurant, where there is an excellent choice of fayre. You can choose from the à la carte or table d'hôte menus, the cold buffet bar or the vegetarian menu. There is also a trolley bearing a selection of roast joints daily. The hotel also boasts a wide range of fine wines. Snacks are served in the Private Members Golf Restaurant, or in the conservatory which has lovely views over the golf course. The comfortable bedrooms have been built to a high standard and are decorated in pale blues. There are some large suites opening onto the terrace, which overlooks the golf course. The suites can also be used as syndicate rooms. The two bridal suites are very special, with canopy beds, jacuzzi baths and every other luxury. The hotel caters for conferences and private parties, with four large conference rooms, such as the Green Suite. This seats 250 for banquets, and there are other rooms for smaller meetings. One of the hotel's claims to fame is the snooker table; this was used by Alex Higgins when he won the World Championship. On Saturday nights they have a Dinner Dance and Sunday brunch is served from 12 noon till 4 p.m. Tariff on application.

THE KEDLESTON COUNTRY HOUSE HOTEL AND RESTAURANT

Kedleston Road, Derby, Derbyshire DE6 4JD

Telephone: (0332) 559202 *Fax: 0332 558822*

Derby 3, London 127, Ashbourne 11

F licence; 15 en suite bedrooms (1 ground floor), all with telephone, col. TV; full central heating; last orders 9.15 p.m.; bar meals; diets; children welcome; no dogs; dancing monthly; leisure centre 3 miles; golf 200 yards; riding 2 miles; all major credit cards accepted.

Although only three miles from Derby city centre, Kedleston Country House Hotel is situated in lovely countryside with a golf course only a few minutes away. The hotel was originally an Inn for visitors to the Kedleston Quarndon health spas, and was built by the Curzon family, who live in nearby Kedleston Hall. This elegant 18th century building was taken over by Ralph and Jean Allcock in 1983. Since then they have carried out major refurbishments whilst retaining the original Georgian charm and character of the building. All the bedrooms are en suite and are beautifully decorated and there is a bridal suite with four poster bed. A pianist plays for your enjoyment most nights of the week in the spacious restaurant, which seats over 60 people. The food is personally supervised by Jean and offers an excellent selection of well-cooked dishes and an extensive and varied wine list. The restaurant has recently been attractively refurbished. During lunch time and evenings, the buttery serves hot and cold gourmet cuisine (except Sat. and Sun). An à la carte menu is also available. You can be assured of a very warm welcome at the Kedleston, as the comfort of guests is of great importance to Ralph and Jean, as it is to their pleasant and cheerful staff. Room and breakfast from £45.00 single, £57.00 double. Special weekend rates available. Always open.

IZAAK WALTON HOTEL

Dovedale, Nr. Ashbourne, Derbyshire DE6 2AY

Telephone: (033 529) 555 *Telex: 378406* *Fax: 033 529 539*

Derby 14, Ashbourne 5, Leek 10, M1 (Junction 24) 24

F Licence; 34 en suite bedrooms (3 ground floor), all with radio, telephone, TV; full central heating; night service; late meals to 9.30 p.m.; bar meals available lunchtime and evening; diets; children welcome; baby listening; dogs welcome; conferences up to 50; dancing on Saturday; river bathing; trout fishing; squash 5 miles; riding by arrangement; 24 hour Prestel information; credit cards accepted.

The Izaak Walton Hotel is situated just above the river Dove in the idyllic hills of Dovedale. Originally built as a farmhouse in the 17th century, the hotel, although extensively modernised, retains its original charm. There are 4 miles of river fishing, but it is necessary to book a rod well in advance, as it is extremely popular. There are magnificent views from all the public rooms as well as all the bedrooms, which are comfortably furnished to a high standard. A beautiful and newly refurbished bridal suite boasts a lace-covered four poster bed. High peaks drop down dramatically to the river below, and gently rolling fields immediately surround the gardens of the hotel. There is a most welcoming bar with a large open stone fireplace as well as four comfortable lounges which have recently been refurbished. A well appointed dining room caters for all tastes with both table d'hôte and à la carte menus. There is a purpose built conference room capable of accommodating up to 50 delegates. Whether you are looking for a quiet restful lazy holiday, or an hotel for your business conference, the Izaak Walton certainly would be an excellent choice. Within easy reach of many tourist attractions in the Midlands the hotel guarantees a memorable and very comfortable stay. Room and breakfast from £45.00 single, £68.00 double/twin including VAT. Open all year.

BUTTERFLY HOTEL	**BUTTERFLY HOTEL**	**BUTTERFLY HOTEL**
A45 Bury East Exit Symonds Road, Moreton Hall	A10-A47 Roundabout Hardwick Narrows	Thorpe Meadows Off Longthorpe Parkway
Bury St. Edmunds IP32 7BW	**Kings Lynn** PE30 4NB	**Peterborough** PE3 6GA
Tel: (0284) 760884 *Fax: 0284 755476*	*Tel: (0553) 771707* *Fax: 0553 768027*	*Tel: (0733) 64240* *Fax: 0733 65538*

F. licence: 70 bedrooms (50 at Kings Lynn) all en suite with direct dial telephone, and col. TV; night porter; last orders for dinner 10.00 p.m. bar meals; special diets; children welcome; no dogs; conference facilities; Mastercard, Visa, Diners & Amex cards accepted.

The Butterfly Hotels are best described as 'Modern Coaching Inns'. Each situated close to the junctions of major trunk roads, they are ideally situated for a stop on your travels or as a meeting place. Each hotel is similar in its layout with an informal atmosphere and very pleasant staff. The public rooms are furnished with pine furniture and decorated with dried flowers, copper vases and comfortable settees. In the Restaurants you will find a buffet with a choice of hors d'oeuvres, joint of the day, soups and desserts or a menu featuring fresh food at excellent value. The bedrooms are on two floors, one floor all with extra wide single studio rooms with showers, settees and a bar with tea and coffee making facilities and the other floor with twin or double bedded rooms with bath. Single and double rooms are the same price from £52.50. English breakfast £5.00 and continental breakfast £3.00. Conference facilities vary at each hotel, telephone for details. Open all year.

SHIPDHAM PLACE

Shipdham, East Dereham, Norfolk IP25 7LX

Telephone: (0362) 820303

Norwich 20, London 100, Newmarket 35, Cambridge 50, Norfolk Broads 25, Coast 25

R & R licence; 8 en suite bedrooms, all with telephone; full central heating; last orders 9.30 p.m.; diets on request; children welcome; baby listening; dogs accepted; conferences max. 20; golf, fishing nearby; riding, shooting 2 miles; Access, Visa credit cards accepted.

Shipdham Place, is to be found up a short leafy drive and is the old rectory of the parish church in the middle of the conservation area of Shipdham. The house dates back to the early seventeenth century, but in 1800 an elegant Regency block was added to the front of the building and a further flint-clad extension was built in the middle of the nineteenth century. It is now furnished with a mixture of antique furniture with the eight bedrooms varying in size and character, all with writing desks, direct dial telephone and two rooms have four-poster beds. Each room has its own bathroom, some with marble topped basins and all have cast iron baths and w.c.'s with wooden seats. Staying at Shipdham is like staying at a comfortable private house with the opportunity to relax in friendly surroundings that larger establishments have long forgotten. The main dining room seats about 30 with a smaller room which can be used for private parties or when they are less busy. There is a choice of 3 or 5 course menu, cooked by Tina Poulton who uses many wonderful seasonal vegetables from the garden, accompanied by a large and varied wine list. Room and breakfast from £35.00. Open all year.

SUMMER LODGE HOTEL

Evershot, Dorset DT2 0JR

Telephone: (0935) 83424

Dorchester 12, Yeovil 12, Bath 45, London 120

R & R licence; 17 en suite bedrooms (3 ground floor), all with telephone and full central heating, 6 with colour TV; last orders 8.30 p.m.; bar lunches; diets; children over 8; dogs allowed; outdoor heated swimming pool; tennis, grass and hard courts; fishing 2 miles; riding 4 miles; sea bathing, golf, sailing and boating 12 miles; hotel closed 2nd January to 18th January; Visa, Access and Amex accepted.

This lovely Georgian Country House was formerly the Dower House of the Earls of Ilchester, and on your arrival at Summer Lodge, the feeling is one of entering a private house. The elegant drawing room, with its French windows leading onto the garden, is full of Margaret Corbett's lovely arrangements of country flowers, and the odd local history book or Thomas Hardy novel lying on the table. Roger Jones offers his own delightful version of modern English cooking, producing excellent set dinners, using as many fresh, local ingredients as possible. The bedrooms are individually decorated, all with bathroom en suite, and many have views of the lovely garden, while others overlook the village roof tops to the fields beyond. Tea/coffee trays are provided along with delicious home made short-bread. Evershot is an unspoilt, charming little village, untouched by modern life, a peaceful base from which to explore the wonderful countryside of Hardy's novels, with many places of interest, and the sea is only 12 miles away. Prices from £60.00 per person, including Dorset Cream tea, dinner, bed, breakfast and VAT.

EBFORD HOUSE HOTEL

Ebford, Nr. Exeter, Devon EX3 0QH

Telephone: (0392) 877658 *Fax: 0392 874 424*

Exeter 4, Exmouth 3, Dartmoor 15

F licence; 18 en suite bedrooms (5 ground floor), all with direct dial telephone, colour TV and full central heating; hairdryers and tea/coffee making facilities in rooms; last orders 9.30 p.m.; bar meals; diets; conferences up to 15; sauna, solarium and spa bath; leisure centre; sea bathing, sailing, golf, tennis, squash, badminton, riding, shooting, fishing all nearby; Access and Barclaycard accepted.

Ebford House is a lovely Georgian country house, stylish and elegant, set in beautiful grounds. It is located just beyond Clyst St. George on the A376 Exeter to Exmouth road. The owners, Don and Samantha Horton, a very enthusiastic and energetic couple, have created a homely atmosphere, enhanced by personal attention. Don is justly proud of his Restaurant's reputation for first class cuisine, with menus individually created by the 'chef patron' himself. The dishes are imaginatively cooked, well presented and served by a pleasant and cheerful staff. The personally selected wine list is very comprehensive. Mention must be made of the attractive Frisco's Wine Bar in Ebford Cellars. Frisco's is run by Caron one of the daughters of the house, a highly efficient young lady. All bedrooms are well appointed and, as with the reception rooms, very comfortable, and tastefully furnished. There is also a four poster room available, attractively furnished in pale lemon and green. The Hotel has its own leisure area, which includes a sauna, solarium, spa bath and several pieces of keep-fit apparatus. There are many places of interest nearby, and there are, of course, the perennial favourites of walking, sailing and golf. Room and breakfast from £45.00 single, £60.00 double, and four poster room £75.00 inclusive of VAT. Other terms on application. Open all year.

ROYAL BEACON HOTEL

The Beacon, Exmouth, Devon EX38 2AF

Telephone: (0395) 264886/265269 *Fax: 0395 268890*

London 173, Exeter 11, Plymouth 48, Taunton 42

F licence; 32 bedrooms all with en suite bathroom; telephone, television; satellite TV; room and night service; baby listening; lift; last order for dinner 9.30 p.m.; bar meals; diets; children welcome; dogs allowed; conferences up to 100; games room, snooker; sauna and solarium; sea bathing; sailing and boating; leisure centre, golf and tennis nearby; riding, shooting and fishing by arrangement; hotel open all year; all credit cards accepted.

Situated in a prime position, The Royal Beacon Hotel was originally a Georgian posting house. The hotel has wonderful views of the Exe estuary and Torbay, and there are private gardens for the use of guests. There is sea bathing opposite the hotel, a swimming pool 200 yards away and the East Devon Golf Club is only four miles away. There is a large indoor sports centre nearby as well as sailing, fishing and water-skiing. Guests are welcome at the Bridge Club which meets in the hotel weekly. The newly refurbished and attractively decorated bedrooms are all en suite, and most have a lovely sea view. Honeymooners are welcomed with champagne, flowers and chocolates, and there are two delightful four-poster rooms. Light refreshments may be obtained in the lounge or ''Eccentrics'' Bar. The attractive Fennels Restaurant overlooks the sea and has excellent à la carte or table d'hôte menus, plus a comprehensive wine list. Devonshire Cream Teas are served daily. Business needs are also provided for with conference facilities for up to 100 delegates. The Larke family and their staff are helpful and efficient, ready to ensure that you enjoy a memorable holiday at this pleasant hotel. Room and breakfast from £42.00, demi-pension weekly £375.00.

ROYAL DUCHY HOTEL

Falmouth, South Cornwall TR11 4NX

Telephone: Falmouth (0326) 313042 *Fax: 0326 319420*

London 267, Lizard 20, Penzance 25, Bodmin 34, Truro 11, Redruth 10

F licence; 50 en suite bedrooms (one suite on ground floor suitable for disabled guests), all with telephone, video linked TV; full central heating; lift; night service; meals to 9.00 p.m.; light lunch meals available; diets; children welcome; baby listening; dogs accepted at Manager's discretion; private functions up to 250; conference room for 40; dinner dance Saturday; small snooker table; table tennis; indoor heated swimming pool; sauna; solarium; spa bath; sea bathing; sailing; golf – Carlyon Bay and Falmouth Golf Clubs – special concession rates tennis and squash, membership for residents at the Falmouth Club, ¼ mile; special sporting facilities arranged for children; river and sea fishing can be arranged; riding nearby; most credit cards accepted.

With well kept grounds in the historic, maritime resort of Falmouth on Cornwall's famed riviera coastline, this is the ideal setting for a seafront hotel. It is just a short, level walk to the town centre and harbour, with views across Falmouth Bay to Pendennis Castle. Owned by the Brend family (who own other luxurious hotels, including the Victoria Hotel at Sidmouth – see page 231) the Hotel is expertly managed by John Allen. With very good furnishing and colour schemes, both bedrooms and public rooms are comfortable and relaxing, with a friendly atmosphere. The food is distinguished by its high standard and choice of dishes which are interesting, admirably cooked and well presented with a well chosen wine list to complement. I thoroughly recommend the Royal Duchy at all seasons, whether for relaxation or a more active holiday, either way you will enjoy first class service. Room and breakfast from £44.00 single, £39.00 double per person inclusive of VAT. Write for attractive brochure. Other terms, including special breaks, on application.

BUDOCK VEAN GOLF AND COUNTRY HOUSE HOTEL

Nr. Falmouth, South Cornwall TR11 5LG

Telephone: (0326) 250288 *Fax: 0326 250892*

London 276, Falmouth 6, Lizard 17, Penzance 19, Truro Station 14

F licence; 58 en suite bedrooms, all with colour TV, direct dial telephone; lift; night service; diets; meals till 9.00 p.m.; children welcome, baby listening; dogs allowed; games room; dancing throughout season; own 9 hole (18 tee golf course); tennis including two deluxe all weather tennis courts; sailing, fishing and windsurfing from own foreshore; splendid indoor heated pool kept at above 80°; riding 3 miles; most credit cards accepted.

Located amidst rolling parkland, this historic Cornish Manor House, on the shore of the beautiful Helford River, provides ample opportunity for a break from the stresses and strains of daily life. The building itself is almost 300 years old yet successfully blends yesteryear with all the requirements of the modern traveller. Owned by the Barlow and Start families, both have a long acquaintance with the art of good hotel keeping and have done much to build this hotel up to the high standards it now maintains. Ted and Barbara Barlow also own the Treglos Hotel in Constantine, and Bud and Joan Start are former proprietors of the Windsor Hotel, Newquay. There are three very comfortable lounges cheered by blazing log fires during the winter months. Bedroom furnishings and décor are restful, and sometimes romantic, as with the lovely four poster beds in some rooms. The Cocktail Bar is intimate and inviting, leading to a dining room where you can enjoy an imaginatively chosen table d'hôte or à la carte menu featuring the locally caught sea-food, complemented by a selective wine list. The 9 or 18 hole golf course is beautifully laid out and is free of charge to residents. As well as the fabulous indoor pool, the hotel has its own private beach, on the Helford River and the walk through the woods is a sheer delight. Room and breakfast from £42.00 per person including VAT. Hotel closed 5th January to mid February but office open for enquiries.

THROWLEY HOUSE HOTEL AND RESTAURANT

Ashford Road, Sheldwich, Nr. Faversham, Kent ME13 0LT

Telephone: (0795) 539168 *Fax: 0795 535086*

Canterbury 7, Faversham 2, Ashford 14, M2/A2 2, Leeds Castle 10

F licence; 9 bedrooms, with en suite bathrooms (a further 18 planned); TV & telephone; room & night service; baby listening; last orders 9.30 p.m.; diets by arrangement; children welcome; dogs allowed; conferences max. 25; open all year; all major credit cards accepted.

Throwley House is situated deep in the heart of this particularly unspoilt part of the Kentish countryside, surrounded by typically rolling North Downs farmland. The buildings are Georgian in style with Adam features, and are set in 16 acres of garden and parkland, with lovely views from the terrace. Whilst the hotel is only 1½ miles from the M2 (leave at Junction 6 on A251 towards Ashford to the village of Sheldwich), this could not be a more secluded and peaceful place. The hotel interior is decorated and maintained to a very high standard. Each bedroom, with en suite bathroom, is individually styled with every possible convenience and luxury available. The dining room is both elegant and spacious, and combines exquisite cuisine with excellent service and attention to detail. A fine selection of wines is kept, from which you can make your choice. A substantial programme of improvements has taken place over the last few months, which have taken this hotel to its present high level of facilities. A fully equipped nursery brings extra freedom, and time to relax, for those with young children. Kent has so many wonderful and historic places to visit – castles, cathedrals, gardens and beautiful scenery, all within easy driving distance of Throwley House. Room and full English breakfast from £95.00. Special weekend rates.

FLITWICK MANOR

Flitwick, Bedfordshire MK45 1AE

Telephone: (0525) 712242 *Telex: 825 562 FM* *Fax: 0525 712242*

London 40, Oxford 35, Cambridge 35, Bedford 10

F licence; 16 en suite bedrooms (3 ground floor), all with colour TV, telephone and full central heating; limited night service; last orders 9.30 p.m.; diets; children welcome, baby listening; no dogs; conferences up to 14; games room; tennis; Amex, Access and Barclaycards accepted.

This classic manor house, listed Grade 2*, is set in 7 acres of lawns and gardens, studded with specimen trees and approached by a magnificent avenue of enormous lime trees. The gardens themselves form the northern part of a former deer park of 40 acres, and round the house there is a haha, a grotto, the parish church, two lakes and even a tunnel, the whole in a ring of woodland. This peaceful setting on the south side of Flitwick is complemented by the luxury of the manor, antique furniture, fine pictures, log fires and sumptuous soft furnishings, all in well proportioned rooms, which create a warm, welcoming feel to the house. In the kitchens, above the vaulted cellars (home to 150 bins of carefully chosen and stored wines, mainly French), is a team of award winning chefs who pride themselves on the quality of supplies and presentation of imaginative food. A sea-water tank, many hives of bees, the best senders on the coast, a kitchen garden and free range hens all add to the quality of the food. The bedrooms offer every sybaritic luxury with large beds, many four posters, bowls of fresh fruit, iced water, soft towels and dressing gowns and a host of bathroom goodies. A quiet night's sleep is followed by excellent breakfasts helped by those hens and bees. Bedfordshire offers a perfect centre to visit both Oxford and Cambridge, is an easy drive from London, and one can visit scores of stately homes and fine country houses. Room and breakfast from £75.00 single, £95.00 double, inclusive of service and VAT.

FOSSEBRIDGE INN

Fossebridge, Nr. Cheltenham,
Gloucestershire GL54 3JS

Telephone: (0285) 720721

Cheltenham 12, Burford 13, Cirencester 18, London 87, Oxford 30

F licence; 14 bedrooms all with en suite bathroom, telephone, colour TV; room service; baby listening; night service till 11.00 p.m.; last orders 9.30 p.m. except Saturday, till 10.00 p.m.; extensive bar lunches, and special diets catered for; children welcome; dogs accepted; conferences up to 20 taken; shooting and fishing; golf 5 miles; major credit cards accepted.

The Fossebridge Inn is situated on the edge of the River Coln which flows alongside the hotel and into the Fossebridge Lake at the foot of the Hotel's lawned gardens. The Fossebridge was originally built as a coaching Inn in Tudor times, and has such charming features as inglenook fireplaces, original oak beams and flagstone floors, all typical of the fifteenth century. The Bridge Bar is located in the oldest part of the hotel and offers an extensive menu, ranging from Roast Rack of English Lamb or Whole Smoked Pigeon with Hazelnuts and Port, to simple light dishes. A special cold table is available at lunch time and a wide variety of English puddings is always included on the menu. The elegant River Restaurant offers a varied table d'hôte menu which is well renowned locally, and offers fine cuisine of the highest quality. Both restaurants possess extensive wine lists. The hotel bedrooms are all tastefully decorated with all the qualities demanded by today's visitor. The distinctive Drawing Room offers guests a peaceful place in which to relax, and provides diners with a delightful venue for pre-dinner drinks. The Fossebridge Inn is the ideal base from which to explore the beauty of the Cotswolds. It offers a unique blend of charm and elegance where fine cuisine is matched by excellent service. Room and full English breakfast from £37.50 single, and £55.00 double.

FOWEY HOTEL

The Esplanade, Fowey, Cornwall PL23 1HX

Telephone: (0726) 832551 *Fax: 0726 832125*

London 270, Plymouth 36, Truro 24, Land's End 60, Bodmin 12, Penzance 49

F licence; 30 bedrooms (12 suitable for disabled), 27 with en suite bathroom; telephone and TV; room service and night service; baby listening; lift; last orders for dinner 9.00 p.m.; bar meals; special diets to order; children welcome; dogs allowed; conferences up to 25; sea bathing, fishing, sailing and boating; riding 2 miles; golf 5 miles; hotel open all year; Amex, Diners, Visa and Master Cards accepted.

The Fowey Hotel commands a magnificent position overlooking the sea, and is close to the Royal Fowey Yacht Club. The ancient borough of Fowey supplied Edward III with many men and ships for the siege of Calais. Still an important port, large ships can still be seen in the harbour. The extensive hotel gardens run down to the private and secluded foreshore, where sea, as well as river bathing, is available. There is much to do and see from Fowey, with Polperro, Looe and Readymoney Cove close by, and there are first class golf courses at Lostwithiel, St. Austell and Carlyon Bay. The attractive dining room overlooks the sea and harbour, and offers a table d'hôte menu, fresh vegetables and a large and sensibly priced wine list. Interesting old photographs line the downstairs walls. Bedrooms are mainly en suite, and most with sea views, and all have colour television, radio and direct dial telephone. There is also a lift, and car parking. Self-catering flats are also available, all with harbour and sea views. The hotel is run by resident proprietors William and Mavis Stobbs, who, with their excellent staff will make your stay comfortable and relaxing. Tariff on application.

THE PICKERINGS

Catterall, Garstang, Lancashire PR3 0HA

Telephone: (0995) 602133 *Fax: 0995 602100*

Lancaster 10, Preston 8, Blackpool 12

Restaurant licence; 16 en suite bedrooms (2 ground floor), 3 with four poster beds, 2 with whirlpool baths, all with colour TV, bedside telephones; full central heating; late meals to 10.00 p.m.; diets; conferences max. 20; golf locally; Access, Diners, Visa credit cards accepted.

The Pickerings is a delightful country house surrounded by large floodlit gardens. Taken over three years ago by Mr. Allan Leck, many improvements have been made to the hotel and more are planned. There is now an air of charm and elegance about the house and a warm welcome is assured from Allan and his staff. Dinner is a five course affair, prepared by the Head Chef, Nigel Marsden. A master in the art of cooking he produces such delicious dishes as Avocado Fool with Tipsy Shrimps, Sirloin Steak stuffed with Crab and Lymeswold Fritters with Cumberland sauce. Vegetarians are also catered for with delights such as Stilton, Celery and Walnut Pie or Vegetable Vindaloo. A fine wine list accompanies this tempting menu. After dinner what a pleasure it is to retire to your tastefully decorated bedroom, some of which have four-poster beds and some even have whirlpool baths. Naturally, there is a colour TV, tea and coffee making facilities, hair dryers, etc., and fresh flowers from the garden to give that more personal touch. Room and breakfast from £37.00 single, £58.00 double. Open all year.

EUROPA GATWICK

Worth, Gatwick, Nr. Crawley, Sussex RH10 4ZR

Telephone: (0293) 886666 *Fax: 0293 886680*

Gatwick 5, Heathrow 30, Croydon 18, London 30

F licence; 211 en suite bedrooms (75 ground floor), including 24 Club rooms and 4 Suites; all have colour TV with satellite channels, tea/coffee making facilities, telephone and full central heating; lift; night service; coffee shop; bar meals; diets; children welcome, baby listening; conferences up to 180; indoor heated swimming pool; sauna and solarium; leisure centre; horse riding nearby; courtesy coach to airport; all major credit cards accepted.

The Europa Gatwick opened its doors in the spring of 1990, in its setting of 5½ acres of grounds on the B2036 Balcombe Road; and is only 5 miles from Gatwick Airport. With brilliant white walls and a terracotta tiled roof, the hotel's Spanish styling is enhanced by soft landscaping and many mature trees within its grounds. Controlled car parking ensures visitors of a space at all times, and special arrangements can be made for long-term car parking for residents flying off from Gatwick. An extensive leisure facility offers a comprehensive range of amenities, including swimming pool, spa, sauna and solarium, steam room, hair salon and beauty room, gymnasium, dance studio, creche, restaurant and bar facilities. The hotel has two galleried restaurants, a cocktail bar and a lounge bar on the ground floor of the lobby. This area will be a popular meeting place for both businessmen and local residents alike. The conference and banqueting facilities reflect concern and desire for good service. The largest of the rooms, seating approximately 120 people is complemented by two rooms for 40 people, one for 80, and 12 syndicate rooms for 12 people each. Please telephone for details of special rates available.

MALLYAN SPOUT HOTEL

Goathland, Nr. Whitby, North Yorkshire YO22 5AN

Telephone: Goathland (094 786) 206

London 247, Pickering 14, Whitby 9, York 41

F licence; 24 en suite bedrooms, including 3 honeymoon suites; TV and direct dial telephone in all rooms; children welcome; dogs accepted; last orders at 8.30 p.m.; diets; conferences; sea bathing and golf 9 miles; sailing and riding 7 miles; fishing; moorland walking.

Set in the heart of the North Yorkshire Moors lies the typical moorland village of Goathland. Close to the church and facing a large and lovely green is the ivy clad, stone built Mallyan Spout Hotel. When I entered I felt, as always, a great sense of warmth and friendliness, the three spacious lounges have roaring fires and the hotel's decoration is tasteful and unobtrusive. The standard of cuisine has been consistently superb, the wine list is exceptional; the St. Emilions in particular being chosen by Mr Ian Martin of Castle Howard, who is Chancellor of the Jurade de St. Emilion for the North of England. I have always appreciated the high degree of comfort found throughout the hotel. My congratulations to Mrs Heslop for ever improving on her high standards especially on this last extensive and imaginative refurbishment of the bedrooms. The honeymoon suites have balconies with superb views over the countryside, and such luxuries as remote-controlled curtains. As a matter of interest, the hotel derives its name from the waterfall of that name which is within easy walking distance of the hotel. For those whose desire is to lounge, read or potter round the countryside, here is an uninterrupted calm. If you are unable to stay, why not call in for a superb evening meal in the restaurant or for a bar meal. Both are excellent and walkers are welcome in the bar. Other local interests are a well-preserved stretch of Roman road, a steam railway, Rievaulx Abbey, Castle Howard and of course, the East Coast resorts. Always open. Prices from £45.00 single, to £100.00 for luxury double with balcony. Mini breaks available all year.

GOMERSAL PARK HOTEL

Moor Lane, Gomersal, West Yorkshire BD19 4LJ

Telephone: (0274) 869386 *Fax: 0274 861042*

M62 motorway 4

F licence; 53 bedrooms, all with en suite bathroom, telephone, TV with satellite channels; room and night service; baby listening; last orders for dinner 10.00 p.m.; bar meals; special diets; children welcome; no dogs; conferences up to150; hotel's own helicopter, & minibus; indoor heated swimming pool; leisure centre; sauna, solarium, spa pool and gymnasium; golf and riding nearby; hotel open all year; all major credit cards accepted.

Gomersal Park is an ideal hotel for any visitor to this area, for a wide variety of reasons. For the business man, it is literally at the centre of the Bradford, Leeds, Wakefield, Huddersfield and Halifax circle and thus it is perfect for conferences, meetings, and so on. It is also a superb base for the holiday maker from which to explore the industrial archaeology of these historic towns and the dramatic countryside of the Yorkshire Dales and the Pennines. Again, for the business man, every modern aid is provided for a conference including the hotel's own helicopter, and the tourist can take advantage of the many Mill shops that abound in the area to buy woollens at bargain prices. The hotel itself is tastefully decorated in a muted style and all the rooms are extremely comfortable. The atmosphere is cool and relaxed, and the staff are friendly and efficient. The super dining room has an excellent menu and wine list, and anyone contemplating holding a function of any nature will find this a delightful venue. There are seven acres of well tended grounds in which to ''wind down'', or to provide a scenic backdrop for wedding photographs, making the hotel a haven in the midst of this bustling area. Tariff on application.

GRAYTHWAITE MANOR HOTEL

Grange-over-Sands, Cumbria LA11 7JE

Telephone: (05395) 32001/33755

London 261, Lake District (Windermere) 15, Carlisle 58, Liverpool 76

F licence; 22 bedrooms (some ground floor), 20 with private bathrooms and all with telephone, TV, tea/coffee making facilities, electric blankets; drying room; small conferences; billiards; attractive gardens; golf locally, putting green; hard court tennis; municipal sea water pool; riding nearby.

What first impressed me here was the courtesy and thoroughness with which one of the owners showed me round. As a result of what I saw and felt, I returned a few days later for a night's lodging and this is what I found. A largish and substantial house, beautifully appointed and with every indication that the detailed comfort of visitors had been most conscientiously achieved. The armchairs were cosy enough to go to sleep in. The dining room, an imposing affair, displays cut glass chandeliers and some fine oil paintings. And, incidentally, the dinner table d'hôte with choice was excellently cooked and served. I made a special note, too, of how pleasant and attentive the staff were, obviously taking their cue from the owners. Bedrooms, most with private baths, fulfilled the expectation of the downstairs comfort and elegance. Faithful guests return year after year for Graythwaite and Grange are within easy reach of the Lake District. Dinner, room and breakfast from £50.00 single, £90.00 twin. Special terms available on request from November to March.

NETHERWOOD HOTEL

Grange-over-Sands, Cumbria LA11 6ET

Telephone: (05395) 32552

London 262, Lake District (Windermere) 5, Carlisle 58, Liverpool 82, Kendal 12, Keswick 41

F licence; 32 bedrooms (1 for disabled); 29 with en suite bathroom, 2 pairs of intercommunicating bedrooms; all have radio, telephone, TV; night service; lift to 1st floor; late meals; special diets; children welcome; baby listening; dogs allowed; conferences; parking for 160 cars; dancing; 11 acres of gardens; sea bathing & sailing 100 yds; leisure centre with indoor pool (opening 1991); tennis ½ mile; squash, badminton, riding, shooting and fishing all 5 miles; credit cards not accepted.

This imposing hotel, set in its own topiary gardens on a woodland slope, dominates the main road into Grange-over-Sands. The house dates back to 1893, and retains all the original panelling, wood-carvings and fireplaces. Modern conveniences also have their place here, however; you will find a lift servicing the first floor bedrooms and the dining room, and all the dining areas are fully air conditioned. The ten new bedrooms have been furnished in harmony with the rest of the hotel, and all are non-smoking. The Honeymoon Suite still has its original, built-in furniture, to help you re-live the romance of days gone by. Netherwood is very much a family run establishment and the imaginative menus are based on local produce, wherever possible. There is a lot to see and do nearby; Grange-over-Sands itself has many intriguing shops, and there are ornamental gardens, and a promenade on which to stroll. The area is famous for its historical landmarks, including the nostalgic Haverthwaite railway, Holker Hall, and there is the racecourse at Cartmel. There are many possibilities for nature lover and explorer alike, with Morecambe Bay and its estuaries to discover, or you can venture into the Lakes and the Lune Valley. Room and breakfast from £32.75 single, £65.50 double. Open all year.

AYNSOME MANOR HOTEL

Cartmel, Nr. Grange-over-Sands, Cumbria LA11 6HH

Telephone: (05395) 36653

London 263, Manchester 84, Ulverston 10, Coniston 15, Bowness-on-Windermere 12

R and R licence; 13 bedrooms, 12 with private bathroom and all with colour TV, alarm radio, direct dial phone, tea/coffee making facilities; full central heating; night service until 11.00 p.m.; meals until 8.30 p.m.; coffee service until 11.00 p.m.; diets to order; children welcome; dogs welcome by arrangement; conferences 12–20; drying room; riding 1 mile; sea bathing; outdoor swimming pool, golf (4 courses), tennis, fishing 2 miles; sailing and boating 6 miles; indoor heated swimming pool 10 miles; Access, Visa and Amex cards accepted.

This beautiful old manor house, parts of which date back to 1510, was once the residence of the Earl of Pembroke, founder of the historic Cartmel Priory. It is now in the experienced hands of its owners, Tony and Margaret Varley, their son, Christopher and his wife, Andrea. The elegant, yet comfortable atmosphere has been retained by the tasteful furnishings and décor, which are to be found throughout the hotel. The superb candle-lit dining room with its view of the Priory is an ideal setting in which to enjoy the imaginative and carefully chosen menu, which offers the best of fresh local produce, well cooked and presented. The bedrooms, including the four-poster honeymoon suite, are quite charming in their individuality. After a day spent visiting the local places of interest, such as Holker Hall, Beatrix Potter's home, Sizergh Castle and Levens Hall or after pursuing a day's sporting activities, the visitor can relax in the tranquil atmosphere that the hotel provides. Dinner, bed and breakfast from £41.00 including VAT. Other terms on application including special terms for winter breaks. Closed first three weeks in January.

THE WORDSWORTH HOTEL

Grasmere, Ambleside, Cumbria LA22 9SW

Telephone: (09665) 592 *Telex: 65329*

London 271, Ambleside 4, Kendal 17, Keswick 13

F licence; 37 en suite bedrooms, including 2 suites (2 ground floor), all with colour TV, telephone and full central heating; lift; night service; last orders Fri–Sat 9.30 p.m.; bar meals; vegetarian diets; children welcome, baby listening; no dogs; conferences up to 100; games room; dancing by arrangement; indoor heated swimming pool; sauna and solarium; mini gym; jacuzzi; free golf on weekdays; squash, riding and fishing nearby; all major credit cards accepted.

Set in the centre of Grasmere, in 1½ acres of landscaped gardens, this hotel offers all that is best for a holiday in the Lakes. It is spacious, airy and has all the modern amenities to be expected by the discerning traveller. One bedroom has retained its original Victorian bathroom and is very much in demand, as the shower facilities must be seen to be believed. There is also a romantic four poster room. The public rooms are tastefully furnished in keeping with the period of the buildings, without the gloomy atmosphere inherent in so many Victorian hotels. The swimming pool has large doors opening onto a patio and makes an excellent place in which to relax after a few days of walking, climbing or sightseeing. The hotel is owned by Reg Gifford of Michael's Nook Country House Hotel, so little more need be said of the food here, other than that the fame which he has gained as an hotelier is more than justified. What could be better than the fresh air of the Lake District and, maybe, a little exercise, coupled with the cuisine of the hotel's "Prelude Restaurant"? Christmas and New Year house parties. Winter breaks available; open all year. Prices from £45.00 per person.

LANGDALE HOTEL AND COUNTRY CLUB

Gt. Langdale, Nr. Ambleside, Cumbria LA22 9JD

Telephone: (09667) 302

Ambleside 4½, Windermere 12½, Kendal 19

F licence; 65 twin/double rooms all with luxury bathroom, satellite TV, radio, direct dial telephone; some with impulse shower, balcony, four poster bed; full central heating; night service; dinner till 10.00 p.m.; coffee shop 10 a.m.–10.30 p.m.; diets; children welcome; baby sitting; sauna, solarium; games room; heated swimming pool; jacuzzis, health and beauty salon; trim trail; squash; fishing; golf, tennis and riding nearby; shooting and badminton by arrangement; conferences; credit cards accepted.

Langdale Hotel and Country Club is situated in a superb setting in what is arguably the most spectacular valley in the Lake District. It is surrounded by beautifully landscaped grounds with streams running through wooded glades and bubbling into miniature tarns. The hotel is modern yet warm, bright and welcoming. There is the outstanding Hotel restaurant overlooking the millpond with its mill wheel and the tropical Tamarind Terrace where one can enjoy a drink or a light meal whilst looking down on the magnificent swimming pool. Hidden among the trees are the luxury lodges of the exclusive Langdale time ownership. Available in the Country Club are squash, solaria, sauna, steam room, spa bath, impulse showers and a sports shop. The Langdale Hotel is unique in this area and offers the standard of service and facilities one would expect to find in capital cities. Rates based on double occupancy £59.00–£75.00 per person per night. From April 1st 1991 £65.00–£83.00. Special Breaks available. Always open.

LENWADE HOUSE

Great Witchingham, Norwich, Norfolk NR9 5QP

Telephone: (0603) 872288 *Fax: 0603 872355*

Norwich 10, London 120, Cambridge 60, Newmarket 45, Yarmouth 30, Cromer 25

R & R licence; 36 en suite bedrooms, all with direct dial telephone, TV; trouser press, hairdryer, tea and coffee making facilities; full central heating; last orders 9.30 p.m.; children welcome; dogs accepted; conferences; heated outdoor swimming pool, fitness gym; golf 6 miles; tennis, squash, shooting 3 miles, trout and coarse fishing; Access, Amex, Diners, Visa cards accepted.

I could not believe the way Lenwade House has been transformed since Harmony Hotels acquired the property. There is a new extension, comprising 19 bedrooms, conference centre and gymnasium. Lenwade is set in 18 acres of beautiful woods and gardens, and there are several improvements underway within its environs, including a herb garden to provide fresh ingredients for the kitchen. The lake is brimming with trout, and the hotel can provide visitors with rods for fly or coarse fishing in the river. The restaurant, featuring pink table-cloths and napkins, is most relaxing, with its views over the gardens. The food is delicious, with à la carte and table d'hôte menus, all superbly prepared by chef, Brendan Ansbro, who uses as many local products as possible. Adjoining the restaurant is the new conservatory, where you can take a relaxing breakfast, looking out over the beautiful landscape. The conservatory can also be booked for private parties. There is now a wide range of bedrooms from which to choose, from the luxurious and spacious newly built rooms, to the original rooms, which are both comfortable and full of character. The new gymnasium is superbly equipped, so there is no excuse not to keep fit! Room and breakfast weekdays from £46.00 single, £56.00 double, weekend rates from £41.00 single, £51.00 double. Weekly rate from £240.00. Hotel open all year.

THE MAYNARD ARMS HOTEL

Grindleford, Derbyshire S30 1HP

Telephone: (0433) 30321 *Fax: 0433 30445*

Bakewell 5, Sheffield 9, Chatsworth 4

F licence; 13 bedrooms, 11 with private bathrooms, all with radio, telephone, colour TV and trouser press; 2 separate bathrooms; central heating; night service to 11.30 p.m.; last orders at 9.30 p.m. (10.00 p.m. Saturdays); vegetarian meals, other diets on request; children welcome; dogs by arrangement; conferences max. 100; outdoor swimming pool 4 miles; golf 5 miles; fishing at Ladybower and Chatsworth by arrangement; major credit cards accepted.

This beautiful 19th century building was bought in 1982, and transformed into the attractive country house it is today. It is situated in the Peak District National Park off the A625 road from Bakewell to Sheffield, ideal as the centre for a holiday in this lovely area or as a peaceful retreat. The Residents' Lounge and the bedrooms have been refurbished to a high standard of décor and comfort and two rooms have four-poster beds. There are some beautiful views across the Derbyshire hills. The Padley Restaurant, overlooking the private garden, offers an excellent menu, with a wide choice which is changed seasonally. The Longshaw Bar, popular with local residents, has a choice of fifteen dishes plus a superb cold table and is open for lunch and in the evenings. There are many routed walks and if you choose to arrive by train at Grindleford Station, please ask to be met. Close by are Chatsworth House, historical Bakewell and in the summer, the well-dressing festivals take place. Room and English breakfast from £45.00 single, £58.00 twin including VAT and newspaper. Bargain breaks available. Open all year.

WEST LODGE PARK

Cockfosters Road, Hadley Wood,
Nr. Barnet, Hertfordshire EN4 0PY

Telephone: 081-440 8311 *Fax: 081-449 3698*

London 12, St. Albans 10, Hatfield 10, London Airport 25

R and R licence; 50 en suite bedrooms, all with radio, direct telephone, TV; full central heating; lift; night service; late meals to 9.30 p.m.; children welcome; baby listening; conferences; indoor swimming pool 3 miles, golf 1 mile, tennis and squash 2 miles, riding 2 miles, putting, croquet, bar billiards, fitness trail; credit cards accepted.

I had such a pleasant surprise when I arrived at West Lodge Park to find the hotel, although only 12 miles from central London, standing in its own 34 acres of park surrounded by beautiful rolling country, with hardly a house in sight. Guests enjoy lovely views of the countryside, a lake and the arboretum created by Mr. Ted Beale and his family, who have owned the hotel since 1945, in which time they have gathered a fine collection of Old Masters, mostly by the 17th century artist, Mary Beale. I was greeted by Mr. Beale in the hall of the mansion, which dates back to the 16th century and has been rebuilt over the years, in front of a welcoming log fire. There were fresh flowers throughout the hotel. The four reception rooms are used on occasions for elegant musical evenings and other functions. Much thought and imagination are shown in the à la carte menus, supported by an extensive wine list. The bedrooms are individually furnished and beautifully appointed in keeping with the country house atmosphere. The Beales and their long-serving staff, headed by General Manager John Phillips, add so much to this delightful environment with their constant attention to providing a service that ensures the comfort and happiness of their guests. Single room with English breakfast £75.00, double room from £99.50. Always open.

GRANTS HOTEL

Swan Road, Harrogate, North Yorkshire HG1 2SS

Telephone: (0423) 560666 *Fax: 0423 502550*

London 208, Leeds 15, Manchester 70, Hull 70

F licence; 37 bedrooms, all with en suite bathroom, telephone and TV; room and night service; baby listening; lift; last orders for dinner 9.30 p.m.; bar meals; special diets; children welcome; dogs allowed; conferences up to 14 in board room, 25 in theatre; golf and tennis ½ mile; riding 3 miles; hotel open all year; major credit cards accepted.

I will not dwell on the delights of Harrogate and the beautiful county of Yorkshire other than to say that there can be nowhere in England with so much to do and see, in either town or country, within so short a walking or driving distance. To me, one of the greatest attractions is Grants Hotel. It is rapidly gaining a well deserved reputation as one of the best small town house hotels in the country. From the first warm welcome to the final departure, the efficient and courteous staff ensure that a stay here is a memorable one. The beautifully decorated rooms exude an air of luxury and the bedrooms are superbly comfortable, with all the touches that make life so easy these days in a top class establishment. The Chimney Pots Restaurant, also building a name for itself over a wide area, is excellent and the food is varied, interesting and delicious. The running of the hotel is orchestrated by the proprietors Peter and Pam Grant, along with Ian Kimberley, who are to be congratulated on the many accolades and awards that they receive. The hotel is ideally situated for shopping, conferences, touring and so on, but it is also particularly suitable for short breaks either of a quiet nature or of a more sporting type. These breaks can include romantic weekends, ballooning, theatre visits, and many others. Room and breakfast from £42.50 per night, or £297.50 weekly.

NEWTON HOUSE HOTEL

5-7 York Place, Knaresborough, Nr. Harrogate,
North Yorkshire HG5 0AD

Telephone: (0423) 863539 *Fax: 0423 869614*

London 200, Edinburgh 200, York 12, Harrogate 4, Dales 20

R licence; 12 en suite bedrooms (2 suitable for disabled), all with minibars and TV, 11 with direct dial telephone; 2 four poster rooms; baby listening; last orders for breakfast 9.00 a.m. (weekends 9.30 a.m.); diets by arrangement; children welcome; dogs by arrangement; conferences up to 50; snooker/billiards next door; leisure centre 20 yards; tennis ½ mile; many golf courses and riding stables nearby; walking, shooting and fishing; closed Christmas week only; Visa, Amex and Master Card accepted.

This hotel is a beautiful, 350 year old listed building, built with stone from nearby Knaresborough Castle. The cellars are reputed to have housed condemned prisoners en route to York to be hanged. Today, however, it is very picturesque, complete with a courtyard, which is very important in this area, where parking space is at a premium. Inside, the rooms are most comfortably furnished, and a warm and friendly atmosphere pervades. Homely is the best word I can find to describe it, for indeed, one feels immediately at home. This relaxed air, however, hides the fact that the hotel is professionally run by Len and Jackie Cohen. Nothing is too much trouble, and almost any activity can be arranged, from fishing to painting, and advice on what to do or see in the area is readily imparted. Newton House is an excellent base for sightseeing in beautiful Yorkshire. Unlike most hotels featured in *Signpost*, Newton House does not normally cater for meals other than breakfast, though your hosts will be happy to provide evening meals for eight people or more by arrangement. There are many super restaurants locally, and nearby Harrogate is a veritable gastronomic paradise. Room and traditional full English breakfast from £50.00 per couple, per night (£5 per person supplement for four posters). For weekly stays, 7th night FREE (not including Bank Holidays, trade fairs, conferences or exhibitions).

NIDD HALL HOTEL AND COUNTRY CLUB

Nidd, Harrogate, North Yorkshire HG3 3BN

Telephone: (0423) 771598 *Fax: 0423 770931*

Leeds/Bradford Airport 22, Harrogate 5, York 22

F licence; 80 bedrooms, all with en suite bathroom, TV and telephone; 24 hour room service; baby listening; lift; last orders for dinner 9.30 p.m.; bar meals; special diets; children welcome; conferences up to 200; games room; billiards; indoor heated swimming pool, leisure centre, sauna, solarium, gymnasium, squash court, sailing and boating, tennis, shooting and fishing; golf and riding nearby; natural spa pool in Harrogate; hotel open all year; major credit cards accepted.

Take an old country mansion, restore it and its grounds to their former splendour, sympathetically and discreetly install all the modern conveniences that a hotel guest now expects, add a superb leisure centre, and what do you get? At Nidd Hall you have your answer; a premier hotel, with courteous, efficient staff, set in this beautiful part of England. There is only one dilemma facing visitors – choice! Whether to relax in the peace of the library or in the lovely grounds? Whether to take advantage of the many sporting facilities that exist here, or that can be arranged? Whether to study the hall itself and its history, or explore the many historic houses that abound in the area? Whether to dine in the sumptuous dining room, or to have a more informal meal in the Brasserie, located in the vaulted cellars? Wherever you choose to eat, the food is most carefully prepared, cooked and presented, as well as being truly delicious, and the extensive wine list is a revelation. In short, Nidd Hall is the epitome of country house hotels, where the "Bon Vivant", the country sportsman, nature lover and historian can stay in the utmost comfort. Tariff on application.

BEAUPORT PARK HOTEL

Battle Road, Hastings, East Sussex TN38 8EA

Telephone: (0424) 851222 *Telex: 957126* *Fax: 0424 852465*

London 58, Hastings 3, Brighton 36, Dover 44, Rye 11, Tunbridge Wells 30

F licence; 23 en suite bedrooms, all with radio, TV, auto-dial telephone; full central heating; night service; late meals to 10.00 p.m.; diets; children welcome, baby listening; dogs welcome; conferences; dancing once a month in winter; outdoor heated swimming pool; all weather tennis court; sea bathing, sailing 3 miles; golf, squash 50 yards; riding on the premises; shooting by arrangement; croquet lawn, country walks, putting green; fishing 3 miles; most credit cards accepted.

Built in the early 18th century, this imposing house is set in thirty-three acres of gardens and woodlands. The hotel is situated on the main A2100 south of Battle, 58 miles from London. East Sussex is an area rich in history and beauty, with many interesting towns, houses and gardens to visit. In recent years additions have been made to the original buildings of the hotel to provide increased facilities. This has not in any way detracted from the friendly and efficient atmosphere which has been created by the residential proprietors and their staff. The dining room, overlooking the formal Italian garden, provides an excellent cuisine with flambé dishes being a speciality. Afterwards the Georgian style lounge with its open log fire is a perfect place to relax. The elegantly furnished bedrooms, including a room with a four poster bed, are equipped with all modern amenities and all have bathrooms en suite. The hotel is happy to cater for conferences and special occasions. A wide range of leisure facilities are available in and around the hotel (see above). Room and breakfast from £50.00 (single), £68.00 (twin/double). Open all the year round.

TUDOR COURT HOTEL

Rye Road, Hawkhurst, Kent TN18 5DA

Telephone: (0580) 752312 *Telex: 957 565 TCH* *Fax: 0580 753966*

Rye 13, Hastings 16, Maidstone 20, London 60, Tenterden 10, Tunbridge Wells 17

F licence; 18 bedrooms, all with private bath or shower, direct dial telephone, radio alarm, colour TV, hair dryers and tea making facilities; full central heating; late meals to 9.15 p.m.; diets; children and dogs welcome; small conferences; children's play area; sea bathing 15 miles; sailing, boating and fishing Bewl Bridge Reservoir 7 miles; golf 1 mile (9 hole 5 miles); tennis by arrangement; squash 1 mile; riding 5 miles; ballooning by arrangement; open all year; most credit cards accepted.

This attractive hotel is situated on the A268, a mile outside the picturesque village of Hawkhurst in the heart of the Kentish Weald. Mr David Hill L.H.C.I.M.A.is an experienced and understanding host, who works hard to maintain a high standard. The hotel offers its visitors a refreshingly simple and relaxing stay. Great care is taken over the preparation and presentation of the meals – home-made shortbread, apple pie and steak and kidney pie are only a few of the specials that are always available. The recently completed Garden Wing adds a modern, sophisticated dimension to this charming and comfortable establishment. The hotel is ideally situated for touring this part of the Garden of England, with its many beautiful houses open to the public. Room with bath and breakfast from £51.50 single, £82.00 twin. Other prices on application.

EDWARDIAN INTERNATIONAL

Bath Road, Hayes, Middlesex UB3 5AW

Telephone: (081) 759 6311 *Fax: 081 759 4559*

Heathrow 1, Windsor 7, London 12, Hampton Court 10

F licence; 450 en suite bedrooms all with telephone, TV, baby listening; 24 hour room service; lift; special diets; coffee shop brasserie; children welcome; dogs accepted by special request; conferences max. 450; leisure centre with indoor heated swimming pool, sauna, solarium, gymnasium; credit cards accepted.

One of London's newest and most luxurious five star hotels, the Edwardian International (previously the Skyway Hotel), has been refurbished to enormously high standards. The visitor should leave the M4 at Junction 4 following signs to Terminals 1, 2 and 3, and just before the tunnel, turn left, signposted A4 and Central London. When on the A4, the hotel is 200 yards on the left. The décor throughout is simply superb, including beautiful hand woven Thailand carpets. All rooms are triple glazed and air conditioned, and all bedrooms have hand painted furniture, crested sheets, 16 channel TV and bathrooms of Sicilian marble. There are 17 beautifully decorated and luxuriously equipped suites, some with four posters and all with jacuzzi baths. A new innovation is the express check out system, where your account can be displayed on your room TV for you to check, so speeding your departure. A luxurious Drawing Room provides afternoon tea or cocktails and Henley's Restaurant serves food from à la carte menus. The Polo Lounge serves drinks all day and the Continental Brasserie has an 18 hour menu for travellers. Conferences may be held for up to 450 delegates. There is a swimming pool, health club and gymnasium, while shops include a hairdresser, florist and newsagent. Single room and breakfast from £140.00. Open all year.

THE BEL ALP HOUSE

Haytor, Nr. Bovey Tracey, South Devon TQ13 9XX

Telephone: Haytor (0364) 661217 *Fax: 0364 661292*

Exeter 18, Plymouth 34, Bovey Tracey 2½, Newton Abbott 8

R and R licence; 9 en suite bedrooms (2 on ground floor), all with colour TV, radio, intercom, direct dial telephones, tea/coffee making facilities; central heating; lift; out of season small conferences, functions and dinner parties; full size billiards table; games room; riding by arrangement; golf nearby; Access and Visa accepted.

The Bel Alp House is a small Country House, set in 8½ acres of well kept, attractive grounds at 900 ft. on the south east edge of Dartmoor, with magnificent views extending over the surrounding countryside. The House is finely furnished in a style in keeping with the original Edwardian Mansion. Colour schemes are soft and restful, and with the country house furnishings you find comfort in a home of distinction and dignity. Bel Alp is superbly run by the owners, Roger and Sarah Curnock and their family, and you are assured of a warm welcome, considerate service and really good food. The Dining Room, with its beautifully set tables, offers a different 5 course dinner each evening with alternative courses. The view from the dining room, as with most of the hotel rooms, is panoramic and seems to stretch forever into the distance. The interesting menus, with both English and Continental recipes are prepared with imagination, using fresh local produce whenever possible, and the service is very good. There is a well chosen wine list. The bedrooms are individually furnished and well appointed. I can thoroughly recommend Bel Alp House at any time of the year – an ideal centre for exploring Dartmoor and surrounding countryside. Room and breakfast from £54.00. Dinner, room and breakfast from £72.00 per person, inclusive of VAT. Other terms on application. The Hotel has received "highly commended" grading from the English Tourist Board. Closed December and January. Open November and February by prior booking only.

THE BLACK SWAN HOTEL

Helmsley, North Yorkshire YO6 5BJ

Telephone: (0439) 70466 *Fax: 0439 70174*

York 24, Thirsk 14, London 233, Leeds 48

F licence; 44 en suite bedrooms, including 4 suites all with telephone, col. T.V.; full central heating; night service; last orders 9.30 p.m.; bar meals; diets; children welcome, and baby listening; dogs accepted; conferences; golf, riding, shooting, fishing by arrangement; outdoor swimming pool nearby; all credit cards accepted.

The Black Swan epitomises all that is best in hotel keeping. To begin with, this historic hotel is sited in a prominent position in the lovely old market town of Helmsley which itself is situated perfectly for touring Yorkshire, one of the most interesting and scenically beautiful parts of England. Secondly, the building itself is full of the warmth and charm embodied in it during its many hundreds of years of existence. This atmosphere is discreetly complemented by all those modern comforts that make staying in today's hotels such a joy. There are even such innovations as "floating" floors to deaden the sound of the creaking old boards! But enough of this or there will be no room to write of the food. The Black Swan must surely be the proudest of hotels as its team of chefs is carving a well deserved niche in the annals of haute cuisine. Executive Head Chef John Benson-Smith and Head Chef Alec Howard give monthly culinary demonstrations in the hotel and John frequently demonstrates at other far-flung locations. The incredible menus are so imaginative and adventurous and yet they are unbelievably delicious. The wines to complement these repasts have been selected by Ian Martin, the Chancellor of the Jurade de Saint Emilion of the North of England, and these can be chosen from the rack by visiting the cellars. Space allows no more than to say that The Black Swan is a gourmet's paradise, a hedonist's heaven and a tourist's Garden of Eden. Tariff on application. Open all year.

FEVERSHAM ARMS HOTEL
Helmsley, North Yorkshire YO6 5AG

Telephone: (0439) 70766

York 24, Teeside Airport 35

F licence; 18 en suite bedrooms (6 ground floor), some four poster, all with radio, telephone, TV, full central heating; late meals to 9.30 p.m.; diets; children welcome; baby listening; dogs welcome; conferences up to 30 (18 residential); games room; swimming pool; tennis; riding; golf nearby; Access, Amex, Barclay and Diners Club cards accepted.

Originally an old coaching inn, this hotel has been tastefully modernised and improved to a high standard not often found in this country. The bedrooms are well appointed with every modern convenience, including hair drier, safe, trouser press and tea/coffee making facilities, and the reception rooms are relaxing and comfortable. Food is interesting and varied, for the noted restaurant specialises in both game and seafood, but the menu also caters for many tastes other than these. The wine list is truly incredible: the largest selection of Spanish wines that I have ever seen in the UK and a fairly comprehensive selection of French 1st Cru and other wines in all price ranges. With a superb tennis court, an attractive swimming pool and an acre of gardens in which to relax, what more can one ask for when staying in this most beautiful part of England? It need hardly be added that Helmsley is an excellent centre for many outdoor sporting activities and for exploring the North York Moors National Park. Room and breakfast from £45.00 single, £70.00 twin or double and four poster or suite £80.00. Bargain breaks available all year round. Open all year.

THE PHEASANT

Harome, Helmsley, N. Yorkshire YO6 5JG

Telephone: (0439) 71241

Helmsley 3, York 22, London 220, Scarborough 28, Leeds 48, Edinburgh 160

R &R licence; 14 en suite bedrooms (1 ground floor), all with telephone, colour TV, tea/coffee making facilities; full central heating; last orders 8.00 p.m.; bar meals (lunch); diets; children over 14 welcome; dogs by arrangement; conferences max. 12; golf, tennis, riding, fishing, outdoor heated swimming pool all nearby; credit cards not accepted.

The Pheasant was recommended to me by another hotelier of note in Yorkshire and how right he was to guide me to it. Set in a pretty village, overlooking the village pond, it has been imaginatively created from a group of buildings on two sides of a courtyard. Inside, the log fires, the antiques and the numerous beams lend an air of warmth and comfort to the tastefully decorated rooms. Old fashioned in atmosphere the hotel might be but the best of all the modern conveniences are also there where needed. The bedrooms, for example, all have colour television, telephone, tea/coffee making facilities, etc. Mrs 'Tricia Binks provides the most delicious food and many of the ingredients come from the hotel's own large garden and paddock. Holly Cottage is also available – this is a charming, thatched 16th century cottage just 350 yards from the hotel, with 2 double bedrooms and two sitting rooms, all attractively furnished to the same high standard as the hotel. It is serviced by the hotel staff and meals are taken in the hotel. A quiet and peaceful haven with a delightful atmosphere. Having said all this, the Pheasant makes an ideal base from which to explore this most beautiful part of England, where there is so much to see and do. Dinner, room and breakfast from £37.50, weekly from £262.50–£350.00 including VAT. Closed January and February.

RYEDALE LODGE

Nunnington, Nr. Helmsley,
North Yorkshire YO6 5XB

Telephone: (04395) 246

Helmsley 5, York 20, East coast 30, London 230, Edinburgh 160

R licence; 7 en suite bedrooms (1 ground floor), all with colour TV, telephone and full central heating; last orders 9.30 p.m.; diets; children welcome, baby listening; no dogs; conferences up to 20; fishing; golf and riding 5 miles; shooting by arrangement; Visa and Access cards accepted.

What a delightful find! In what used to be a country railway station, Jon and Janet Laird have created a superb little hotel. Where trains once ran, you can now stroll and listen to the evening bird song and the distant lowing of cattle. It is an idyllic setting. However, Ryedale Lodge is exceptional not only for its situation, but for its comfort; inside every room is tastefully and beautifully furnished, and an air of warmth and serenity pervades throughout. As the reader can no doubt deduce, I find this hotel particularly inviting, but it is for its food that I shall be most tempted to return. Not only is Janet Laird a good cook, but she chooses the finest and freshest ingredients to produce the most varied and imaginative menu. The results are stupendous! I look forward eagerly to visiting this hotel again and again. If you look at a map of Yorkshire, Nunnington is almost in the middle and as such Ryedale is truly the centre of all that is best in this lovely and historic county. Hotel closed for three weeks in January only. Room and breakfast from £38.00, weekly rates from £295.00.

HOAR CROSS HALL

Hoar Cross, Nr. Yoxall, Staffordshire DE13 8QS

A Health and Leisure Hotel in a Stately Home

Telephone: (0283) 75671 *Fax: 0283 75652*

London 120, Lichfield 12, Airports – East Mids. 22, Birmingham Int. 30

F licence; 90 bedrooms (4 suited to disabled), all with en suite bathroom, telephone and TV; room and night service; 2 lifts; last orders 9.30 p.m.; 2 restaurants for residents; special diets; over 16s welcome; no dogs; conferences max. 30; full health & beauty spa facilities; hair dresser; dance studio; indoor Roman-style hydrotherapy pool & whirlpool spa; sauna and solaria, gymnasium; badminton, tennis; golf improvement facility; riding, shooting and fishing by arrangement; boules, croquet; bicycles; open all year; all major credit cards accepted.

It is said that health is the ultimate luxury, and to that end, Hoar Cross Hall is a health resort in a luxurious stately home. Recreated in keeping with its original splendour, conducive to total relaxation, this magnificent Grade II listed building is approached by a drive lined with lime trees. The splendidly wooded grounds also boast a ha-ha and formal gardens with fountains. Professional, caring therapists help you to relax with body baths, massage, facials, beauty treatment, swimming exercises, aerobic and dance classes. Guests may luxuriate in the whirlpool, steam rooms, sauna or spa pool. Bedrooms are beautifully furnished with the choice of water bed, four poster, half tester, crown tester, king sized beds. All are en suite with every conceivable luxury. The original leather lined library has been discreetly adapted into a champagne and cocktail bar. Meals may be taken either in the traditional Dining Room with ornate ceiling and crystal chandeliers, or in the restaurant overlooking the pools. Hoar Cross eating has a healthy aspect and much of the food is calorie controlled. Hoar Cross Hall can be found off the A515 between Lichfield and Ashbourne. The very reasonable rates include bed, breakfast, lunch, dinner, all facilities and some inclusive beauty treatments from £95.00 per person. Single supplement of £20.00 per day.

COMBE HOUSE HOTEL

Holford, Nr. Bridgwater, Somerset TA5 1RZ

Telephone: (027 874) 382, Guests 213

London 153, Birmingham 132, Bridgwater 12, Bristol 45, Minehead 15, Dunster Castle 12

R and R licence; 23 bedrooms all with direct dial telephone and tea/coffee facilities; colour TV; 14 with private bathrooms, four poster bed; central heating; children welcome; meals to 8.30 p.m.; dogs welcome but not in public rooms; tennis; croquet; indoor swimming pool; solarium.

This 17th century house is situated off the A39 at Holford amid romantic and beautiful surroundings in the heart of the Quantock Hills, famous for their wildlife, red deer and ponies. Combe House Hotel, which was acquired in 1976 by the resident proprietors, Mr and Mrs Bjergfelt, stands in its own grounds of five acres half a mile from the main road, with lovely garden and a wonderful 100 year-old Monkey Puzzle tree. For the actively inclined there is a hard tennis court, croquet lawn and indoor heated swimming pool. The hotel is furnished to a high standard with genuine period furniture and attractive décor throughout and there is a fine collection of Royal Danish Christmas plates. Of the well appointed and comfortable bedrooms, fourteen have private bathrooms en suite. Great care is taken over the preparation and presentation of the meals, where fresh fruit and vegetables feature prominently on the menu. Good riding stables nearby provide suitable mounts for all ages to ride over the moors and forests of the surrounding hills. Golf is available at Minehead and Enmore and a championship course at Burnham-on-Sea. Room and breakfast from £29.50 (single) and £60.00 (twin). Open all year. Write for colour brochure to R. S. Bjergfelt.

COMBE HOUSE

Gittisham, Nr. Honiton, Devon EX14 0AD

Telephone: (0404) 42756 and 43560 *Fax: 0404 46004*

London 155, Birmingham 149, Bristol 61, Exeter 16, Honiton 2, Airport 14

R and R licence; 15 en suite bedrooms (one suite), 2 with four poster beds, all with colour TV, direct dial telephone and hairdryers; diets available, including a vegetarian menu; children welcome; dogs welcome; small executive conferences; weekend house parties up to 20 welcome; small wedding receptions; croquet; trout fishing; riding by arrangement; tennis nearby; golf at Honiton; sea bathing 7 miles; lovely walks and well kept gardens.

This 14th century Elizabethan Mansion lies in 2000 acres of parkland adjoining the Otter Valley, off the A30 Honiton–Exeter road to Gittisham. John and Thérèse Boswell own and care for the hotel, and enhance the historic Country Mansion atmosphere with many antiques from the Boswell ancestral Scottish home. The staff work as a cheerful, efficient and attentive team. The spacious, restful bedrooms are dignified and well appointed. Among the magnificent rooms downstairs are the Entrance Hall – a fine example of Caroline grandeur – and the large, panelled drawing room. The cosy Cocktail Bar (adjacent to the smaller drawing room) features John's interest in horse racing. He owns some wonderful horses and pictures of them adorn the walls. A wonderful candlelit dinner is served in the two lovely dining rooms. The chef de cuisine is Rosy Higgott who has been at Combe House for many years, and produces superbly cooked dishes, full of imagination. The wine list is excellent in its range and quality. Room and breakfast from £55.00 per person (single), £85.00 (double/twin), inclusive of VAT and service. Other terms on application, including out of season rate. Member of Pride of Britain. Open all year, but closed on Sundays and Mondays in January and February.

WORSLEY ARMS HOTEL

Hovingham, North Yorkshire YO6 4LA

Telephone: (0653) 628234 *Fax: 0653 628130*

London 213, Malton 8, Helmsley 8, York 16

F licence; 23 bedrooms, all with en suite bathroom, radio, telephone and TV; room service; night service till midnight; baby listening; last orders for dinner 9.00 p.m.; bar lunches; special diets; children welcome; dogs accepted; conferences up to 40; 1 squash court; golf, tennis, riding, shooting and fishing in the locality; hotel open all year; Master Card and Visa accepted.

There is too little space to really do justice in writing about this delightful hotel and its surroundings. It is a Georgian building set in a beautiful Yorkshire village where the local cricket match is often the major topic of conversation in the bar. Indeed on the day that I last visited, the click of bat against ball and the call of the cuckoo were the only sounds to punctuate the talk on this particular evening. Outwardly little has changed here for generations, but the hotel exterior hides a tastefully decorated and superbly modernised establishment. The staff, supervised by Mr John Adcock, the manager, are impeccably efficient, and yet a quiet and friendly atmosphere prevails. The menu is excellent and the food is perfectly prepared and cooked. Hovingham is situated in the centre of all that is best in the North Riding, and it makes a perfect base for the walker, historian, archaeologist, general country lover or for anyone, who like myself, just wants peace and quiet with good food and congenial surroundings. This is one of my favourite hotels. Room and breakfast from £52.00 single, £74.00 double.

HUNSTRETE HOUSE

Hunstrete, Chelwood, Nr. Bath, Avon BS18 4NS

Telephone: (0761) 490490 *Telex: 449540* *Fax: 0761 490372*

Bath 8, Bristol 8, London 120

F licence; 24 en suite bedrooms, all with colour TV, telephone and full central heating; night service; last orders 10.00 p.m.; diets; children 10yrs and over welcome; no dogs; outdoor heated swimming pool; croquet, tennis; Visa and Access cards accepted.

This elegant 18th century country house has been carefully and thoughtfully converted into a very special hotel. Set in classical English countryside on the edge of the Mendip Hills, many rooms have uninterrupted views over the undulating fields and woodlands, and deer graze in the park beside the house. It is hard to believe you are only eight miles from Bath and Bristol. The reception rooms are beautifully furnished with antiques, paintings and a profusion of flowers from the lovely gardens. In the drawing room, hall and library, log fires burn in the winter and on cooler days. The bedrooms are all individually decorated and furnished to a high standard combining the benefits of an hotel room with the atmosphere of an elegant private country house. The Terrace dining room overlooks a delightful flower-filled courtyard which features a fountain. The Head Chef and his eight man team offer light and interesting dishes using the best English meat and fish together with produce from their own immaculate kitchen garden. Hunstrete House is a member of Clipper Hotels, who are all recommended by *Signpost.* Room and breakfast from £95.00 single, £170.00 double. Open all year.

HUTTON COURT

Hutton, Avon BS24 9SN

Telephone: (0934) 814343

London 145, Bristol 20, Bath 25, Wells 18, Glastonbury 20

R & R licence; 10 bedrooms with en suite private facilities, all with TV, telephone, tea/coffee making facilities; full central heating; meals to 9.45 p.m.; diets; dogs welcome; conferences; bathing, sailing, golf, riding all within 5 miles; sea fishing from Weston, trout at Chew and Blagdon; shooting by arrangement; Amex and USA Mastercard credit cards accepted.

Hutton Court is located in Church Lane in the village of Hutton, and is set in 5 acres of grounds. This is an historic Manor House, granted by William the Conqueror to the Bishop of Coutances, mentioned in the Domesday Book, and with rooms and architecture that show its development from the 1400's to the present day. The baronial hall (now the dining room), with its 30 foot high vaulted ceiling, was built in the 15th century, and work of this period is very much in evidence. In 1603, the Bishop of Bath and Wells bought the Court and built the Jacobean part of the house. Antique furniture and fine original paintings contribute to the atmosphere, and there is a panelled cocktail bar and a conservatory where breakfast can be served. All the bedrooms are individually decorated and furnished, the Master Bedroom having a magnificent Jacobean fireplace. Excellent food is provided by the experienced chef, and guests can choose from a list of over 100 wines, selected not only from the classic areas of France and Germany, but ten other producing countries around the world. This is a marvellous base for visits to many famous places – Wookey Hole, Cheddar Gorge and Caves, the Quantocks, Longleat, Montacute, Bath, Wells and many more. Bed and full English breakfast from £35.00 per person including VAT. Open all year.

COW AND CALF HOTEL

Ilkley Moor, Ilkley, West Yorkshire LS29 8BT

Telephone: (0943) 607335

London 207, Leeds 16, Bradford 13, Harrogate 17, York 35, Bolton Abbey 5

F licence; 17 en suite bedrooms, including 5 executive rooms; all have colour TV and radio, telephone and full central heating; last orders 9.30 p.m.; diets by arrangement; children welcome, baby listening; dogs allowed; conferences welcome; games room; indoor and outdoor heated swimming pool 1 mile; golf, tennis, squash, badminton, fishing and riding 1 mile; grouse shooting locally when in season; Amex, Diners, Access and Barclay cards accepted.

From its imposing location on the edge of Ilkley Moor, the Cow and Calf Hotel commands magnificent views of the Wharfe Valley and the surrounding countryside. Its position is also ideal for those who wish to indulge in the many outdoor activities for which this part of the country is so well known, whether hiking or just rambling on the Moor. The hotel is a small family run affair, under the supervision of brothers, Andrew and Philip Norfolk and their parents. In all rooms, the choice of décor, including many hand embroidered fabrics contributes to the warm and cosy atmosphere of the interior, a welcoming contrast to the splendid isolation of the landscape. The hotel also features a conservatory and private garden for you to stroll through, as an alternative to the rugged countryside. In the restaurant, both traditional food and cuisine from further afield are served from an à la carte and table d'hôte menu. Lunch is offered in "Le Jardin", beautifully designed in pastel greens which enhance the light and airy effect. Close to the hotel are many places of interest; the world of the Brontës at Haworth, and the Dales of James Herriot to name but two, while for the businessman, the centres of Leeds, Harrogate and Bradford are within half an hour's drive. Room and breakfast from £55.00 single and £65.00 twin. Open all year.

ROMBALDS HOTEL & RESTAURANT

West View, Wells Road, Ilkley,
West Yorkshire LS29 9JG

Telephone: (0943) 603201 *Telex: 51593* *Fax: 0943 816586*

Harrogate 17, Leeds 18, Skipton 9, York 35, London 219

R & R licence; 15 bedrooms, all with en suite bathroom, telephone and TV; 24 hr. room service; baby listening; night service; last orders for dinner 9.30 p.m.; bar meals; special diets; children welcome; dogs accepted; conferences up to 50; presentation theatre; leisure centre, sauna, solarium, spa pool and gymnasium ½ mile; indoor/outdoor heated swimming pool, golf, squash and tennis 1 mile; riding 2 miles; hotel open all year; Amex, Diners, Master Card and Visa welcome.

Rombalds Hotel has so much to recommend it, from its position on the edge of Ilkley, with the moor behind it and the town centre below. It is known for its high standards of service and comfort, and the tastefully decorated bedrooms offer a choice from single rooms to suites. There are two private dining rooms, and the elegant lounge, cocktail bar and restaurant are linked by attractive arches, which add to the intimate ambience of an hotel that happily manages to be 'all things to all people'. There is also a 'state of the art' presentation studio, for which congratulations are in order to owners, Mr. and Mrs. Guthrie; for this theatre has just won The White Rose Award for Excellence and Innovation. Everything that a visiting business man could command is discreetly available. From the impressive modern kitchens flow meals, beautifully cooked and presented by Chef Chris Brown and his team. Selecting the best of meat, fish and game, his creations make a great contribution to the star quality of this small hotel. Companion to the menu is an excellent wine list, offering wines from the modest to the exceptional. Ilkley lies on the A65, half way between Skipton and Leeds, with the Dales and Yorkshire Moors, Harrogate and York itself, in easy reach. The hotel has plenty of books and an information board to aid decisions. Room and breakfast from £55.00, weekly from £400.00.

THE COMMODORE HOTEL

Marine Parade, Instow, North Devon EX39 4JN

Telephone: (0271) 860347 *Fax: 0271 861233*

London 210, Barnstaple 6, Bideford 3

F licence; 21 en suite bedrooms, all with direct dial telephone, colour TV, radio/intercom, hairdryer, trouser press, baby listening, tea and coffee making facilities; full central heating; dinner to 9.15 p.m.; diets; bar snacks; morning coffee, afternoon teas; conferences up to 180 and receptions welcome; games area; 3 moorings; water ski-ing; sea bathing; sailing; golf, tennis, squash, riding all nearby.

The Commodore, a great favourite of mine, is run with quiet efficiency by the owners, Bruce and Patricia Woolaway, who with their son Gary, and daughter Vanessa, personally look after this highly recommended hotel, where quality and service is their first consideration. The Commodore is sited in an outstanding position at the mouth of the Taw and Torridge estuary. There is lots to do and enjoy whatever the time of the year, an ideal place for autumn and spring holidays. I was most impressed with the conference facilities – those interested do make a careful note. The public rooms are spacious, nicely furnished and comfortable. The bedrooms, with their individual colour schemes, most with balconies, are very comfortable and well appointed. The Commodore has a great reputation for its food. Locally caught fish, shellfish, lobster and salmon are a speciality and all dishes are interesting, well presented and served by a cheerful and willing staff. The wine list is selective and good. You will receive a warm welcome and if you are looking for good living, peace and a happy atmosphere, you will find it at The Commodore, and will want to return again and again. In high season, room and breakfast from £50.00 single, £82.00 double inclusive of VAT. Other prices on application. Open all year.

RIVERSIDE HOTEL

Stramongate Bridge, Kendal, Cumbria LA9 4BZ

Telephone: (0539) 724707 *Fax: 0539 740274*

London 280, Windermere 8, Manchester 52, Edinburgh 94, Glasgow 82, York 72, Sedbergh 8

F licence; 47 bedrooms, all with en suite bathroom, telephone, and TV; baby listening; 24 hour service; lift; last orders for dinner 10.00 p.m.; bar meals; special diets; children welcome; guide dogs only accepted; conferences up to 200; indoor heated swimming pool, solarium, spa pool, gymnasium; squash court, riding and fishing all locally; local shooting club; sailing and boating on Lake Windermere; 2 golf courses within 8 miles (Windermere, Kendal); sea bathing 15 miles, Morecambe; hotel open all year; Visa, Master Card, Amex and Diners accepted.

Unusually for this part of the country this hotel is a town hotel, but it is one with a difference. It is full of charm and character, and is a converted 17th century tannery, right on the banks of the river Kent. It is both convenient for exploring and shopping in the interesting and historic town of Kendal, and yet it is an excellent base from which to tour the Lune Valley, even as far as the Yorkshire Dales to the east, The Lake District to the west, and the Eden Valley as far as the Borders and Hadrian's Wall to the north. Southwards, the towns of Lancaster, Morecambe Bay and Blackpool are all within an hour's drive. The hotel itself offers extreme comfort, with all the modern conveniences that we now expect of a good hotel. Excellent food is served in the delightful dining rooms. For the businessman looking for a comfortable, yet unusual venue for a conference, the Riverside is certainly different. For the holiday maker, a more centrally placed base could hardly be found in this beautiful region. Room and breakfast from £50.00 single, £66.00 double. Dinner, bed and breakfast, £318.50 weekly.

LYZZICK HALL HOTEL

Underskiddaw, Keswick, Cumbria CA12 4PY

Telephone: (07687) 72277

Edinburgh 128, London 300, Keswick 2, Stranraer 139, Hull 169

F licence; 20 en suite bedrooms (1 ground floor); all with telephone, colour TV, central heating; last orders 9.30 p.m.; bar meals; diets; children welcome; baby listening; conferences up to 15; outdoor heated swimming pool; sailing 3 miles; riding, fishing nearby; Visa, Access, Amex, Diners credit cards accepted.

Taken over five years ago by Mr. and Mrs. Fernandez, Lyzzick Hall has been steadily improved. The Hotel has splendid views over the Derwent Valley, with its own extensive grounds including a swimming pool on a sunny terrace, there is everything here for the visitor to the Lake District, whether on business or pleasure. The food, from a most imaginative menu, is excellent, served in the spacious dining room. There is an à la carte menu, into which dishes from the table d'hôte menu can be incorporated, and the food is delicious. There are 125 bins in the wine list, chosen by Mr Fernandez himself, who is a most knowledgeable enthusiast about Spanish wines. I have rarely found more than one of my favourite Spanish wines on any list but here there are three amongst many that I had not heard of. This is a fairly new venture for the young Fernandez family but I feel sure that, with the improvements planned and those already in the pipeline, this friendly hotel will soon make a well deserved name for itself amongst the many excellent hotels in the area. This hotel is well worth a visit and one to look forward to visiting in the future. Room and breakfast from £23.50. Closed in February.

STAKIS LODORE SWISS HOTEL
Keswick, Cumbria CA12 5UX

Telephone: (059684) 285 *Fax: 059684 343*

Carlisle 42, Penrith 23, Keswick 3

F licence; 70 bedrooms all with en suite bathroom, TV and telephone; room and night service; baby listening; lift; last orders 9.30 p.m.; bar lunches; special diets; children welcome; no dogs; conferences up to 80; games room; outdoor/indoor heated swimming pool; leisure centre; sauna and solarium; gymnasium; squash and tennis; sailing, boating and riding nearby; golf and fishing by arrangement; hotel closed January 3rd–February 14th; all major credit cards accepted.

The Lodore Swiss, situated overlooking Derwent Water and at the foot of the famous Lodore Falls, is an hotel of international class and reputation. It caters superbly for all manner of guests and their families. One of the most impressive aspects is the way in which children are looked after by N.N.E.B. nurses, with their own playroom and kitchen, providing parents with a welcome rest. The public rooms are all bright and airy, the bedrooms are spacious and well appointed, and the whole hotel is beautifully decorated and cheerful.Many of the excellent dishes served are from original Swiss recipes, and the staff are all courteous and friendly. The gardens are a delight, and the immediate environs have the most imposing views, yet there is also a gentler beauty in the landscape. All the Lake District, with its sporting facilities, as well as its natural and historical features is easily accessible, so whether you are holidaying as a family or alone, there is something here to suit you. The hotel also has its own many and varied facilities for guests to enjoy. Room and breakfast from £53.00, weekly rates (including dinner) from £329.00.

ARMATHWAITE HALL HOTEL

Bassenthwaite, Nr. Keswick, Cumbria CA12 4RE

Telephone: Bassenthwaite Lake (059 681) 551 *Fax: 059681 220*

London 310, Carlisle 24, Keswick 8

F licence; 42 en suite bedrooms all with telephone, radio and TV; 5 studio suites; children welcome; lift; dogs welcome; indoor leisure complex including heated swimming pool, sauna, solarium, spa, gymnasium, dance floor, bar, grill menu; games room; conferences; diets; golf 3 miles; squash; tennis; swimming; boating; lake fishing; riding (own stables).

Forget the crowds and coaches that clutter up most parts of the Lake District and spend a quiet, relaxing few days or even a night, in the peaceful surroundings of the Hall, standing amidst 133 acres of private parkland, graced by fine trees and magnificent views down to Bassenthwaite Lake. The public rooms are spacious and bright; the lounge is impressive with its large open hearth and panelling, so too are the cocktail bar with its magnificent 16th century fireplace, and the restaurant with the exceptional view it commands. All the bedrooms have their own private facilities and are well equipped with telephone, colour TV and in-house video, radio and central heating. A magnificent new leisure centre with heated indoor swimming pool, sauna, solarium, spa bath, gymnasium, beautician and hairdresser has recently been added to supplement the superb sports and conference facilities. As the late Sir Hugh Walpole once wrote: "Is there anything more romantic than Armathwaite Hall with its lovely habit of drawing Bassenthwaite in a sheet of silver or orange to its very doors? With the trees that guard it, and the history that inhabits it and the lake that stretches before it, it is a house of perfect and irresistible atmosphere". Privately owned and managed. Rooms from £45.00 single, £100.00 twin, £160.00 studio suites. Winter Weekend breaks. Special Christmas and New Year programme.

THE BORROWDALE HOTEL
Borrowdale, Nr. Keswick, Cumbria CA12 5UY

Telephone: (0596) 84224 *Fax: 0596 84338*
B.T. advise change due, to: (07687) 77224

London 290, Keswick 5, Carlisle 36, Penrith 24

F licence; 34 bedrooms (28 with bath, 6 with shower), all with colour TV, telephone and full central heating; last orders 9.30 p.m.; bar meals at lunch time; diets; children welcome; baby listening; dogs allowed; conferences up to 30; lake bathing; sailing, boating and riding nearby; local fishing; golf and swimming pool 4 miles; Access and Visa cards accepted.

The impressive grandeur of the Lake District is relieved now and then by a softer, prettier scene. Such is Borrowdale. Sylvan paths lead down to the lake or riverside, lending a cheerful, lighter relief from the surrounding sombre hills; the Borrowdale Hotel strikes such a note. In light and airy public rooms, the chatter of happy people discussing their day's activities, or perhaps the culinary delights to come, brings joy to the weary traveller as he enters. For this hotel is noted for its warmth and comfort, its service and food, as well as for its position. The table d'hôte menu features both continental dishes and traditional English fare, and this is complemented by a remarkably comprehensive wine list. For those visiting the Lake District, whether on holiday, business or a conference, the Borrowdale offers a venue central for all that is best in the area and a warm, friendly base from which to explore it. Dinner, bed and breakfast from £35.00. Open all year.

SCAFELL HOTEL

Borrowdale, Nr. Keswick, Cumbria CA12 5XB

Telephone: (059684) 208 *Fax: 059684 280*

London 291, Keswick 6, Carlisle 36, Kendal 36, Penrith 24

F licence; 20 en suite bedrooms (8 ground floor); all with direct dial telephone, tea and coffee making facilities; TV; full central heating; children welcome and dogs accepted; bar meals; drying room; river bathing; boating; fishing; pony trekking; tennis 6 miles; golf 10 miles.

It is not surprising that the Scafell is becoming one of Lakeland's leading hotels following its recent improvements and the consistent efforts of its management. Situated almost at the head of the beautiful Borrowdale Valley, its position is as outstanding as the service and comfort which it provides for all its guests. There is an excellent table d'hôte menu and, for those wishing to dine later, a comprehensive à la carte supper menu. Both menus are accompanied by a well balanced wine list. Year after year guests return to walk and climb for they know that they are going to be comfortable and well looked after. For the less energetic there are cosy and homely lounges. The bedrooms are comfortable and attractively furnished, all of them having their own private bathroom. Pleasant views are to be had of the sheltered garden ringed by mighty mountains on which internationally famous climbers have learned their craft. Yes, this is a home for the visitor seeking peace or exercise and wishing to get away from it all. Hotel open all year except January. Special weekend and midweek breaks November to April. Tariff on application.

THE MILL HOUSE HOTEL AND RESTAURANT

Kingham, Oxfordshire OX7 6UH

Telephone: (0608) 718188 *Fax: 0608 71492*
Telex: 849041 SHARET G TVH 003

Stow on the Wold 5, Oxford 20, Cheltenham 18, London 80
Chipping Norton 5, Stratford upon Avon 18

F licence; 21 bedrooms (4 disabled), including 1 suite, all with en suite bathroom; telephone and television; hairdryers; tea and coffee making facilities; room service (not 24 hour); last orders for dinner 9.30 p.m.; light lunches; special diets; children over 5 welcome; no dogs; conference annexe for up to 30 delegates; fishing in River Evenlode nearby; golf, tennis and riding 5 miles; hotel open all year; credit cards accepted.

The Mill House Hotel stands in a rural spot on the edge of the pretty Cotswold village of Kingham. The building was originally an old flour-mill, though the passing years have seen much renovation, making it the charming hotel it is today. A warm welcome awaits, as you enter the flagstoned hall. The heavily beamed bar, which has a log fire burning during the winter, still has two of the original bread ovens, one for proving and the other for baking bread. The adjacent restaurant is predominantly pink, and there are fresh flowers on every table. The table d'hôte menu, changed daily, consists of three courses, and is inventive, as well as reasonably priced. The à la carte menu is always available, and offers a selective choice of international dishes. Take a close look at the wine list, for there are some excellent clarets. The cellar boasts 180 bins, so you can be assured of something to suit all palates. The lounge is spacious and airy, and is a quiet place in which to relax. All bedrooms are tastefully furnished, in keeping with the Cotswold atmosphere, and offer the necessary conveniences required by today's guest. The old millstream, now the Corwell Brook, winds slowly through the gardens, and there are plenty of walks nearby. Prices from £45.00 single, £40.00 double for room and breakfast, including VAT.

COBWEBS COUNTRY HOUSE

Leck, Cowan Bridge, Kirkby Lonsdale,
Lancashire LA6 2HZ
Telephone: (05242) 72141

Kirkby Lonsdale 2, M6 (Junc. 36) 8, Kendal 15, Settle 13

R & R licence; 5 en suite bedrooms all with direct dial telephone, colour TV; room service; last orders for dinner 8.00 p.m.; special diets; children over 12 welcome; no dogs; golf, shooting & fishing nearby; Master Card and Visa accepted; closed January to March.

Set just 2 miles from the Yorkshire dales and only 10 from the Lake District, this gem of a country house is ideally situated as a base for exploring, or simply for a relaxing break amidst lovely unspoilt countryside. Previously owned by two sisters, whose portraits still hang on the walls, it is now in the extremely competent and hardworking hands of Paul and Yvonne Kelly, from whom we received a warm welcome. This small Victorian house is a delight, and comprises five enchanting bedrooms, individually decorated and enhanced with pretty drapes, Victorian furniture, and each has its own modern bathroom; there are also two sitting rooms and the new conservatory dining room. It is certainly the exquisite food that I should be writing about. Reservations are always required as Yvonne Kelly shops daily for fresh ingredients before deciding on her menu for the evening. These dishes are described in detail by Paul in the 'parlour' where we enjoyed an aperitif before dinner, and selected wine from the collection of over 350 bins from all over the world, some at reasonable prices, some very rare and expensive. Two complementing soups served in the same bowl, sometimes one hot and the other cold illustrate the imagination of Yvonne's cooking. Her food is extraordinarily delicious, perfectly cooked, enhanced by wonderful sauces and exquisite vegetables. Puddings are first class and the cheese board is a masterpiece. All this for £17.50 each and room and English breakfast for £25.00 per person in a twin room including VAT or £30.00 for a single. What excellent value for money!

LASTINGHAM GRANGE HOTEL

Lastingham, Nr. Kirkbymoorside, Yorkshire YO6 6TH

Telephone: (075-15) 345 or 402

London 232, Malton 15, Scarborough 24, Thirsk 24, Whitby 26, York 33

R and R licence; 12 en suite bedrooms, all with telephone, trouser press, hair drier; children welcome, baby listening in all rooms; drying room; diets; fire certificate; golf 5 miles; riding 1 mile.

You can discover this delightfully situated, elegant country house by leaving the A170 at Kirkbymoorside and making for Hutton-le-Hole. The Grange is stone-walled and built round a courtyard. It is set within 10 acres of well-kept gardens and fields, on the edge of the moors, in the historic village of Lastingham, a peaceful backwater in the heart of the National Park. Lastingham Grange is owned and personally run by Mr and Mrs Dennis Wood. The atmosphere, even during the height of the season, is unhurried and peaceful, the south-facing terrace providing a pleasant setting in which to relax and enjoy the beautiful rose garden, noted for the variety and rarity of its many flowering shrubs and trees. The spacious and homely lounge, with its open fire, and the comfortable bedrooms, with their impressive views, are all tastefully furnished. The food is excellent – speedily and cheerfully served. Room and breakfast from £45.50 single. Short breaks available. Open March to the beginning of December.

MYTTON FOLD FARM HOTEL
Langho, Nr. Blackburn, Lancashire BB6 8AB

Telephone: (0254) 240662 *Fax: 0254 248119*

M6 (Junction 31) 11, Blackburn 5½, Clitheroe 5½, Burnley 8

R & R licence; 27 en suite bedrooms (3 ground floor), all with colour TV, telephone and full central heating; last orders 9.30 p.m.; bar meals mid week lunchtimes; diets; children over 7 welcome; no dogs; conferences up to 300; local riding; golf within 5 miles; Access and Visa cards accepted.

Here must be the epitome of family hotels. The proprietors have owned the farm for three generations and the present Mr. and Mrs. Hargreaves are running the hotel with their son David, and twin daughters, Barbara and Carole. The old stables were originally converted and these, together with various extensions, provide a real home from home for any weary traveller. Warm and comfortable furnishings contribute to the relaxing atmosphere and, in the evening, to sit in front of the fire, after a good meal and perhaps a bottle of wine, how good it is to reflect on the success that the family have had. The hotel is useful for the business man, since Preston, Blackburn, Clitheroe and Burnley are all within 10 miles and, for the tourist, Blackpool, The Lake District and the Yorkshire Dales are all easily accessible by car. Of particular interest locally is the Ribble Valley. All these places can be toured from a base at Mytton Fold Farm, only 11 miles from junction 31 on the M6. Prices start at £29.00 single, and £46.00 double, and from April 1991, £31.00 single, £50.00 double. Open all year.

ALEXANDER HOTEL

9 Sumner Place,
South Kensington,
London SW7 3EE

Telephone: (071) 581 1591
Fax: 071 581 0824

R licence; 40 bedrooms all with en suite bathroom, telephone and TV; baby listening; night service; lift; dogs by arrangement; all major credit cards accepted.

The Alexander Hotel is an elegant early Victorian town house with a pretty, well designed interior. The bedrooms are beautifully furnished, some with four poster beds. There is also a suite, complete with its own patio and terrace. A 24 hour room and valet service is also provided for guests' convenience. In your room you will find complimentary newspapers, a hospitality tray with tea/coffee, chocolate and biscuits, along with ironing board/trouser press, and hair dryer. An international facsimile machine is also available on request. The recent concept of bed and breakfast luxury hotels is now very popular in London as there are so many wonderful restaurants to visit in this great city. This hotel is well located for London's prestigious shopping areas, such as Knightsbridge, and the West End. The reception staff can also reserve theatre tickets, and arrange all your travel requirements, both in Britain and abroad. The hotel is in walking distance of Hyde Park and Kensington Gardens, and many great museums and Exhibition Halls. Along with its sister hotel, The Diplomat, it is run by Mr Akbar Verjee, who takes a good deal of pride in the every day running of his establishments. They are great value for money, and prices include a full English breakfast, served in the pretty Garden Restaurant, which adjoins an attractive private garden. Tariff on application.

THE BEAUFORT
33 Beaufort Gardens, London SW3 1PP

Telephone: 071-584 5252 *Telex: 929200* *Fax: 071 589 2834*

R licence; 28 en suite bedrooms (4 ground floor) all with telephone, TV; full central heating; lift; limited room service; children over 10 years or babes-in-arms welcome; no dogs; telex; facsimile; photocopying; health club; Access, Amex, Diners, Visa credit cards accepted.

The Beaufort is an early Victorian house in a pretty, tree-lined square right in the centre of London. Although only 100 yards from Harrods and the bustle of Knightsbridge, it has a very tranquil atmosphere. The principal aim is to give everyone who visits the hotel the feeling of entering an English country home, where one may expect the warmest of welcomes. Because first impressions are so important, comfort, warmth and friendliness are all in abundance. When you first arrive, you ring the doorbell and you are given your own front door key, which adds to the feeling of home. One of the charms of the Beaufort is that all the rooms have their own bathroom and are different both in decoration and in size. In every room there are flowers, soaps and chocolates. Breakfast arrives in the room on a large tray with pots of steaming hot coffee or tea. There is a fresh supply daily of croissants, brioches and rolls, with English butter and home-made marmalade, jam, honey and very lemony lemon curd. The Beaufort is an English country home set in the heart of London. Drinks from the bar, room service and membership of a nearby health club are included in the room rate. Tariff on application.

BERKSHIRE HOTEL

Oxford Street, London W1N 0BY

Telephone: 071-629 7474 *Telex: 22270* *Fax: 071-629 8156*

Heathrow 15, Gatwick 28, London city airport 7, Luton 31

F licence; 147 en suite bedrooms, including 3 suites with jacuzzi, all with computerised security locks, telephone, colour TV, video, mini bar, trouser press; full central heating; lift; night service; valet; laundry; bar meals in drawing room; diets; children welcome; dogs at Manager's discretion; all major credit cards accepted.

Conveniently situated just off busy Oxford Street, the Berkshire Hotel is remarkably peaceful, whilst being central for shopping, theatres and business. Recently re-named and refurbished, the hotel attains very high standards. The bedrooms, which have computerised locking systems, are comfortable, attractive and, above all, quiet. All are air-conditioned and boast all the latest equipment, including colour television with satellite link to receive international stations including CNN. A harpist plays in the comfortable and elegant drawing room which is attractively furnished in Chinese style. Conference rooms are available on two floors, one incorporating an adjoining double bedroom. These rooms are wonderfully well-equipped and, in addition, are sound-proofed. The meal that I enjoyed in Ascots Restaurant was excellent, with efficient and caring staff. Prints from great racing artists, including Stubbs, contribute to the tasteful décor. If you are either on business or exploring London, this hotel is a good central base, with parking adjacent to the hotel. Single rooms from £155.00, double from £200.00, suites from £425.00. English breakfast from £13.00, continental breakfast from £10.00. Rates are subject to change without notice. Open all year.

THE COBURG HOTEL

129 Bayswater Road, Hyde Park, London W2 4RJ

Telephone: (071) 221 2217 *Fax: 071 589 9526*

F licence; 134 bedrooms all with en suite bathroom, telephone and TV; room and night service; baby listening; lift; last orders for dinner 9.30 p.m.; bar meals; children welcome; dogs accepted; all major credit cards accepted.

This wonderful Edwardian building has recently been superbly restored to its former glory. The new owner has taken great personal pride in the workmanship and décor of this well known hotel, which overlooks Hyde Park. The bedrooms have been decorated to the highest standards and are designed to provide every convenience and comfort. The tariff rate includes a full, buffet-style English breakfast. Amongst a host of other amenities, a hospitality tray, ironing centre, satellite television, safe, complimentary newspapers and minibar are all provided. An amazing luxury penthouse suite has been created in the famous Coburg Dome, offering unparalleled views over London. A charming reception area and bar/lounge offer a peaceful setting for meeting one's friends, or just quiet relaxation. The bar leads on to the wonderful new restaurant called The Spice Merchant, which offers a unique blend of the best cuisine from the Indian sub-continent, along with a number of dishes which evolved from East Africa. I am very much looking forward to my next visit to this lovely hotel, and I cannot recommend it too highly. Tariff on application.

THE DIPLOMAT

2 Chesham Street, Belgravia, London SW1X 8DT

Telephone: (071) 235 1544

27 bedrooms, all with en suite bathroom, direct dial telephone and TV; baby listening; night service; lift; children welcome; dogs by prior arrangement; all major credit cards accepted.

If you are looking for value for money, and a great place to stay, complete with an excellent breakfast, in the most prestigious part of London, then The Diplomat is for you. Built in 1882 by Thomas Cubitt, this former family residence is listed as a building of architectural distinction. Dominating the entrance is the splendid, glass-domed stairway, which leads up to twenty seven comfortable and well appointed bedrooms. All rooms are equipped with hairdryer, ironing facilities and trouser press, as well as a hospitality tray with tea, coffee and chocolate biscuits. Complimentary newspapers are also provided. Included in the price is a sumptuous, buffet style English breakfast, served in the most elegant and cheerful little dining room. The Diplomat is part of the Linbar Group of hotels. The management takes great pride in its standards of care and attention, down to the last detail, in the every day running of the hotels. The Diplomat is within easy walking distance of Harrods, and Sloane Square, or there you can visit elegant Knightsbridge and Chelsea. One is spoilt for choice by the number of lovely restaurants in this area, making this hotel an ideal location for both business and pleasure visits. Tariff on application.

DUKES HOTEL
St. James's Place, London SW1A 1NY

Telephone: (071) 491 4840 *Fax: 071 493 1264*

F licence; 62 bedrooms with en suite bathrooms, including 26 suites; telephone and television; room and night service; lift; last orders for dinner 10.00 p.m.; special diets; guide dogs only; conferences up to 60; all major credit cards accepted.

This intimate and elegant hotel tucked away in St. James's Place is yet another addition to Cunard Hotels, which also include The Stafford just around the corner, and The Ritz in Piccadilly. All these hotels are under the personal supervision of Terry Holmes, the Vice President and Managing Director. This beautiful Edwardian building is approached through a flower filled courtyard, complete with gas lamps, which are lit by hand every evening, evoking an air of romance and times gone by. Dukes Hotel is just like a country house hotel, set in the middle of London. The bedrooms, of which 26 are suites, are beautifully designed. No two are alike, though all feature fine, classic furniture, and include such thoughtful extras as bathrobes, hairdryers and personal toiletries. There is a superb team of staff, under the direction of the Hotel Manager, Hugh Williamson-Noble, who offer excellent service and their personal attention. There is an intimate dining room, which provides English cooking at its very best, with an equally well thought out wine list. There is an abundance of fresh flowers throughout, and a cosy little sitting room, where you can read the newspapers, and take coffee or tea. There is also a lovely little bar. This hotel is really very special, and a great asset to the Cunard Company. Tariff on application.

THE GORING HOTEL

Beeston Place, Grosvenor Gardens, London SW1W 0JW

Telephone: 071-834 8211 *Telex: 919166* *Fax: 071-834 4393*

100 bedrooms all with private bathroom, radio, colour TV and telephone; children welcome; late meals to 10.00 p.m. (last orders to 9.30 p.m.); night service; diets; valet services; conferences; full central heating; credit cards accepted.

It is not easy to find an hotel operated for three generations by the same family, which still bears that family's name. Such a gem is the Goring Hotel, situated just behind Buckingham Palace in a very quiet yet central location with its own large garden. All bedrooms and public rooms are very tastefully decorated and maintained to the highest standards of luxury and cleanliness. Mr. Goring and his staff succeed in giving personal and attentive service and nothing seems to be too much trouble for them. The Goring restaurant and private dining suites are often used by guests prior to attending investitures or garden parties at Buckingham Palace. A sensibly sized and priced menu offers excellent, traditional dishes and the wine list is imaginative and very comprehensive. A number of rooms have now been fully air-conditioned and others have splendid marble bathrooms as a result of an extensive refurbishment programme. The management team, headed by Mr. William Cowpe and directed by Mr. George Goring, describe themselves as "forward looking in a traditional way". In the Goring Hotel you will find a "home from home". Single room from £115.00, double from £165.00, breakfast and all meals extra.

LE MÉRIDIEN HOTEL

Piccadilly, London W1V 0BH

Telephone: 071-734 8000 Telex: 25795 Fax: 071-437 3574

F licence; 284 en suite bedrooms all with radio, telephone, satellite TV with a wide choice of stations; air-conditioning; lifts; 24-hour room service; diets; children welcome; baby sitting; conferences; business centre; sauna, solarium; Turkish bath; jacuzzi; health club dancing classes; beauty salon; hairdresser; massage; billiards; indoor heated pool; squash; golf 30 mins. away; most credit cards accepted.

This hotel, built in 1908, and restored to its original splendour, was bought in May 1986 by the French company Société des Hotels Méridien. Located in fashionable Mayfair, Le Méridien has 284 beautifully appointed rooms decorated in restful pastel shades, including 30 individually designed luxury suites and marble-clad bathrooms. The magnificent Oak Room restaurant, with its wood-panelled walls, decorated with gilded trophies, garlanded leaves and crystal chandeliers, is one of London's most elegant dining rooms, where the consultant chef, Michel Lorain, holder of 3 Michelin stars, together with the British Executive chef, David Chambers, recreates his unique style of cuisine. At lunchtime, from Monday to Friday, business executives can enjoy in the Oak Room's spectacular surroundings, a 3-course lunch for £21.00, including coffee and VAT. In the evening there is the 'menu gourmand' of 4, 5 or 6 courses, starting at £40.00. The nearby lounge offers light snacks and, in the afternoon, to the soft melodies of a harpist, traditional English tea, with over 20 varieties of tea. On the second floor is the Terrace Garden, a stunning glass-domed restaurant with trees, shrubs and hanging baskets, where you can enjoy sunny lunches or intimate dinners – open from 7.00 a.m. until 1.00 a.m. (last orders 11.30 p.m.). Located on the lower ground floors of the hotel, Champneys Club offers swimming, squash, a workout in the Nautilus Gym or therapeutic treatment. A full range of secretarial and translation services and all the latest office machines are provided by the Business Centre within the hotel. Tariff on application.

THE MONTCALM

Great Cumberland Place, London W1A 2LF

Telephone: 071-402 4288 *Telex: 28710* *Fax: 071-724 9180*

London Airports: Heathrow 12, Gatwick 27, Luton 31, Stansted 34

F licence; 116 bedrooms and suites, all fully air-conditioned with private bathrooms, radio, complementary in-house films, mini-bars; 24 hour room service; children welcome; valet and laundry services; all major credit cards accepted.

Located on a charming tree-lined crescent in the centre of London, The Montcalm has the quiet air of an exclusive London club. The emphasis in the hotel is that of discreet individual service to each guest. The restaurant 'Les Celebrites' offers an exceedingly attractive table d'hôte luncheon menu and a full à la carte menu at dinner. The elegant bar and 24 hour room service reflect a standard and style of British hospitality no less than superb. A personal welcome begins with registration at a lovely antique desk where guests may sit and relax. The Montcalm Hall Porters are the traveller's perfect mentor, helping you arrange theatre tickets, sightseeing, limousines and almost everything you may request. If you'd like to turn back the clock to Georgian style and forward to flawless comfort, The Montcalm is your London connection. Single rooms are £152.00, twin/double rooms from £169.00, including service at 15% and VAT. English breakfast £11.00, Continental £8.00. Rates are subject to change without notice. Open all year.

NUMBER FIVE, SUMNER PLACE
South Kensington, London SW7 3EE

Telephone: (071) 584 7586 *Fax: 071 803 9962*

Heathrow 15, Gatwick 26

R licence; 13 bedrooms with en suite bathroom (2 downstairs); telephone and television; room service; baby listening; lift; children welcome; honesty bars in double rooms; all credit cards accepted.

Number Five, Sumner Place is quietly tucked away in an elegant Kensington street, yet is conveniently placed for both business and shopping. The house has been tastefully and thoughtfully converted from a home to a hotel by the owners, Mr. and Mrs. Palgan. This lovely terrace was built in the mid nineteenth century and is of great architectural merit. South Kensington tube station is two minutes from the hotel and Heathrow Airport is half an hour from the station. The Albert Hall and the Kensington museums are within walking distance, as are the large Knightsbridge shops, Sloane Square and the Kings Road. West End shopping is a few minutes away, by taxi, tube or bus. After registration, a front door key is yours for the duration of your stay. Bedrooms are attractively decorated and are all en suite, double rooms having fitted bars. All have radio, colour television and telephone. Furnishings are in period style, in harmony with the building. Buffet breakfast may be taken in the Victorian style conservatory which is light and airy, and overlooks a small, sunny terrace, complete with attractive shrubs. Bed and breakfast only, from £55.00 single, £70.00 double.

THE PORTLAND

7 Montague Street, Bloomsbury, London WC1B 5HB

Telephone: (071) 323 1717 *Fax: 071 636 6498*

F licence; 27 bedrooms, all with en suite bathroom; telephone and television; room and night service; lift; last orders for dinner 10.00 p.m.; bar meals; special diets; children welcome; no dogs; no conferences; hotel open all year; Mastercard, Visa, Amex and Diners Cards accepted.

This lovely new Bloomsbury Hotel has gardens, restaurant and some bedrooms backing onto The British Museum, thereby ensuring peace and privacy for visitors. Mr Iain Russell-Jarvie, a very experienced hotelier, offers his guests style, comfort and value for money. The elegant marble-floored reception area has a lift to all four floors and is decorated with wonderfully original paintings and antiques, as is the comfortable residents' sitting room. The fabrics used throughout are superb, reflecting the country house style of the hotel. The Room Service Menu is available 24 hours a day, and the restaurant is open from breakfast till late evening. The restaurant, which opens out onto the gardens, also serves a wide range of freshly cooked dishes, and mouth watering Italian desserts. There is an attractive and well appointed suite, and some of the 26 bedrooms are gently rounded, following the curves in the outline of the Regency period building. All bedrooms have en suite bathrooms, every modern luxury, lovely paintings and antique furniture. The hotel is well-positioned near Russell Square Underground, with its 50 minute link to Heathrow Airport. Theatres are also close by, and West End shopping is a brief taxi ride away. This hotel is well worth a visit, for business or pleasure. Room and breakfast from £100 per double. Hotel open all year.

THE REGENCY HOTEL

One Hundred Queen's Gate, London SW7 5AG

Telephone: 071-370 4595 *Telex: 267594* *Fax: 071-370 5555*

Heathrow 15, Gatwick 26, Earls Court 1, Olympia 1, Knightsbridge 1, West End 3, Science Museum ½

F licence; 210 en suite bedrooms (including 11 suites) all with direct dial telephone, colour TV, trouser press, hair dryer; 2 lifts; 24 hour room service; last orders 10.30 p.m.; bar meals; diets; children welcome; no dogs; conferences up to 250; sauna; leisure centre; Access, Air Plus, Amex, Diners, Visa cards accepted.

The elegant Regency Hotel stands in Queen's Gate in the heart of South Kensington. It takes its name from the Prince Regent, later King George IV, who was society's leading figure in the early 19th century. For those on holiday, the hotel is conveniently situated for museums, shopping in Kensington and Knightsbridge, including Harrods. For those on business, Earls Court and Olympia are at hand, and the hotel offers excellent conference facilities. It is decorated with luxurious silk tapestries, specially woven oriental rugs and crystal chandeliers. Light meals, coffee and traditional English tea may be taken on the attractive Terrace. The Pavilion Bar is to the right, perfect for meeting friends and unwinding after a hard day. The Pavilion Restaurant serves international cuisine with vegetarian options and a most comprehensive wine list. A lunch time Brasserie menu is also available. Beneath the hotel is the magnificently equipped Elysium Club, an ideal venue for healthy relaxation and revitalisation. The spa features sauna and steam rooms, solarium, floatarium, multi-gymnasium and an exciting vibrosauna. The décor is classical Greek, incorporating a large tiled whirlpool. The fully trained staff include beauty therapists and masseuses. The club is open for non residential membership. Single room from £99.00, double from £115.00. Suites on request. Open all year.

THE RITZ
Piccadilly, London SW1V 9DG

Telephone: (071) 493 8181 *Telex: 267200* *Fax: 071 493 2687*

F licence; 130 en suite bedrooms, all with telephone, TV, satellite TV and personal bar; air conditioning in all public rooms and most bedrooms; lift; room and night service; valet service; last orders 11 p.m.; special diets; children welcome; baby listening; no dogs; conferences; dinner dances Fri./Sat. in Restaurant; Big Band Fri./Sat. in Palm Court; all major credit cards accepted.

The name 'Ritz' gives the impression of utter luxury and style, perhaps beyond the reach of many, and although the hotel is sumptuous in the extreme, it is by no means the most expensive hotel in London. It is, however, famous for its cocktails and teas, and Big Band dances in the Palm Court, and regular dinner dances in the restaurant on Fridays and Saturdays. The Ritz, along with The Stafford and Dukes Hotel, is now part of the Cunard Hotel Group, and is under the personal supervision of Vice President and Managing Director Terry Holmes. The hotel was opened in 1906 by Swiss born Cesar Ritz. The pink and gold beauty of the ground floor remains faithful to the original splendour, and the bedrooms have been lovingly restored, many with original fireplaces and gold leaf decoration in the style of Louis XVI. The terrace and gardens have been re-opened for dining al fresco. The elegant restaurant, overlooking Green Park is one of the most beautiful dining rooms in Europe. The menu is complemented by an extensive selection of wines including the Ritz's own family of champagnes. David Hopkins, the Manager, and his skilled and friendly staff provide a personal and caring service. The hotel is close to some of the best shopping in the world, as well as theatres, restaurants and museums. The concierge is also on hand to give any necessary assistance. Tariff on application.

ROYAL GARDEN HOTEL

Kensington High Street, London W8 4PT

Telephone: 071-937 8000 *Telex: 263151* *Fax: 071-938 4532*

Heathrow 15, Gatwick 30, Luton 40

F licence, 395 en suite bedrooms, all with radio, colour TV, cable TV, telephone, air-conditioning, complementary in-house films, mini-bar; 24 hour room service; valet; four lifts; business centre; children welcome; diets; guide dogs welcome; conferences; dancing Friday and Saturday evenings; all major credit cards accepted.

Uniquely situated on one of London's Royal Parks and taking pride of place next to the royal residence – Kensington Palace – the Royal Garden is renowned for its breathtaking views across Kensington Garden and Hyde Park. It is the nearest five-star hotel to Heathrow Airport and is just two minutes' walk from Kensington High Street underground station, has easy access to Knightsbridge, Piccadilly, Earls Court and Olympia and the many museums and antique shops of Kensington and Chelsea are close by. All bedrooms are luxuriously furnished, offering the ultimate in style and comfort. On the ground floor, the Garden Cafe is a lively, popular venue for either a simple snack or full meal, any time of day. The famous Royal Roof Restaurant, situated on the tenth floor, offers the ultimate in French cuisine with a panoramic view of London's skyline. With three further bars, a large underground car park and excellent banqueting facilities, the Royal Garden richly deserves its five star rating and has most competitive rates. Single rooms from £135.00, double from £168.00, inclusive of VAT. Rates are subject to change without prior notice. Open all year.

SHERATON PARK TOWER

101 Knightsbridge,
London SW1X 7RN

Telephone: 071-235 8050
Telex: 917222 PARKTO G
Fax: 071 235 8321

Heathrow 15, Gatwick 27

F licence; 295 en suite bedrooms including 147 executive rooms, 19 suites, 6 penthouse suites all with private bathrooms, direct dial telephone, radio, colour TV, in-house films, refrigerator, mini bar; full air conditioning; non smoking rooms available, room suitable for disabled person, valet service; 24-hour room service; diets; baby sitters on request; small conferences; business centre; hairdressing salon, barber shop; theatre desk; garage; currency exchange; all major credit cards accepted.

It is not surprising that the Sheraton Park Tower has an international reputation, and that many overseas visitors choose to stay here. The location is ideal for shopping, and such places of interest as Hyde Park and Buckingham Palace are within easy reach. The main building has been cleverly designed, in that it is circular and every bedroom has a large bay window. These provide panoramic views of London from the upper floors. Moving to the ground floor, be sure not to miss the Champagne Bar. It is a very popular meeting place and there is a choice of an extensive cold buffet or a hot snack if you require something to go with your glass of champagne. If the waistline will permit, you also have the choice of a gourmet menu in the restaurant, which is open from 7.00 a.m. and last orders are taken at 11.30 p.m.; it is situated on the Knightsbridge forecourt and features a raised dais under a cathedral stained glass canopy. The latest addition at The Sheraton Park Tower is the introduction of Butler floors, offering the ultimate in personalised service. Complementary valet unpacking services are also provided, and there is a choice of bed size, and an additional telephone on the writing desks in the Executive rooms. Tariff on application. Open all year.

THE STAFFORD
St. James's Place, London SW1A 1NJ

Telephone: (071) 4930111   Telex: 28602 STAFRD   Fax: 071 493 7121

F licence; 62 en suite bedrooms, all with colour television, and satellite channels; room telephone; lift; night service; bar meals; diets; children welcome; baby listening; conferences; valet service; all major credit cards accepted.

More like a private club than an hotel, there is always a warm welcome for guests from the Manager, Denis Beaulieu, and his skilled and experienced staff. A careful note is made of each guest's preferences, so when you return, you have the same room and service, wherever possible. The 62 bedrooms and 5 suites are luxuriously furnished – one room even has its own private garden! The elegant dining room, with its superbly painted ceiling (which includes the famous Stafford Black Cat!) can offer a host of mouth watering specialities, created by master chef, Armando Rodriguez. Pre-theatre dinners are available from 6.00 p.m. There are over 200 wines, supervised by Master Sommelier Guio Nardella. The Stafford caters for private parties in any of the four salons, which are air conditioned and sumptuously decorated in the late Victorian style, or you can dine in unique surroundings, in the famous 300 year old cellars. The American Bar is intimate with a varied collection of ties, hats, photographs and mementoes from hotel guests and friends. Charles, who has been head barman for many years, will certainly make your visit a memorable one! The Stafford is part of the Cunard Group (which also includes the Ritz and Dukes Hotel) under the personal supervision of its Vice President and Managing Director, Terry Holmes. Guests may sign in any of these hotels and charges will be put to their room account. Tariff on application.

WHITES HOTEL

90 Lancaster Gate, London W2 3NR

Telephone: (071) 262 2711 *Fax: 071 262 2147*

Heathrow 15, Gatwick 30

F licence; 54 bedrooms, all with en suite bathroom, direct dial telephone and TV; room and night service; baby listening; lift; last orders for dinner, 10.30 p.m.; bar meals, special diets; children welcome; no dogs· conferences up to 25; car park facilities; valet service; riding in Hyde Park by arrangement; all credit cards accepted.

Luxury from a bygone era is easily discovered at the elegant Whites Hotel. Overlooking Hyde Park and Kensington Gardens, it is wonderfully situated for the London visitor. The hotel is approached through one of its unique, glass tunnel-canopies, and staff welcome you warmly in the foyer, which has beautiful chandeliers, Chinese ornaments and lovely portraits. Bedrooms are the height of luxury, with bathrooms in Italian marble, and brass accessories. Furnishings are in elegantly draped moire silks, and carpets echo these lovely muted greens, pinks and blues. The bar, complete with sunny terrace overlooking Royal Kensington Gardens, has a large and interesting collection of caricature engravings, with carved figures and porcelain, thoughtfully displayed against primrose coloured walls. The décor in The Grill Room is classically elegant, in peach and cream, part of the ornate ceiling being draped in dark peach, with spectacular chandeliers and many superb paintings. Restaurant menus are both imaginative and unusual, featuring items such as marinated salmon, with guacamole and yoghurt and feuillete of seafood on spinach with a watercress sauce. The wine list is both discerning and excellent. I have known and loved this hotel since my childhood and cannot recommend it too highly. Room and breakfast from £137.00. Hotel open all year.

QUORN GRANGE

Wood Lane, Quorn, Loughborough,
Leicestershire LE12 8DB

Telephone: (0509) 412167 *Fax: 0507 415621*

London 98, Birmingham 40, Nottingham 15, Leicester 9, Derby 12, Loughborough 3

R & R licence; 17 bedrooms all with en suite bathrooms (1 suitable for disabled); telephone and TV; room and night service; last orders for dinner 10.00 p.m.; bar meals; special diets; children welcome; dogs allowed; conferences up to 80; ladies' fashion shop; riding and golf, tennis, sauna, solarium, leisure centre, gymnasium, squash courts 2 miles; shooting and fishing 3 miles; sailing and boating 4 miles; hotel open all year; all major credit cards accepted.

Quorn Grange is a charming Country House Restaurant with luxury accommodation. The 19th century house stands in ten acres of lovely landscaped gardens. It is situated off the A6 between Loughborough and Leicester. Quorn village features a variety of shops, and the area is famous for its horse riding. Quorn Grange has an excellent reputation for its modern English cuisine. The chef, Gordon Long, offers you a choice from his vegetarian, à la carte or daily menus. The emphasis is on freshly cooked seasonal dishes, with no frozen products. The Restaurant is charmingly decorated in blues and pinks, with linen napkins and pretty china, and opens into the conservatory. Here one can relax and enjoy the beautiful garden. Recently a new wing has been added, and includes a banqueting room which opens onto the garden, and some charming bedrooms, all with their own patios. These are suited to wheelchairs, since there are special ramps at the banqueting entrance. Bedrooms are well furnished and overlook the gardens, some with king-size beds, and there are also family rooms with communicating doors. There are superb, white marble bathrooms. The hotel is owned and run by the Lord family, who offer their guests personal care and attention, aided by their efficient team. A hotel to be recommended, for pleasure or business. Room and breakfast from £65.00 single, and £85.00 double per night. Weekly from £365.

SOUTH LODGE

Lower Beeding, Nr. Horsham, West Sussex RH13 6PS

Telephone: (0403) 891711 *Fax: 0403 891766*

London 40, Gatwick 12, Brighton 15

F licence; 39 en suite bedrooms (9 ground floor) all with telephone, colour TV; full central heating; night service; last orders 10.30 p.m.; bar meals, diets; children welcome; baby listening; no dogs; conferences max. 80; tennis; shooting; fishing; croquet; golf nearby; credit cards accepted.

This is one of West Sussex's luxury country house hotels, set in 90 acres of parkland, close to Gatwick and only 20 miles away from Brighton, set on the A281 south of Horsham. Surrounded by picturesque villages with many places of interest nearby to visit and enjoy, South Lodge was originally built as a family house in 1883 by Lord Fredrick Ducane Godman. After extensive renovation and refurbishment, it now offers beautifully proportioned reception rooms with ornate ceilings, wood panelling and open fires, creating a feeling of comfort and elegance. Outstanding food and fine wines are provided in the graciously appointed dining room, where menus change with the seasons. The individually furnished bedrooms are light and spacious, many with fine views of the South Downs, all have private bathroom, colour television and direct dial telephone. Private facilities in the original drawing room are available for senior executive and director level meetings, also weddings and special family celebrations. In the grounds, leisure and sporting facilities are provided, such as croquet and tennis. Golf, riding and shooting are nearby by arrangement. Tariff on application. Hotel open all year.

SCALE HILL HOTEL

Loweswater, Cockermouth, Cumbria CA13 9UX

Telephone: Lorton (090085) 232

Cockermouth 6, Keswick 12

F licence; 17 bedrooms (2 suitable for disabled), including 1 four poster room, 15 with en suite bathroom, all with electric fires, hairdryers; last orders for dinner 7.45 p.m.; drying room; children welcome; dogs accepted; pony trekking nearby; squash courts in Keswick; 2 golf courses within 8 miles; lake fishing in the valley; sailing and boating; peace and tranquillity; hotel closed in winter.

What a gem of a country inn! Scale Hill is an hotel offering the best of simple life. Set in a delightful garden amidst some of the most stunning scenery in the Lake District, it has the peace and quiet so seldom found in larger, more expensive establishments; as I heard one guest, a Mrs. Stanton from the Midlands, so aptly quote, that here both inside and out, is "where every prospect pleases". The bedrooms have all that one needs for a comfortable stay, but deliberately, they have no televisions or telephones. The public rooms are beautifully furnished with many antiques and interesting pictures, and they are warm and inviting. Fresh flowers abound, there are open fires when necessary, and the "well polished" look adds to the homely and welcoming feel. The area is a nature lover's and walker's paradise and to that end, the food, prepared by Mrs. Sheila Thompson, the wife of owner, Michael Thompson, and her daughter, is both wholesome and plentiful enough to replenish the energy of the most ambitious walker or climber. Also of interest to active guests is the laundry and drying room, should they get caught in the rain. To "get away from it all" is increasingly difficult in many parts of the Lake District, yet you can do so here. I cannot recommend this hotel too highly. Dinner, room and breakfast from £48.00, weekly from £300.00.

THE FEATHERS AT LUDLOW
Bull Ring, Ludlow, Shropshire SY8 1AA

Telephone: 0584 875261 *Telex: 35637 Fether* *Fax: 0584 876030*

Hereford 25, Shrewsbury 30, Knighton 17, Leominster 11, Birmingham 37

F licence; 40 en suite bedrooms, several of which are four-poster suites, all with telephone; colour TV, radio, tea/coffee making facilities, mini-bars, some with air conditioning; lift to all floors; night service; meals to 9.30 p.m.; bar lunches; diets; children welcome; ideal for incentive and reward conferences; receptions; billiards room; riding, golf, by arrangement; indoor heated swimming pool nearby; most credit cards accepted.

The Feathers was named in honour of Prince Charles, son of James I, who was created Prince of Wales in 1616. On the King's orders great celebrations took place at Ludlow, the seat of the important Council of the Marches. This historic Inn boasts some of the finest half timbered work and plaster ceilings in the country. The furnishings and appointments in all rooms are tasteful, comfortable and of high quality, with fine Tudor and Jacobean effects, antiques and period furniture. The bright and cheerful bedrooms are beautifully equipped, several with four poster beds, whilst the banqueting suite has been refurbished as a baronial hall. This ancient Inn, owned by Mr. Osmond Edwards and ably managed by Mr. and Mrs. Peter Nash, enjoys a wide reputation for first class food and service. It is situated in the centre of Ludlow, one of the most beautiful rural towns in England, a superb centre for touring the Marches and the Heart of England. Room and breakfast from £60.00 (single), £43.00 per person (twin). Budget terms on application. Open all year.

ALEXANDRA HOTEL

Pound Street,
Lyme Regis, Dorset DT7 3HZ

Telephone: (029 74) 2010; Guests 5428

London 152, Southampton 76, Birmingham 156, Taunton 28, Exeter 28, Bristol 66

F licence; 24 en suite bedrooms all with telephone, colour television, radio, intercom, baby listening, tea/coffee making facilities; full central heating; meals to 8.30 p.m.; diets; children welcome; sea bathing; fishing and boating 200 yards; golf, tennis, squash and riding within 2 miles; credit cards accepted.

The Alexandra Hotel, set within its own large and peaceful garden, is ideally situated for those seeking a quiet and restful holiday. It is within easy reach of both the sea front with its famous Cobb harbour and the town and shops. Most of the comfortably furnished bedrooms have fine sea views across Lyme Bay, as does the spacious dining room and the sun lounge. The original house dates from 1735, when it was the Dower House of the Dowager Countess Poulett, later owned by the Duc de Stacpoole. The Alexandra became an hotel around the turn of the century and is now under the personal care and supervision of Mr. and Mrs. David Haskins, whose aim is to offer their guests comfort and hospitality in beautiful surroundings. A varied choice of menu is provided at all meals and fresh local produce is used whenever possible. Hot and cold bar lunches are available and a comprehensive but reasonably priced wine list is maintained. The delightful and unspoilt town of Lyme Regis has many historical and literary associations, and with its sandy beach and safe bathing is a perfect spot for a family holiday. Room with breakfast from £35.00 single, £70.00 twin. Brochure on application. Closed mid-December to 1st February.

KERSBROOK HOTEL

Pound Road, Lyme Regis, Dorset DT7 3HX

Telephone: (02974) 2596

London 152, Exeter 28, Taunton 28, Bristol 66, Southampton 76, Birmingham 156

R and R licence; 14 en suite bedrooms (3 on ground floor), all with tea, chocolate & coffee making facilities; meals to 9 p.m.; diets; children over 12 welcome; well behaved dogs welcome; colour TV lounge; restaurant open to non residents; receptions and conferences up to 20; sea bathing; wind surfing; sailing, boating, golf, riding, shooting, river and sea fishing all nearby; Visa and Master Card accepted.

The Kersbrook Hotel is truly a gem set amidst the unspoilt beauty of Lyme Regis, nestling unobtrusively on the majestic Dorset coastline. Kersbrook Hotel is a charming 18th century house with 1½ acres of pretty "cottage style" gardens. The care and attention of the proprietors, Eric and Jane Stephenson, have made this hotel quite immaculate. Rooms are individually decorated and provide "welcoming packs", novels for reading and a basket of fresh fruit providing that "special something" for their guests. There is a fine 1820 oak panelled bar providing a splendid atmosphere, enhanced and decorated with well chosen antiques, all of which truly complement a connoisseur's selection of outstanding scotches, brandy and superb wines. The charming and spacious, split-level, pink and white dining room is a joy, providing the ideal surroundings in which to savour the superb cuisine. Norman Arnold, the talented chef, uses fresh produce daily, to prepare and present varied and comprehensive table d'hôte and à la carte menus, also catering admirably for vegetarians. The "Quiet Room" lounge too, is most charming, following the cottage-theme of this delightful hotel. The hotel truly deserves its datastar and blue ribbon accolades. Treat yourself to the charm of Kersbrook Hotel, a sojourn here is most highly recommended. Prices from £40.00 single, and £58.00 double.

THE STANWELL HOUSE HOTEL

Lymington, Hampshire SO14 9AA

Telephone: (0590) 677123 *Telex: 477463G* *Fax: 0590 677756*

Southampton 12, Brockenhurst 6, Motorway M27 10

F licence; 35 en suite bedrooms (8 ground floor) all with telephone, colour TV, tea/coffee making facilities, hairdryer, trouser press, full central heating; night service; diets; children welcome; baby listening; dogs not accepted; conferences max. 20; sea bathing, sailing, golf, tennis, squash, badminton, riding, shooting, fishing all nearby; Visa, Access credit cards accepted.

The Stanwell House Hotel is an attractive 18th century house in the centre of Lymington. Over the years it has been carefully modernised and refurbished creating an atmosphere of a country house hotel and a new bedroom wing has recently been added. Lymington, founded by the Romans, is a bustling little Georgian town full of charm and character; it has now become a major yachting centre and the Lymington river provides endless interest. The New Forest is on one side and the Solent on the other, so there is much to see and do on the doorstep. The Hotel public rooms are furnished to a high standard of comfort and the restaurant and cocktail bar have been extended. The bedrooms are quiet and well appointed, all have bathroom en suite, colour TV, tea and coffee making facilities, hair dryer and trouser press. Each room is named after one of the great Bordeaux chateaux, reflecting the outstanding reputation of the Railings Restaurant's wine list. Both table d'hôte and à la carte menus are offered and the fresh fish, meats, poultry and vegetables are brought directly from the markets. Behind the Hotel is an attractive walled garden for the use of guests. The Hotel which offers a purpose built Garden Suite for executive meetings and functions for up to 25 people is run by charming and helpful staff. Room and breakfast from £62.50 single, £80.00 double, including service and VAT. Hotel open all year.

PASSFORD HOUSE HOTEL

Nr. Lymington,
Hampshire SO41 8LS

Telephone: (0590) 682398 *Fax: 0590 683494*

London 93, Lymington 2, Brockenhurst 3½, Bournemouth 17

F licence; 54 bedrooms (13 ground floor), 2 suites, all with private baths, telephone, radio, colour TV; children welcome; dogs by arrangement; diets on application; indoor leisure complex (details below); tennis court; croquet lawn; putting green; outdoor swimming pool – heated in season; sea bathing, sailing, golf, riding all nearby; fire certificate; major credit cards accepted.

This lovely country house hotel is set in nine acres of grounds on the edge of the New Forest and was originally the home of Lord Arthur Cecil. It has been carefully adapted to an elegant hotel run under the personal supervision of the owners, Mr and Mrs Patrick Heritage. Passford House is ideally suited for the pursuit of many interests and forest walks and drives begin at the hotel entrance. In addition to the many outdoor activities, a very comprehensive purpose-built leisure centre has been added recently, providing an indoor swimming pool, spa pool, sauna, solarium, multi-gym, including cycling, rowing and treadmill equipment, pool table and table tennis. In the hotel the spacious lounges are elegantly furnished and comfortable with wood fires in autumn and winter. The restaurant prides itself on its high standard of cuisine which is complemented by an extensive and varied wine list. All bedrooms have bathrooms en suite with shower and are maintained to a very high standard; trouser press and hair dryers are also provided. Room and breakfast from £65.00 single, £90.00 double. Hotel open all year.

THE RISING SUN HOTEL
Harbourside, Lynmouth, Devon EX35 6RQ

Telephone: (0598) 53223 Fax: 0598 53480

London 195, Minehead 17, Barnstaple 23, Ilfracombe 22

F licence; 16 bedrooms, all with en suite bathroom, TV and telephone; room service; baby listening; last orders for dinner 9.00 p.m.; bar meals; special diets; no dogs; conferences up to 10 (winter only); sea bathing, sailing and boating; golf, tennis, riding and shooting nearby; hotel open all year; all major credit cards (except Diners) accepted.

The Rising Sun can be found right on the edge of Lynmouth harbour. Originally a fourteenth-century smugglers' inn, the hotel is romantically covered with climbing roses and attractively thatched. R. D. Blackmore wrote 'Lorna Doone', whilst staying at The Rising Sun, and in 1812, the poet Shelley spent his honeymoon in the adjacent Shelley's Cottage, now part of the hotel. The cottage has its own private garden and lovely double bedroom with four poster bed. The main building has sixteen pretty, olde worlde bedrooms, including two with four poster beds, and all have views of either the hillside or the harbour. Recently refurbished, all are attractively decorated and are reached by a series of tiny corridors and staircases. Ceilings are far from straight, oak floors are uneven and the whole is charming. Gordon Kelly is the talented young chef and the restaurant enjoys a fine reputation for good food beautifully prepared and presented. Sea food and game are specialities, and it was hard to choose from the excellent bar menu, but I very much enjoyed a tasty sea food vol au vent. The Rising Sun is owned and expertly run by Hugo and Pamela Jeune and their charming staff. An ideal venue from which to explore the delights of North Devon. Room and breakfast from £35.00, weekly rate from £195.00.

THE LYNTON COTTAGE HOTEL

Lynton, North Devon EX35 6ED

Telephone: (0598) 52342 *Fax: 0598 52597*

London 140, Barnstaple 18, Exeter 48

F licence; 17 en suite bedrooms, all with TV and telephone; room service; last orders for dinner 8.45 p.m.; bar meals; special diets; children over 10 welcome; dogs accepted; conferences up to 20; bar billiards; sea bathing; riding; tennis 1 mile; shooting and fishing locally; hotel closed in January; credit cards accepted.

The Lynton Cottage Hotel is set in its own grounds high above Lynmouth Bay, and the original house dates back to the seventeenth century. The present-day hotel has a warm and friendly atmosphere, echoed by the proprietors, Mr. and Mrs. Jones. Lynton Cottage has many regular visitors who feel it to be a very special place. Situated on the edge of Exmoor National Park, there is much to see and do, and activities include walking the moor, fishing the Lyn and simply relaxing and absorbing the splendid sea views. Bedrooms are attractively furnished and include a four poster room; all have views of either Exmoor or Lynmouth Bay. The special, romantic Champagne Weekends are very popular, including pink champagne with dinner on your second night, and breakfast in your room. Fresh flowers welcome you in the foyer, and the attractive restaurant, decorated in pastel shades overlooks the sea. Guests may choose from à la carte or table d'hôte menus; there is much to tempt the palate, including a wide range of fish, meat and game. There is an excellent wine list. Bar lunches and snacks are available during the day. Double room and breakfast from £40.00 per person; weekly rate for half board, £320.00 per person.

SUTTON HALL

Bullocks Lane, Sutton, Nr. Macclesfield,
Cheshire SK11 0HE

Telephone: (02605) 3211 *Fax: 02605 2538*

London 240, Macclesfield 1, M6 (J18/19) ½ hour, Manchester airport ½ hour

F licence; 10 en suite bedrooms, all with four poster beds, colour TV, direct dial telephones, tea/coffee maker & trouser press; full central heating; late meals to 10 p.m.; diets; dogs welcome; conferences up to 20; golf, tennis, riding nearby; Peak National Park adjacent; most credit cards accepted.

If like myself you enjoy staying at an hotel of character, then here at Sutton Hall is one of the finest in which to indulge yourself. A wealth of beams, log fires and four poster beds are all in evidence, and the ales, conditioned in cask, are matched by the choice of food from an excellent menu. As with the inns of old, there is an atmosphere of warmth, hospitality and good cheer. This, married to such modern conveniences as en suite bathrooms and colour TV, makes a very happy amalgam of past and present. To travel, even from afar, is well worth while and this is made easy by the fact that the M6 and Manchester Airport are less than half an hour away. Also in the area are many other famous old houses, as well as the scenic beauty of the Peak District. The hotel is personally run by Mr. and Mrs. Bradshaw. Room and breakfast from £55.95 single, £36.50 double, per person, inclusive of VAT and full English breakfast. Open all year.

FREDRICK'S HOTEL AND RESTAURANT

Maidenhead, Berkshire SL6 2PZ

Telephone: (0628) 35934 *Telex: 849966* *Fax: 0628 771054*

London 28, Oxford 30, Heathrow 14, Henley 9, Windsor 8

F licence; 37 en suite bedrooms (14 ground floor) all with telephone, colour TV with satellite network, radio; full central heating; night service; last orders 9.45 p.m.; diets; children welcome; baby listening; conferences max. 140; golf, tennis, nearby; all major credit cards accepted.

The proprietor, Fredrick W. Losel, has created a fine hotel here on the outskirts of Maidenhead. Although it is not far from the railway station and junctions 8 and 9 of the M4, the hotel is in a very quiet situation in its own lovely gardens. On entering Fredrick's there is an immediate sense of the hotel's stylish ambience, emphasised by the stunning flower arrangements and plants throughout the hotel. The Restaurant, bar and lounge are most comfortable and sumptuously furnished. In addition to the good à la carte menu there is a table d'hôte at luncheon, with a choice of five main course dishes – the food is excellent and the wine list has a large selection of the finest wines. The suites are magnificent, the bedrooms luxurious and the furnishings typify that of the English country house. The interior design of the new wing is almost indistinguishable from the earlier main building. I found the service throughout was efficient, courteous and most helpful. Windsor and Henley are very close and Runnymede, Ascot and Wentworth not much further. Bed and full English breakfast from £98.50 single, £135.00 double, inclusive of VAT, daily paper and early morning tea/coffee. Open all year, except 24–30 December.

MONKEY ISLAND HOTEL
Bray-on-Thames, Maidenhead, Berkshire SL6 2EE

Telephone: (0628) 23400   Telex: 846589 MONTEL   Fax: 0628 784732

Maidenhead 2, Windsor 5, London 30, Heathrow 13

F licence; 27 en suite bedrooms (12 ground floor) all with telephone, colour TV, room service; night service; last orders 9.45 p.m.; bar meals; children welcome; dogs not accepted; conferences max. 120; boating, private moorings; croquet lawn; fishing; riding, golf, tennis, squash all nearby; all major credit cards accepted.

This famous hotel has been completely refurbished to a very high standard of luxury, but of course the one thing you cannot change is its sensational position on the River Thames. In fact, Monkey Island is a true islet on a beautiful part of the river in Berkshire. On arrival at the hotel, having parked your car, a footbridge beneath the willow trees leads you across the water to an island of sweeping lawns and sheltering trees. Each of the twenty seven tastefully appointed bedrooms and suites is furnished and equipped to the highest standard and all have picturesque river and garden views. Naturally, room service is available for your convenience, but breakfast can be served in the pretty terrace room. I recently had dinner in the Marlborough Room which also overlooks the river and which is stunningly decorated in pale apricots and creams. The food was superb, as one would expect, and the service excellent. Visit the famous Monkey Room for pre-dinner drinks or coffee afterwards. It is a most interesting room with a painted domed ceiling, dating from the early 18th century, depicting monkeys in several river scenes, all dressed in the fashions of the day. Monkey Island is a most romantic setting and one that will leave you with the feeling that you have experienced an adventure, dining at this unique hotel. Room and breakfast from £70.50 (effective to 31.3.91), weekly from £505.00. Rates inclusive of service and VAT. Hotel open all year.

THE OLD BELL HOTEL

Malmesbury, Wiltshire SN16 0BW

Telephone: (0666) 822344

Bath 25, Cirencester 24, Lacock 14, Castle Combe 14, Badminton 10, Swindon 13

F licence; 37 en suite bedrooms, all with telephone, radio, TV; tea/coffee making facilities; full central heating; late meals to 9.30 p.m.; diets; children welcome, baby listening; conferences; golf 5 miles; riding; Access, Visa credit cards welcome.

Possibly the oldest hotel in England, the Old Bell stands in the shadow of the old Norman Abbey and was built as its hostelry around 1220. It has a number of interesting architectural features including part of the castle wall, a medieval spiral staircase, a 13th century window, and a unique stone hooded fireplace from the early 13th century. At the back is a truly delightful sheltered garden on two levels with a pretty octagonal gazebo providing a pleasantly furnished sitting area which overlooks the river Avon as well as the garden. The bedrooms all have a style and décor of individual character and, like the lounge, are both attractive and comfortable. In addition to the Castle Bar, there is a cocktail bar, and both have log fires in the winter. The well-appointed restaurant has an interesting à la carte menu as well as table d'hôte for luncheon and dinner, complemented by a carefully selected and extensive wine list. Malmesbury is England's oldest borough and as such is full of interest. It is also an excellent centre with many famous sights within easy reach, such as Westonbirt Arboretum and the lovely villages of Lacock and Castle Combe. Bed and full English breakfast from £65.00 single, £80.00 double, inclusive of VAT; no service charge. Christmas and New Year programmes. Bargain Breaks available. Open all year.

CRUDWELL COURT HOTEL AND RESTAURANT

Crudwell, Nr. Malmesbury, Wiltshire SN16 9EP

Telephone: (06667) 7194, 7195 or 355 *Fax: 06667 7853*

London 97, Cirencester 6, Swindon 12, Malmesbury 3

R & R licence; 15 en suite bedrooms, all with telephone, remote control colour TV, radio, tea/coffee making facilities, full central heating; night service until 12 midnight; last orders 9.30 p.m.; bar meals; diets; children welcome; baby listening; dogs accepted; conferences max. 25; heated outdoor swimming pool; croquet; leisure centre, sailing, golf, tennis, squash, badminton, riding, shooting, fishing all nearby; Access, Visa, Amex, Diners credit cards accepted.

What a lovely surprise to find this enchanting little hotel on my travels near to Cirencester and Malmesbury. It is a 17th century former Vicarage, set alongside a Saxon church in 3 acres of beautiful walled gardens. It is really like staying in a private home – I had the most warm welcome and I certainly look forward to a return visit. The house has recently been completely refurbished and all fifteen bedrooms are individually decorated. The gracious panelled dining room overlooks the church. The excellent cuisine is freshly prepared to order, all complemented by an extensive wine list. Crudwell Court is run by its resident owners, Brian and Susan Howe, who give that extra personal touch to the warm, country house atmosphere. Room and breakfast from £40.00 single, £77.00 double. Weekly terms on application. Hotel is open all year.

WHATLEY MANOR

Easton Grey, Nr. Malmesbury,
Wiltshire SN1G 0RB

Telephone: (0666) 822888 *Telex: 449380* *Fax: 0666 826120*

London 98, Chippenham 10, Swindon 16, Bristol 30

R and R licence; 29 en suite bedrooms (12 ground floor), all with telephone, TV; radio on request; full central heating; night service; diets; children welcome, baby listening; dogs welcome; conferences; sauna; solarium; jacuzzi; croquet; billiards; heated outdoor swimming pool; tennis; fishing; golf 5 miles, squash 2 miles, riding 1 mile; Amex, Access, Diners, Visa cards accepted.

Whatley Manor, located on the borders of Wiltshire and Gloucestershire and on the edge of the Cotswolds, is noted for the luxury and spaciousness of both the bedrooms and public rooms. It has a real feeling of comfort and opulence, backed by unobtrusive service and excellent cuisine. The dining room has lovely views over the gardens, beyond which paddocks run down to a peaceful stretch of the river Avon, well stocked with brown trout, where the hotel has fishing rights. The pine panelled lounge and oak panelled drawing room, both with log fires, are elegant and provide relaxing surroundings. The Library Bar offers drinks and volumes of *Punch* dating back to the 19th century. The Manor bedrooms are furnished to a very high standard indeed. The Court House, 70 yards from the Manor and recently refurbished, has ten more bedrooms overlooking the tennis court and grounds. The hotel is within easy reach of Badminton, Westonbirt Arboretum, Stonehenge and Longleat, to name but a few places, and the towns of Bath, Bristol, Cheltenham and Swindon. Convenient for M4 and M5. Bed and full English breakfast from £66.00 single, double £92.00, inclusive of VAT and service. Short breaks also available throughout the year.

AUBURN HILL HOTEL

Norton-on-Derwent, Malton, North Yorkshire YO17 9PZ

Telephone: (0653) 695335

York 18, Pickering 8, East coast 23, Railway station 1½, London 193

R & R licence; 8 en suite bedrooms, all with colour TV, telephone and full central heating; last orders for dinner 9.00 p.m.; vegetarian diets, others by request; children over 12 welcome; dogs allowed; conferences up to 10–15 welcome; indoor pool, sauna and solarium nearby; golf 1 mile; shooting 2 miles; fishing 5 miles; Visa and Access welcome.

I enjoyed my visit to Auburn Hill Hotel. Surrounded by lovely mature gardens, it stands high above the old Malton Racecourse. Inside, it is spacious and comfortable, with the most lovely decorations. The tasteful dining room, dressed in warm tones is a delightful place in which to relax over dinner and enjoy a good bottle of wine. The bedrooms are large, all with bathrooms, and beautifully styled to blend in with this quiet Victorian house. The hotel is owned by Patrick and Jane Johnson, whose personal attention will ensure your stay is relaxing and memorable. Auburn Hill is situated in the midst of a picturesque and historic part of Yorkshire. York, which offers historic remains, racing, good shops and a wonderful variety of fascinating museums, the famous antique shops of Harrogate and the city of Leeds, are all about half an hour's drive away, as are the east coast resorts and the breath-taking scenery of the North Yorkshire Moors National Park. To find Auburn Hill, take the Langton Road out of Norton-on-Derwent, and drive for 1 mile; the hotel is on the left just before the road rises to the wolds. Hotel open all year. Room and breakfast from £45.00 single, and £68.00 double.

IVY HOUSE HOTEL

Marlborough, Wiltshire SN8 1HJ

Telephone: (0672) 515333   Telex: 449703 Attn. Ivy   Fax: 0672 515338

British Rail 15, Heathrow 80, Avebury 6, Stonehenge 30, Bath 35, M4 8

R & R licence; 35 en suite bedrooms (8 ground floor), all with telephone, full central heating; last orders – meals 9.30 p.m.; drinks 11.00 p.m.; vegetarian diets; smoking and non-smoking lounges; children over 12 welcome; dogs accepted; residential conferences max. 35; special functions; golf, tennis, squash nearby; shooting and fishing weekends arranged; Amex, Visa, Access, Diners credit cards accepted.

Ivy House is a Listed Grade II Georgian residence on the south side of the famous Marlborough High Street. During the 19th century it became well known as a coaching inn and has been a traditional hostelry until the present day. The interior contains many architectural and decorative features of the changing eras. The Garden Restaurant, with its high ceiling and Palladian-style décor in pale pink and Wedgwood blue, is particularly attractive. I enjoyed a very good luncheon with efficient, friendly service and there is a first-class wine list with a large selection of excellent wines. The bedrooms are attractively furnished and individually decorated and have all the latest facilities – 12 rooms are in the main building and 14 are in the Beeches wing, newly built but so well designed that it is almost indistinguishable from the earlier building. Adequate car parking is provided at the rear from which there is a wheelchair ramp leading to four ground floor bedrooms. Marlborough is an excellent centre for visits to Stonehenge, Avebury, Savernake Forest and Salisbury Plain and nearby stately homes include Littlecote, Bowood House and Blenheim Palace. Tariff on application. Hotel open all year.

DANESFIELD HOUSE

Medmenham, Marlow, Buckinghamshire SL7 3ES

Telephone: 0628 891010 *Fax: 0628 890408*

London 35, Marlow 2, Heathrow 20, Windsor 10, Henley 5, Oxford 25

F licence; 90 en suite bedrooms all with direct dial telephone, TV, 24 hour room service; lift; last orders dinner 10.30 p.m.; bar meals; special diets; children welcome; dogs accepted; conferences max. 100; outdoor swimming pool; sailing & boating & fishing on Thames; tennis; golf 5 miles; riding, shooting by arrangement; credit cards accepted.

This very beautiful house, in sixty five acres of outstanding grounds and formal gardens on the River Thames, opens as a luxury hotel in early March. No expense has been spared to create a very exclusive hotel in this lovely part of England. Danesfield is only 30 miles away from London and at the centre of the English Season, with the Henley Regatta, Ascot and Polo at Windsor all close by. If your tastes are more peaceful, however, you can enjoy a quiet picnic on the edge of the Thames. Guests will enjoy the grand drawing room with its magnificently carved timber ceiling, the spacious banqueting hall and the 90 superbly appointed bedrooms, which also include eighteen suites. All the rooms boast extras such as complimentary toiletries, as well as trouser presses, bath robes, hair dryers and even umbrellas! You can enjoy a variety of cuisines from around the world in any of the four restaurants; Swedish, French, Brasserie and Loggia. All the restaurants are beautifully designed, with antiques, fine objets d'art and sumptuous furnishings, all of which will help to make a stay at Danesfield House a truly exceptional experience. Room and breakfast from £150.00. Open all year from March.

RIBER HALL

Matlock, Derbyshire DE4 5JU

Telephone: (0629) 582795 *Fax: 0629 580475*

Derby 20, Nottingham 26, Chesterfield 11, Sheffield 25, M1 Motorway (exit 28) 20 minutes

Take the A38 from Junction 28, M1 motorway, turn on to A615 and follow 7 miles to Tansley, turn left at lane signposted Riber.

R and R licence; 11 en suite bedrooms (7 ground floor), with radio, tea/coffee making and bar facilities, colour TV, direct dial telephone; children over 10 welcome; meals to 9.30 p.m. (last orders); service to 11.00 p.m.; breakfast from 7.00 a.m.; small conferences; all weather tennis court; indoor swimming pool and golf 2 miles; fishing and clay pigeon shooting by arrangement; all credit cards accepted.

This lovely peaceful Elizabethan Manor House is set in the heart of the Derbyshire countryside, surrounded by woods and meadows with a beautiful walled garden to stroll in or sit and soak up its enchantment. Situated on the border of the Peak National Park, and close to five of the finest stately houses in England, Riber Hall is a delightful and luxurious hotel in a most tranquil setting. The bedrooms are set around the courtyard and are of the highest standard. Five rooms have whirlpool baths, and nine have antique four poster beds. There are three luxury double rooms, and all have individual colour schemes, the exquisite work of Gill Biggin, the wife of Proprietor Alex Biggin. Since it was established in 1972, Riber Hall has been renowned for its outstanding cuisine and extensive wine list. There is no room to describe all the pleasures at Riber Hall, so do try it, and I am sure you will return for more. Room and Continental breakfast from £59.00 single and £78.00 double. Other rates, including 'Away Weekends', on application. Hotel and restaurant open seven days a week throughout the year.

FIFEHEAD MANOR

Middle Wallop, Stockbridge, Hampshire SO20 8EG

Telephone: (0264) 781565 *Fax: 0264 781400*

Stockbridge 5, Andover 7, Salisbury 10, Winchester 14, Southampton 20, London 70

F licence; 16 bedrooms all with en suite bathroom (2 suitable for disabled); telephone and TV; room service; baby listening; last orders for dinner 9.30 p.m.; bar meals; special diets; children welcome; dogs accepted; conferences up to 20; fishing, shooting, riding within 5 miles; sports centre 5 miles; hotel open all year except 2 weeks at Christmas; major credit cards accepted.

Legend has it that Lady Godiva once lived here. The current owner and "lady of the manor" for the last 14 years, is a charming Dutch lady by the name of Mrs Margaret van Veelen. Under her expert supervision, Fifehead Manor has literally become a living legend, with its superb style and quality. Dating back to the 11th century, Fifehead Manor is steeped in history, charm and character. The reception area, bar and lounge are tastefully decorated, creating a relaxed and sophisticated atmosphere. The original Medieval hall provides a wonderful backdrop for the hotel's restaurant. Stunning colour schemes, mullioned windows and a Jacobean fireplace complement this setting, where you can savour the most excellent cuisine, which consists of fresh local produce. Fifehead Manor is a most impressive venue for lunches or candlelit dinners, with a comprehensive selection of fine wines, and excellent service. The stylish and peaceful conference room facility is a find for any chief executive. The 16 en suite bedrooms are a joy. The interior design incorporates the beautiful colours of the countryside to perfection. The building has been thoughtfully maintained, and the 3½ acres of grounds provide a picture postcard setting for this lovely hotel. Middle Wallop is ideal for touring the south and west, and I can thoroughly recommend a stay of any duration. Room and breakfast from £45.00 single, £75.00 double.

SOUTH LAWN HOTEL

Milford-on-Sea,
Hampshire SO41 0RF

Telephone: (0590) 643911 *Fax: 0590 644820*

London 96, Lymington 4, Brockenhurst 5, Barton-on-Sea 3

R and R licence; 22 bedrooms and 2 de luxe all with en suite bathrooms, ground floor bedrooms available, colour TV, radio, telephone, trouser press, hairdryers; children over 7 years welcome; no dogs; diets; full central heating; sea bathing, sailing, boating, golf, tennis, squash, riding, shooting and fishing all nearby.

It was a letter of recommendation from a local resident that led me to South Lawn Hotel which is situated about a mile from the sea at Milford. Ernst Barten and his wife have owned the hotel since 1971 and are constantly effecting improvements. Mr. Barten can be justifiably proud of the standard of cuisine that is available. The quality is particularly emphasised and French, German and English dishes predominate. Mr. Barten supervises all the cooking himself and the kitchen is absolutely spotless. The spacious bedrooms are comfortably furnished and all have private bathrooms. Here, then, is a most attractive venue from which to explore the New Forest, or take advantage of the many sporting activities that are available in the vicinity. If you approach the hotel from the direction of Christchurch and Bournemouth, please note that you have to travel through the village of Milford-on-Sea, but then South Lawn is easily found on the left hand side of the road about half a mile beyond. The Bartens are always very helpful and courteous; they extend a warm welcome to every guest. Room and English breakfast from £43.00 single, £71.00 double, including VAT. Two day Winter Breaks (twin/double) Nov–Dec £82.50 (1990), Jan–25th May £85.00 (1991) except Easter and Bank Holidays. Closed mid-December to mid-January.

THE OLD SWAN AND MILL

Minster Lovell, Oxfordshire OX8 5RN

Telephone: (0993) 774441 *Fax: 0993 702002*

Oxford 15, Witney 4, Burford 5, Cheltenham 35, Heathrow 67

F licence; 64 en suite bedrooms all with direct dial telephone & satellite TV; last orders dinner 10.00 p.m.; bar meals; diets by arrangement; children welcome; conferences max. 50; tennis; fishing; billiards; punting; croquet; table tennis; golf & riding 5 miles; credit cards accepted; open all year.

Minster Lovell is a traditional Cotswold village that seems untouched by modern times, with its mill stream, thatched cottages and wealth of local history. The Old Swan and the Mill are located in the middle of this delightful village which is only 15 miles from nearby Oxford and but a short drive from the beautiful town of Burford with its array of antique shops. The Old Swan and the Mill not only offer one of the best local restaurants in the area, but also have superb accommodation with everything you would expect to find in a luxury hotel. The attentive staff are always happy to put themselves out to assist you. Meeting rooms with every modern facility are available for groups of 6–50 people. There are fifty three acres of grounds to wander in and for the active, tennis, punting, croquet and putting are available at the hotel. Tariff on application. Special rates are available at weekends, see Bargain Break section.

MONK FRYSTON HALL

Monk Fryston, Nr. Leeds,
W. Yorkshire LS25 5DU

Telephone: (0977) 682369 *Telex: 556634* *Fax: 0977 683544*

York 18, Harrogate 25, Selby 7, A1 2

F licence; 29 bedrooms (7 ground floor) all with private bathroom, radio, telephone and TV; central heating; late meals to 9.30 p.m.; diets; children welcome, baby listening; dogs welcome; conferences up to 16 residential, day conferences up to 50; credit cards accepted.

This is surely the epitome of a Country House Hotel. In a superb house, with a history going back to the Middle Ages, you can enjoy every modern comfort and convenience whilst wining and dining in a style reminiscent of those former times. The richly panelled rooms are lit by stone mullioned windows and, in winter, are warmed by open fires creating a glowing ambience of well being. Outside, with the splendid stone elevations of the house as a backdrop, you can stroll by the lake or on the terraces of the gardens, both formal and informal. If motoring up the A1, visiting the races at either Doncaster or York, holding a small conference or simply touring in this lovely area, then Monk Fryston makes an excellent place to stay and indulge oneself. Room and breakfast from £54.00 (single) £76.00 (double), service and VAT included. Weekend break, dinner, bed and breakfast (2 nights) £82.00–£92.00 per person. Includes bank holidays except Christmas and New Year. Open all year.

THE KING'S ARMS INN

Montacute, Somerset TA15 6UU

Telephone: (0935) 822513

London 130, Yeovil 4½, Taunton 22, Salisbury 44, Honiton 28

F licence; 11 en suite bedrooms (4 ground floor), all with col. TV, telephone, radio alarm, tea/coffee making facilities, mini bar; full central heating; last orders 9 pm; bar meals; diets on request; children welcome; dogs by arrangement; most credit cards accepted.

This is a 16th century hamstone Inn set in a picturesque village – an ideal West Country touring centre. The Elizabethan Montacute House is only a few hundred yards away, there are many other historic and sporting interests in the area and it takes only thirty minutes to reach the sea. The bedrooms are comfortable and well equipped, all with a pastel shade décor, and one room has an elegant four-poster bed. The à la carte menu, with both classical and more unusual dishes, is served in the attractive Abbey Room and the good wine list also has a wide selection of half bottles, which is less common these days. The standard of food and service was very satisfactory and the Inn also offers a traditional Sunday lunch. The Windsor Room is a comfortably furnished lounge area which is particularly suitable for pre-dinner drinks and coffee afterwards. Hot and cold meals and snacks are available in the Pickwick Bar at lunchtime and there is also a supper menu. Bed and full English Breakfast from £42.00 (single), £58.00 double, inclusive of VAT. Open all year.

THE MILL

Mungrisdale, Penrith, Cumbria CA11 0XR

Telephone: (07687) 79659

Penrith 10, Keswick 10, London 290, Newcastle-on-Tyne 70

R & R licence; 9 bedrooms (2 ground floor) 2 with shower, 4 private bathrooms; 5 with TV; part central heating; dinner 7.00 p.m.; diets on request, with a vegetarian choice on offer each evening; baby listening; dogs allowed; snooker, darts and table tennis; sailing, boating and golf nearby; badminton in summer; riding; local fishing; clay pigeon shooting; no credit cards.

There are, to my mind two main advantages to the location of the Mill. Firstly, Mungrisdale is a secluded and little known part of the Lake District and therefore the crowds and traffic of the many holidaymakers is almost non-existent. Secondly, as this picturesque area is on the Eastern edge of the national park, not only is the centre easily accessible but so are such interesting places as the EdenValley, Hadrian's Wall, the Solway Firth and Carlisle. Even the border regions of Scotland and the Yorkshire Dales are within touring range. Having said this, I am sure that many people would be quite happy to wander no further than a mile or two from this charming hotel, which dates from 1651. I must add that all the activities for which the area is famous, such as pony trekking, rock climbing, sailing and fishing are all available in the vicinity. The Mill stands at the foot of the fells, set in a pretty garden with a mill leat and waterfall, and inside, it is cosy, cheerful and welcoming. The rooms in the Mill are not large but they are well furnished and bright with flowers, the bedrooms are pretty and very comfortable, but it is the dining room that excels. I can wholeheartedly recommend this quiet family hotel, superbly run by resident proprietors, Richard and Eleanor Quinlan. It is BTA commended and offers genuine good value for money. Dinner, bed and breakfast from £30.50 inclusive. Hotel closed from November till mid February.

THE CHEWTON GLEN HOTEL
New Milton, Hampshire BH25 6QS

Telephone: (0425) 275341 *Telex: 41456* *Fax: 0425 272310*

London 97, Bournemouth 10, Lymington 7, Lyndhurst 12

F licence; 58 bedrooms with private bath and colour TV; satellite television; meals until 9.30 p.m.; no dogs; croquet and putting on the lawn; chauffeur service; heated outdoor swimming pool, en-tout-cas tennis court and 9-hole golf course in grounds; squash, boating, fishing, shooting, riding, sea bathing nearby.

Undoubtedly Chewton Glen is one of the finest hotels that Great Britain has to offer. It is somewhat off the beaten track, but within easy reach of such places as Salisbury and Winchester with their famous Cathedrals, Wilton House, Broadlands, Stonehenge, Exbury Gardens, the Mary Rose and Kingston Lacey. The bedrooms are beautifully furnished and spacious and the décor and fittings in the public rooms are of an exceptionally high standard. The guest will particularly appreciate the friendly and attentive service, which is not to be found everywhere nowadays. In November 1990 a luxury Health Club will be completed incorporating two indoor tennis courts, indoor heated swimming pool, seven treatment rooms, gymnasium, saunas, steam room and spa, hairdressing salon. It is hoped that these will be some of the finest facilities of their kind in the UK. To locate this lovely old house the traveller should find Chewton Farm Road in Walkford, off the Ringwood Road, which itself lies between the A35 and the A337. The hotel is at the end of a long drive, thus ensuring quiet and privacy. A member of The Leading Hotels of the World, Relais & Chateaux. Room and breakfast for 2 persons from £173.00, inclusive of service and VAT.

THE OLD ENGLAND

Sutton-on-Trent, Nr. Newark, Nottinghamshire NG23 6QA

Telephone: Newark (0636) 821216

London 128, Newark 8, East Retford 12, Leicester 41, Lincoln 24

C licence; 12 en suite bedrooms; children welcome; dogs welcome; small conferences.

The Old England is a real home from home. The Pike family have run the hotel since we first published *Signpost* and, more than 55 years later, we are still pleased to recommend it. You will find Sutton Village just off the A1, north of Newark. A Hotel sign on the main road points in the direction of the quiet village High Street, and approximately ½ mile down on the left stands this most attractive country house. Situated in a large very well kept garden, which must be a haven of peace on a fine day, the house is continually being updated by its owners. All bedrooms have their own private bathrooms and are cheerful, cosy and well furnished. Those of you who appreciate good furniture, will be delighted with the beautifully polished antique tables and chairs in the dining room, and the many other interesting pieces and lovely old china throughout the hotel. The kitchen door is always open, for they have nothing to hide, and the food supervised by the Pike family, is really good British fare, such as steak, roasts and poached Scotch salmon, and always plenty of it. Later, I was assured by regular diners at the hotel that their high standard of food never varies. If you are travelling north or south, you can be assured of a very warm welcome at this lovely hotel. Single room and breakfast from £42.00, double from £52.00 including VAT. Always open.

REGENCY PARK HOTEL

Thatcham, Nr. Newbury, Berkshire RG13 3RP

Telephone: (0635) 71555 *Telex: 847844* *Fax: 0635 71571*

Newbury 2, Reading 17, London 54, Oxford 30, Windsor 35, Bath 55

F licence; 50 en suite bedrooms (3 ground floor) all with telephone, colour TV; satellite TV, trouser press, hair dryer, mini bar, fresh fruit; full central heating; lift; night service; last orders 10.30 p.m.; bar meals; diets; children welcome; baby listening; dogs accepted; purpose designed business centre; conferences max. 60; dancing occasional Saturdays; Amex, Diners, Mastercard, Visa credit cards accepted.

This new luxury hotel opened in late 1988 and it provides all modern comforts and facilities in surroundings of opulent décor and furnishings. It is located about half a mile north of the A4 at Thatcham and 2 miles east of Newbury, in a quiet situation in five acres of grounds. All the bedrooms are very spacious and provide every comfort; all rooms are triple glazed and have satellite TV and a number of rooms have balconies. The Terraces Restaurant is beautifully furnished with excellent table appointments and warm peach décor. It looks out onto the terraced garden area. There is a fine à la carte menu and a table d'hôte for luncheon and dinner which is changed daily. The wine list is really comprehensive (prices from £10.00 to £150.00) and includes 1937 vintage clarets. The Fountains Bar offers a wide selection of cocktails with a patio area where you can relax with your drink or just a cup of coffee. A feature of the hotel is the large number of lovely pictures throughout. Disabled persons are catered for with a special ground floor bedroom and a cloakroom off the reception area. A high standard of service is provided at this impressive hotel. Single room from £75.00 during the week, £45.00 at the weekend. Weekend breaks from £49.50 dinner, bed and breakfast per person per night, inclusive of VAT. Executive and King size rooms and suites are available. No service charge. Open all year.

THE SWAN HOTEL

Newby Bridge, Nr. Ulverston, Cumbria LA12 8NB

Telephone: (05395) 31681 *Telex: 65108* *Fax: 05395 31917*

London 261, Manchester 83, Bristol 238, Edinburgh 155, Newcastle-upon-Tyne 102, Birmingham 159

F licence; 36 en suite bedrooms all with TV, radio, tea/coffee making facilities and telephone; central heating; night service; late meals by arrangement; wine bar; diets; children welcome, baby listening; conferences up to 20; sailing, boating, fishing; lake and river bathing; marina; riding 2 miles; golf 6½ miles; most credit cards accepted.

Set 'twixt river and lake in what must be one of the most superb situations in the Lake District, The Swan has all the facilities that a traveller or holidaymaker could wish for. It has its own lovely marina, shop, fishing in the river and is close to the steam railway at Newby Bridge; all this at the end of Lake Windermere. The hotel was originally a coaching inn but has now been completely modernised to give every convenience. Special autumn breaks are offered and my only regret is that I could not stay longer to explore this lovely part of Cumbria. Room and breakfast from £46.00 single and £74.00 double, £90.00 de luxe double, and £105.00 in the Lonsdale Suite with its king size bed, luxurious drapes and craftsman-built mahogany furniture to luxury standard. Hotel open for 3-day Christmas Holiday break and 3 day New Year break. 'Swan Breaks' any two nights weekends only (Friday and Saturday or Saturday and Sunday) from £39.00 per person, dinner, bed and breakfast in double room with private bath. A weekend of Gilbert and Sullivan 15–17th November 1990 from £135.00 per person, fully inclusive. There is also a 'Floral Art' weekend, 19th–21st April 1991, prices from £135.00. Dinner, bed and breakfast terms available for a minimum of two nights from £52.00 per person per night. Other terms on request.

HOTEL BRISTOL
Newquay, Cornwall TR7 2PQ

Telephone: (0637) 879347

London 255, Wadebridge 16, Bodmin 20, Penzance 38, Truro 16

F licence; 86 bedrooms, 66 with private bathrooms and colour TV, all with radio and room telephone; full central heating; lift; night service; meals to 8.30 p.m.; diets; children welcome; dogs welcome; sauna, solarium, indoor heated swimming pool; hair dressing salon; billiards (full size table); games room; dancing in season; sea bathing; sea fishing; sailing/boating; golf 1 mile; tennis and squash nearby; all credit cards accepted.

The Hotel Bristol enjoys an idyllic position directly overlooking Tolcarne Beach, which is acknowledged as being one of Europe's finest for surfing. It has been a great favourite of mine for many years and was featured in the 1939 Edition of *Signpost*. The hotel has remained under the ownership of the Young family since its foundation in 1927, and continues to be run under their personal care. This was evident when Mr. Stuart Young, Managing Director, took me round. The Bristol has a charm of its own, and very much the family home-from-home atmosphere with a wealth of hospitality for young and old alike. The décor throughout is pleasant and restful, the furnishings are very good, giving an air of comfort and quality. In the elegant and spacious dining room you are offered dishes that are interesting, varied and expertly prepared, complemented by a fine and carefully chosen wine list. I can thoroughly recommend this well run and comfortable hotel, where the service is friendly, courteous and efficient at any time of the year. Why not enjoy a break away from the hurly burly of the peak holiday months? Room and breakfast from £30.00 per person, weekly from £231.00 dinner, bed and breakfast, inclusive of VAT and service. Always open.

THE HEADLAND HOTEL

Newquay, Cornwall TR7 1EW

Telephone: (0637) 872211 *Fax: 0637 872212*

London 270, Bristol 160, Exeter 84, Plymouth 43, Truro 12

F licence; 100 en suite bedrooms all with telephone, colour TV; part central heating; lift; night service; last orders 9.00 p.m.; coffee shop; bar meals; diets; children welcome; baby listening; dogs accepted; conferences max. 300; games room; dancing Fridays during season; billiards; outdoor and indoor heated swimming pools; sauna; solarium; croquet; putting green; sea bathing; surfing; 9-hole approach golf course; tennis; squash, riding, fishing within 1 mile; shooting 4 miles; Visa and Access cards accepted.

The Headland Hotel stands alone away from the hustle and bustle of a busy seaside resort, for it is situated on its own headland with the sea on three sides. This luxurious hotel was built in a time when elegance was important and its splendid proportions are there for you to enjoy today. There are spacious and comfortable public rooms and a grand staircase takes you to bedrooms that are decorated and appointed to a high standard. Two attractive bars provide ideal areas to relax and meet new friends or there are quiet rooms where guests can sit at peace to read or write. This highly recommended hotel provides just about everything you need for a really good family holiday to be enjoyed by all ages. It is privately owned and personally cared for by John and Carolyn Armstrong who have created a happy and homely atmosphere together with their efficient and pleasant staff. The Armstrongs can be justly proud of their high reputation for good food, their menus offer a wide choice of English and continental dishes aided by a selective list of wines. For leisure, the Headland is a sportsman's paradise, space prevents me from listing all that is offered, do ask for their colourful brochure. For the less energetic, there is plenty to do and see within the precincts of the hotel and its grounds. For the adventurous, there is also the hotel's own hot air balloon, with champagne flights available all year, at £75.00 per person. Room and breakfast from £35.00 per person inclusive of VAT. Other terms on application including special breaks. Hotel is closed in December but office open for enquiries.

TREDRAGON HOTEL

Mawgan Porth, Nr. Newquay,
Cornwall TR8 4DQ

Telephone: (0637) 860213 *Fax: 0637 860269*

Newquay 6, Bodmin 18, Truro 21, Falmouth 30, Padstow 6, St. Austell 18, Lands End 48, Penzance 38, Newquay Civil Airport 1

R licence; 29 en suite bedrooms (10 on ground floor), all with direct dial telephone, colour TV, radio, tea/coffee making facilities; full central heating; night service; meals to 8.00 p.m.; diets, vegetarian dish each night; children welcome; baby listening; dogs welcome; conferences up to 50; dancing 1 day per week; sauna; solarium; games room; indoor heated swimming pool; sea bathing; sailing; golf, squash, riding, shooting, fishing, tennis all nearby; Access and Barclay cards accepted.

Tredragon Hotel is set in nearly 3 acres with its own private path to the beach. This attractive Hotel is owned and run by the Brown family who have combined efficiency with high standards, friendliness and comfort. It has everything that is required for a perfect holiday, with a pool lounge adjacent to the swimming pool, and furnishings and décor that are restful and pleasant throughout. The Tredragon has a high reputation for good food which is under the supervision of Nick Brown and his wife, Jenny. The imaginative menus offer a splendid choice, and the wine list was both carefully chosen and reasonably priced. If you want a friendly, cheerful hotel with good cuisine and first class service with a great deal to offer nearby (Mawgan Porth has a fine surfing beach, 2 riding stables, tennis courts and fishing) then I will always recommend the Tredragon. Room and breakfast from £28.00 per person, inclusive of VAT. Special events include golfing, walking and Heritage holidays. Do ask for their most attractive and informative brochure. Open all year.

SOLBERGE HALL

Newby Wiske, Nr. Northallerton, Yorkshire DL7 9ER

Telephone: (0609) 779191 *Fax: 0609 780472*

The A1 7, Northallerton 3, Thirsk 5, York 30, Harrogate 25, Leeds 45

F licence; 30 en suite bedrooms, all with radio, telephone, TV, trouser press, hairdryer; full central heating; meals to 9.30 p.m.; (9 p.m. on Sundays); diets; baby listening; family rooms; dogs accepted; conferences up to 100; billiards; golf and riding 4 miles; fishing by arrangement; 16 acres of peaceful gardens; all major credit cards accepted.

On the edge of the spectacular North Yorkshire Moors, stands this Victorian mansion, operated as a country house and now owned by the same family as the Mollington Banastre Hotel at Chester. Under the direction of General Manager Linda Mercer and Head Chef Peter Woods and with the friendliness of the staff, a stay in this hotel is a must for all *Signpost* readers. The interior has been restored with great care and attention to detail and outside are such historic diversions as a Roman Encampment, 'Viking' Stones, a walled garden and a haunted clock tower. The grounds are exceptionally suited for a range of activities as well as product launches and incentive days – including karting, archery and clay pigeon shooting, also residential and non-residential shooting days can be arranged. It would be hard to find a better location for exploring Yorkshire's ruggedly beautiful moors and dales, or typical Yorkshire towns like Thirsk (James Herriot's Darrowby), or Helmsley or Leyburn on market day. Castle Howard, the setting for 'Brideshead Revisited' is nearby as are four ruined abbeys: Byland, Fountains, Jervaulx and the hauntingly evocative Rievaulx. Single room from £60.00, twin £68.00, Studio suites from £80.00–£100.00.

THE NORFOLK MEAD HOTEL

Coltishall, Norwich, Norfolk NR12 7DN

Telephone: (0603) 737531

Norwich 7, Yarmouth 20, Wroxham 3, London 130

R & R licence; 10 en suite bedrooms, all with radio, telephone, colour TV and tea/coffee making facilities; full central heating; meals to 9.00 p.m.; diets; children over 3 years welcome; conferences; outdoor swimming pool; boating; tennis; fishing; sea bathing 15 miles; golf, squash, sailing and riding nearby; credit cards accepted.

Driving through the village of Coltishall, past the Church, I saw the sign to Norfolk Mead Hotel and discovered a beautiful Georgian House, part of it dating back to 1740, standing in 12 acres of gardens and parkland gently sloping to a long river frontage. The hotel was originally a manor house and during recent restoration, great care has been taken to preserve its historic character, giving the hotel a homely atmosphere. All the pretty bedrooms, from the honeymoon suite with its jacuzzi bathroom to the spacious family rooms, overlook either the front garden or the walled garden where there is a large swimming pool and a barbecue area leading to the Bar. The Restaurant is a lovely room with soft décor in shades of apricot. Here you have a delightful menu, noted for its outstanding quality and presentation, supported by an extensive wine list. In the grounds there is a slipway and off-river moorings with rowing dinghies available free of charge, also a 2 acre fishing lake for the exclusive use of guests. (See Bargain Breaks section). Room and breakfast from £49.00 single, £65.00 double.

SOUTH WALSHAM HALL

South Walsham, Norwich, Norfolk NR13 6DQ

Telephone: (060 549) 378/591/592 *Fax: 060549 519*

Norwich 9, London 120, Great Yarmouth 11, Cromer 25

C licence; 19 en suite bedrooms all with colour TV and radio/alarm clocks; full central heating; meals to 10.00 p.m.; children welcome; ideal for weddings and conferences; outdoor heated swimming pool; 2 double tennis courts; 2 squash courts; horse-riding school; sea bathing 11 miles; sailing and boating on the Broads 1 mile; golf 6 miles; credit cards accepted.

The first impression of the Hall is magnificent; having driven through a beautiful avenue of rhododendrons and yews, one suddenly sees the Hall which stands back with lawns running down to the lake. This most attractive country mansion has been completely renovated and re-decorated under the present Swiss management. The original part of the Hall is steeped in Norfolk history being Elizabethan with further additions up to Victorian times. The most impressive interior feature is the beautiful 17th century staircase which leads up to eight bedrooms of the Hall all named after European cities, with one magnificent bridal suite opening up to the most sumptuous bathroom. The restaurant offers a wine list for the connoisseur and an extensive menu for the gourmet. In the garden behind the Hall is a rose garden and heated swimming pool with existing plans for future sporting improvements to the 34 acre surrounds. The Hall is nine miles from Norwich and within easy reach of Yarmouth, so is an ideal place to stay, away from the bustle of the city, where one can completely relax in this wonderful setting. Single room and breakfast from £38.00, double from £50.00 including VAT and service. Open all year.

BARNSDALE COUNTRY CLUB

Exton, Nr. Oakham, Rutland, Leicestershire LE15 8AB

Telephone: (0572) 757901 *Fax: 0572 756235*

London 90, Leicester 15, Oakham 2, A1 Stamford 6

CL licence; 24 en suite bedrooms, all with col. TV, telephone and central heating; last orders 9.45 p.m.; beauty shop, hairdressing; coffee shop; bar meals; diets; children welcome; baby listening; no dogs; conferences max. 120; games room; gymnasium, snooker; putting green, squash, tennis and indoor heated swimming pool, croquet, crazy golf, bowls; fishing, sailing, windsurfing, riding, golf nearby; Access, Visa, Diners and Amex accepted.

An amazing new concept in holidaymaking, Barnsdale is a combination of hotel, Country Club and timeshare estate. The complex is situated in 60 acres of garden and woodland, on the banks of the beautiful Rutland Water. It has been constructed around Barnsdale Hall, which was itself built in 1870 as a hunting lodge for the Earl Fitzwilliam and his family. There are three restaurants; the Brasserie and Pool View Restaurant, which both serve delicious, reasonably priced food, and The Westminster Restaurant, which has an à la carte menu. The hotel comprises a whole range of rooms from the large Executive Suites, with dining lounge, balcony views over the lake, to the slightly smaller Deluxe rooms and standard doubles and singles. All are very comfortable and well designed. There are also Scandinavian style lodges which sleep 4–6 people, again excellently appointed, with features such as whirlpool baths, hi-fi, TV and video. Everything is superbly organised, with the most efficient and experienced staff. Prices from £72.00 per night. Open all year.

PEN-Y-DYFFRYN HALL

Rhydycroesau, Nr. Oswestry, Shropshire SY10 7DT

Telephone: (0691) 653700

Oswestry 3, Llangollen 10, Shrewsbury 20, Manchester 54, Birmingham 60, Offa's Dyke ½

F licence; 6 en suite bedrooms, 3 with baths, 3 with showers; all with colour TV; central heating; last orders 8.30 p.m., 9.00 p.m. Sats.; diets; children welcome; baby listening; dogs accepted; conferences max. 30; leisure centre 3 miles; three 18 hole golf courses within 10 miles; pony trekking by arrangement; trout-stream and 2 trout lakes; lovely walks; Access and Visa cards accepted.

Taking the B4580 road from the centre of Oswestry, I soon found myself along a pretty country road amidst the most glorious countryside. Over Offa's Dyke, down a steep hill and the signpost for Pen-y-Dyffryn Hall is on the left, just before you reach the village of Rhydycroesau. This Grade II listed building, built of local stone was once a Rectory and is now the home of Miles and Audrey Hunter and their family. On arrival, I was overwhelmed by the peace and quiet and the serenity of the surroundings. Once inside, you will not find a reception area, only a lovely, small bar and a similar sitting room, furnished with Victorian furniture, not sophisticated, but cosy and homely. The dining room overlooks the patio and pretty south facing garden, which rises up to fields beyond where the border between England and Wales passes through. Audrey Hunter, with a little help from some very pleasant local staff, is the 'Chef de Cuisine' and her menus feature items such as local Welsh lamb casseroled Mediterranean-style, 'Hunters Quail' – quail filled with pork, grapes, chestnuts and brandy, served with redcurrant sauce, vegetarian dishes and many more mouth-watering items. The bedrooms are simply and attractively furnished with matching duvet covers, curtains and wallcoverings, and all are en suite. My stay was all too short, for I believe a few days at Pen-y-Dyffryn with its informal atmosphere, good food and lovely countryside would relax everyone. Dinner, room and full English breakfast from £46.00 (single) £74.00 (double) inclusive of VAT. Winter breaks available, tariff on application. Always open.

THE QUEEN'S HOTEL

The Promenade, Penzance, Cornwall TR18 4HG

Telephone: (0736) 62371 *Fax: 0736 50033*

London 300, Plymouth 60, Lands End 10, St. Ives 15, Truro 23, Helston 10
Gateway to the Isles of Scilly

F licence; 71 en suite bedrooms, all with radio, telephone, TV, free in-house video, tea/coffee making facilities; full central heating; lift; night service; meals to 9.00 p.m.; diets; children welcome; baby listening; dogs welcome; conferences up to 100; dancing during season; snooker room; sauna; solarium; sea bathing; sailing; boating; fishing; golf by arrangement 6 miles; squash by arrangement ¼ mile; riding nearby; major credit cards accepted.

The Queen's Hotel enjoys pride of place on the seafront promenade, with views across Mounts Bay from St. Michael's Mount to the Lizard peninsula. I recently stayed at this splendid Hotel which has been completely refurbished, producing a certain dignity which is enhanced by the appointments. Here, indeed, are rooms of character, quality and comfort. Reception is kind, welcoming and attentive. A superb staircase, flanked by fine paintings will take you to the bedrooms which are restful and well appointed. The food is of a high standard in presentation, quality and service – with the best local produce being used (including freshly caught fish, purchased daily at Newlyn Market). I very much enjoyed my dinner which was complemented by wine from a list that was selective and well chosen. During the day, light lunches are served from a delicious buffet, and individually potted hot dishes are available in the attractive Tudor Bar. Strollers Brasserie, Bar and Restaurant has a superb atmosphere. I can thoroughly recommend this Hotel in all seasons; happy under the management of Anthony Lishman and his cheerful and efficient staff. Room and breakfast from £34.00 per person, inclusive of VAT. Other terms on application, including off season Bargain Breaks and Special Christmas package. Open all year, for restaurant meals; table d'hôte £14.00, Sunday lunch £7.50.

THE WHITE SWAN
Pickering, North Yorkshire YO18 7AA

Telephone: (0751) 72288

York 26, Whitby 21, Scarborough 18, Thirsk 27

F licence; 13 en suite bedrooms, all with telephone, colour TV and full central heating; last orders 9.00 p.m. and 8.30 p.m. on Sundays; bar meals 12.00–2.00 p.m.; diets; children welcome, baby listening; dogs allowed; conferences up to 12; tennis and fishing close by; riding and swimming in town;squash 3 miles; golf 8 miles; sea bathing, sailing and boating from 18 miles; Visa and Access cards accepted.

Pickering has many claims to fame. There is the Parish Church with its Medieval wall paintings; the town itself is the centre from which to tour the North York Moors, the Yorkshire Coast and all that is best in this lovely county, and lastly it is famous for its White Swan Hotel. Here, on arrival you enter a warm and friendly world of log fires, beams and cosy nostalgia. The service too, as in olden times, is courteous and discreet. There is nothing, however, that is old fashioned just for the sake of it. The bedrooms, for instance, have super bathrooms, and all modern conveniences that make staying in a good hotel today such a pleasure. The décor everywhere is pretty and tasteful but these are not the main reasons for recommending this hotel. If you are a gourmet or a wine lover, then a stop here when you are in Yorkshire is a must. The food is varied and interesting, is beautifully prepared and cooked, and above all, it is excellent value. The wine list is nothing short of incredible. What other list can boast 75 St. Emilions alone. Mrs. Buchanan, a connoisseur is a "Dame de la Jurade de St. Emilion". Need I add more! If travelling anywhere in the North of England, what a diversion the White Swan makes! Hotel open throughout the year. Tariff on application.

THE ANCHOR HOTEL AND THE SHIP INN

Porlock Harbour, Exmoor, Somerset TA24 8PB

Telephone: Porlock (0643) 862636/862753 *Fax: 0643 862843*

F licence; 20 en suite bedrooms, all with telephone, colour TV; tea/coffee making facilities; clock radio alarm system; full central heating; late meals to 9.30 p.m.; diets; children welcome, baby listening; dogs welcome; conferences; sailing nearby; golf 6 miles; superb local walking; ½-acre garden; Access, Amex, Eurocard, Visa credit cards accepted.

The 19th century Anchor Hotel and the 16th century Ship Inn are next to each other, 10 yards from the picturesque small harbour, overlooking Porlock Bay and the Bristol Channel. The resident proprietors, Pandy Sechiari and Donald Wade, have a personal objective – to make sure your stay is relaxed and enjoyable. They were certainly much in evidence during my overnight stay, and they invite comments so that they can endeavour to improve still further the high standards of comfort and service. The Anchor has spacious, comfortable lounge areas and an attractive restaurant (candlelit at night), with excellent food and service. The Ship's oak-beamed dining room, which opens during the main season, has an old style quaintness and old world atmosphere. Of the three bars, two are in the Ship and provide good buffet snacks. The accommodation in both houses has a high standard of comfort, and many rooms have sea views. All tastes are catered for in the locality – walks in Exmoor National Park or along the superb coastline, with sailing, fishing, riding and golf all within easy reach. Bed and full English breakfast from £40.00 (single), £62.00 (double) inclusive of VAT and service. Special Christmas breaks and see also Bargain Breaks section. Open all year.

PORT GAVERNE HOTEL

Nr. Port Isaac, North Cornwall PL29 3SQ

Telephone: (0208) 880244 *Fax: 0208 880151*

London 236, Wadebridge 9

F licence; 19 en suite bedrooms all with colour TV, direct dial telephone; 7 self-catering cottages available; late meals by prior arrangement; bar meals, function room; Real ale St. Austell's H.S.D. and Flowers I.P.A. Draught Bitter; children welcome; dogs welcome; sea bathing; boating; riding; sea fishing; golf 6 miles; delightful walks – the Cornish coastal path passes the door; all major credit cards accepted.

This charming 17th century Inn, situated in an unspoilt North Cornish Coastal cove ½ mile from Port Isaac, offers the hospitality and welcome you would expect from a place of this character and hosts such as Freddy and Midge Ross who have owned Port Gaverne for over 20 years. The public rooms retain their old charm, the old baking oven is still to be seen, and many paintings and interesting objects will draw your attention in the three bars and the Residents' drawing room. The bedrooms are well appointed with soft restful colour schemes. Port Gaverne has a high reputation for good food; in an attractive candlelit dining room, you will enjoy a delicious dinner from a choice à la carte menu, augmented by the chef's daily specialities. All dishes are well prepared, imaginative, nicely presented and served, and complemented by a good wine from a cellar kept with pride. Excellent bar meals are also available. Recently, the Ross's acquired the cottages across the lane from the Hotel, and these have been converted (6 with 2 bedrooms and 1 with 3 bedrooms) and may be used either as self catering units, or hotel suites. Now adjoining the "Green Door Cottages" is a most delightful, and thoughtfully designed Function Room, which used to be the "Old Fish Cellar" featuring many objets d'art from bygone days. It has a fully equipped bar, open daily, and is ideal for receptions and private parties. Port Gaverne is noted for its hospitality, comfort, intimate atmosphere, good food, wine and willing attentive service, praised by visitors from all over the world. Terms on application. Special "Breather" rates out of season, and "Tourer" rates during season. A member of the Hospitality Hotels of Cornwall.

RANGEWORTHY COURT HOTEL

Church Lane, Rangeworthy,
Bristol, Avon BS17 5ND

Telephone: (0454 22) 347/473 *Fax: 0454 228945*

Bristol 12, Bath 20, Cardiff 50, Gloucester 23, Cheltenham 30, London 110

R & R licence; 16 en suite bedrooms, with telephone, colour TV, full central heating; last orders 9.00 p.m.; bar meals; diets; children welcome; dogs accepted; conferences up to 16 welcome; outdoor heated swimming pool; riding within 2 miles; golf within 4 miles; hotel open all year; all credit cards accepted.

This beautiful 17th century manor house is a private family run hotel under the ownership of Mr. and Mrs. Mervyn Gillett, whose whole hope is that visitors to Rangeworthy Court can just relax and enjoy the comforts that it has to offer. All the individual bedrooms have private bathrooms or showers, colour TV, movies, telephone, hairdryers and tea/coffee making facilities. The price includes a full English breakfast. The comfortable dining room can seat up to 66 people and features an alcove, if you prefer a more private or intimate atmosphere. The à la carte menu includes traditional dishes, and the table d'hôte menu is changed daily. Rangeworthy Court is very near to the Severn Bridge, the M4 and M5, and only 12 miles from Bristol. Being on the edge of the Cotswolds, close to Bath and Wells, and only an hour from Cardiff, it is a perfect place for both holidays and business visits. The hotel is 15 minutes from Bristol Parkway Station, which has express trains to Paddington. The hotel is set in a beautiful garden, with an unusual and intriguing church hinting at its historic past. There is also ample parking. Room prices start at £44.00–£52.00 single, £58.00–£68.00 double. Bargain Breaks available.

THE BLACK SWAN

Ravenstonedale, Kirkby Stephen,
Cumbria CA17 4NG

Telephone: (05873) 204

London 277, M6 (J38) 6, Kendal 19, Scotch Corner 50

F licence; 17 bedrooms, 15 with private bathroom; full central heating; late meals to 9.30 p.m.; diets; children welcome; dogs welcome; private fishing; tennis; golf nearby; pretty riverside garden.

I was asked by a friend to join him at this hotel and it turned out to be a most pleasant experience. The Black Swan is situated in the lovely Cumbrian village of Ravenstonedale and is surrounded by some of the most spectacular and unspoilt scenery in England. It has a lovely little riverside garden. The hotel itself is efficiently and immaculately run by the resident owners, Mr. and Mrs. Stuart, who offer friendly service, superb food from an imaginative menu, and an excellent wine list. For those wanting to stroll in a beautiful valley, to walk in the peace of the Fells and Moors, or to revel in the wealth of flowers and bird life, there can be no other area better than Ravenstonedale and no place better to stay than the Black Swan. Room and breakfast from £36.50 single, £49.00 double; three, five and seven night inclusive breaks. Winter Break Weekends and Christmas and New Year house parties. Closed January and February.

KIRTONS FARM COUNTRY CLUB AND HOTEL

Pingewood, Reading, Berkshire RG3 3UN

Telephone: (0734) 500885/591885 *Fax: 0734 391996*

Reading 3, Heathrow 30, Newbury 18, Basingstoke 17

F licence; 85 bedrooms all with en suite bathrooms, including 6 suites, all with radio, telephone, TV, tea/coffee facilities; hair dryer; trouser press; safe; room and night service; baby listening; lift; last orders for dinner 10.30 p.m.; bar meals; special diets; children welcome; no dogs; conferences up to 120; games room; snooker/billiards; indoor heated swimming pool; waterskiing and windsurfing; sauna, solarium and spa pool; gymnasium; squash courts and tennis; fishing; credit cards accepted.

This new hotel and country club, parts dating back to 1649, is set in 55 acres on the shores of its private lake. It is a quiet location, yet only five minutes' drive from exits 11 and 12 of the M4. Visitors staying overnight have full membership of the country club for the duration of their stay, and the use of the wide range of sporting and leisure facilities (as above). The members' bar offers traditional pub food and barbecues. In addition there is the Waterfront Bistro, and the Pavilion Restaurant. The former has a large selection of dishes, and the latter provides haute cuisine, with table d'hôte and à la carte menus in attractive surroundings, both have balconies which overlook the lake. The bedrooms are delightful, featuring all modern amenities, and there is a fruit basket to welcome you on arrival, as well as a vase of fresh flowers. All rooms have balconies overlooking the lake. Room and full English breakfast from £85.00 single, £95.00 double, inclusive of VAT. Open all year.

REDCOATS FARMHOUSE HOTEL

Redcoats Green, Nr. Hitchin, Hertfordshire SG4 7JR

Telephone: (0438) 729500 *Telex: 83343 (R.F.H.)* *Fax: 0438 723322*

London 35, Cambridge 25, Hitchin 3, Hatfield 10, Woburn 15, A1(M) 1

F licence; 14 en suite bedrooms (9 ground floor), all with telephone, colour TV; part central heating; last orders 9.00 p.m.; bar meals – weekday lunches; children welcome; baby listening; conferences max. 10; tennis 1 mile; Access, Amex, Diners, Visa credit cards accepted.

Near Little Wymondley village set amidst the rolling Hertfordshire countryside, yet only a few minutes away from the A1, lies the 15th century Redcoats Farmhouse. It has been in the Butterfield family for generations and in 1970 Peter and his sister Jackie converted the building into an Hotel. They started with bed and breakfast before expanding it into the hotel it is today, retaining its relaxed, easy-going country atmosphere. Bedrooms are in the main house or in the converted stable block. Most of them have exposed beams, lovely open fireplaces, antiques and pictures everywhere. One room is particularly suitable for a long stay as it opens onto the very pretty country garden, where marquees can also be erected for weddings. There are three dining rooms, all very intimate, serving delicious food. The menus are very imaginative and varied; the continental and traditional English cuisine is enhanced by the local game, fish and fresh vegetables from their own garden. The bar menu is equally good; mouthwatering dishes can be served in one of the smaller dining rooms, garden or the cosy bar. Room and breakfast from £48.00. Other terms on application. Open all year, except for 10 days at Christmas and Bank Holiday Mondays.

THE ROSE AND CROWN HOTEL

Romaldkirk, Teesdale, Co. Durham DL12 9EB

Telephone: (0833) 50213 *Fax: 0833 50828*

Barnard Castle 6, Alston 26, Kendal 44, London 259

F licence; 11 en suite bedrooms, all with telephone, colour TV and full central heating; last orders 9.30 p.m.; bar meals; diets; children welcome, baby listening; dogs allowed; conferences up to 12; golf, squash, shooting and fishing nearby; credit cards not accepted.

The Rose and Crown sits on the green next to St. Romald's church in what is, arguably, the north of England's prettiest village. The harsh grandeur of the Pennines is tempered by the softness of the Tees Valley, and this is no more evident than here at Romaldkirk. Add to this the warmth, friendliness and comfort of the Rose and Crown, and you have the perfect haven from which to explore this beautiful area. The hotel itself is warm and cosy. There are two bars, and the bedrooms have all the facilities one could wish in a small country hotel. The owners, who have only been here for two years, have already built up a justifiable reputation for their excellent cuisine and imaginative menus. If you are looking for peace, warmth, good food and hospitality, then a visit to the Rose and Crown is to be recommended. This secluded village is a wonderful venue for touring the Dales, the high Pennines and the Lake District. The hotel is open all year. Room and breakfast from £44.00 single, £55.00 double per night, or from £270, including dinner, per week.

MILBURN ARMS HOTEL

Rosedale Abbey, Nr. Pickering,
North Yorkshire YO18 8RA

Telephone: (07515) 312

York 35, Whitby 17, Scarborough 25, Pickering 10

F licence; 11 en suite bedrooms (4 ground floor), all with telephone, col. TV; full central heating; last orders for food 9.30 p.m.; bar meals; diets; dogs by arrangement; conferences max. 60; golf – 6 courses 10–20 miles; riding, fishing locally; Access and Visa credit cards accepted.

What a joy it is to find a civilised small hotel which allows you to walk in off the moors wet, and possibly dirty, and yet not to feel uncomfortable to do so. The bar is sensibly furnished for walkers in a warm, old fashioned way and the friendliness, warmth and excellent food soon restore your energy and well-being. The rest of the hotel is a revelation. Here you have the luxury of thick carpeting, the glow of antiques and the ambience that only a good sense of décor and style can impart. Mr and Mrs Stephen Colling have created a haven for the country lover, be he naturalist, artist, sportsman or tourist. The food here is delicious and generous enough to satisfy the hungriest of gourmands and the choosiest of gourmets and to relax in the cosiness of the Milburn Arms is a tonic after the exertions of your particular pursuit. An inn I look forward to visiting again and again. Prices from £30.00 per night, per person, bed and breakfast in winter.

PENGETHLEY MANOR

Ross-on-Wye, Herefordshire HR9 6LL

Telephone: (0989) 87211 *Telex: 35332 Attn PH* *Fax: 0989 87238*

Take Hereford road A49 from Ross, or 1 mile west from end of M50 spur roundabout linking M5 to Birmingham, London 125, Monmouth 8

F licence; 22 en suite bedrooms (1 ground floor for the disabled) all with colour TV and telephone; 3 suites, 2 with spa bath and 3 with four poster beds; full central heating; last orders usually 9.30 p.m. or by arrangement; diets; children welcome and baby listening; dogs accepted; separate conference centre; pitch and putt; croquet; own trout lake; outdoor heated swimming pool; golf, tennis, squash, riding all nearby; mixed coarse trout and salmon fishing on the River Wye nearby; parking; credit cards accepted.

The Pengethley, this delightful Georgian Country House Hotel, long recommended by *Signpost*, is situated in 15 acres of grounds, with well-stocked gardens and beautiful views of the Herefordshire countryside. The spacious and elegant rooms include a fine panelled library, and the Baysham Bar, where light snacks are available at lunch time. Both these rooms have roaring log fires in chilly weather and, on sunny days, french windows open to the gardens. The smaller Garden Room is available for private dining, and the Georgian Restaurant can be used for private parties and receptions. Executive meetings and small conferences are very much welcomed in the new Chandos Suite. The furnishings and appointments lend character and distinction throughout; the soft and restful colour schemes are particularly welcome in the comfortable and well-appointed bedrooms. In the attractive Georgian Restaurant, imaginative dishes arrive carefully prepared and nicely presented by a cheerful, efficient staff. The wine list is discerningly chosen. The high degree of personal service from Patrick and Geraldine Wisker and their staff provides further reason to recommend this go-ahead hotel. Room and English breakfast from £60.00 single, £100.00 double, including VAT and service. Special breaks and other terms on application, see Bargain Breaks section.

TYLNEY HALL HOTEL

Rotherwick, Nr. Hook, Hampshire RG27 9AJ

Telephone: (0256) 764881 *Telex: 859864* *Fax: 0256 768141*

Basingstoke 7, London 45, Winchester 20

F licence; 91 en suite bedrooms (50 ground floor), all with telephone, colour TV, central heating; lift; night service; last orders 9.30 p.m. weekdays, 10.00 p.m. weekends; diets by arrangement; children over 8 welcome; baby listening by arrangement; no dogs; conferences max. 100; snooker/billiards room; outdoor and indoor heated swimming pools; sauna; leisure centre; multi-gym; croquet in summer; tennis; riding, clay pigeon shooting and golf available by prior notice; all major credit cards accepted; open all year.

Tylney Hall is a beautiful Grade II listed house built at the turn of the century. After a brief period as a school, it has been most carefully restored and turned into a luxurious country house hotel. The main reception rooms are large and elegant with lovely moulded ceilings and the panelled library is now a bar where you can enjoy a pre-dinner drink before embarking on an haute cuisine dinner in the attractive glass-domed restaurant. The ninety-one bedrooms are very spacious and beautifully furnished, reminiscent of the bygone era of country house entertaining; providing everything the most fastidious guest could wish for. Many have fine views over the extensive grounds. Tylney Hall is an ideal setting for special occasions and celebrations; weddings, banquets and conferences are all well catered for and private dining rooms for smaller functions can be arranged. Comprehensive leisure facilities are available, including two lovely swimming pools, one of which is outside in the walled garden and the indoor pool features a whirlpool to help soothe aching muscles after working out in the well equipped multi-gym. For the less energetic, the hotel is set in sixty-six acres of beautifully landscaped grounds ideal for peaceful walks. Room and breakfast from £85.00 single, £99.00 twin.

THE SPA HOTEL

Mount Ephraim, Royal Tunbridge Wells TN4 8XJ

Telephone: (0892) 20331 *Telex: 957188 Spatel* *Fax: 0892 510575*

London 35, Brighton 24, Gatwick 22, Heathrow 50, Canterbury 40

F licence; 76 en suite bedrooms (2 ground floor), all with telephone, radio, TV; diets; children welcome, baby listening; dogs welcome; conferences; hairdressing, spa pool, sauna, solarium, indoor heated swimming pool; gymnasium, jogging trail, tennis court; sailing 3 miles, golf nearby, squash and badminton 2 miles; riding 3 miles; shooting by arrangement; fishing 3 miles; all major credit cards accepted.

Royal Tunbridge Wells is situated in lovely Kentish countryside near the Sussex Borders, with endless places to visit and explore. Where better to stay here than the Spa Hotel? Set in 14 acres of landscaped gardens with its own lake, this family-owned hotel sets out primarily to spoil you. The elegantly furnished bedrooms, equipped with all modern amenities, are prepared each evening with neatly turned down bed covers. The Chandelier Restaurant is both successful and very popular. All the food used in the preparation of your meal is freshly purchased in season from local suppliers. There is an extensive wine list to choose from. The Sir George Kelly suite provides space for conferences of up to 200 delegates. In addition to all the other features, a most luxurious leisure centre "Sparkling Health" has been opened, where electronic equipment enables the staff to assess individual needs and degrees of fitness, and the beauty clinic offers a range of facial and beauty treatments, all designed to relax and revitalise you. The swimming pool (with jetstream system and underwater lighting) is in an air-conditioned conservatory in Victorian style and overlooks the lovely gardens. Room and breakfast from £70.00 single, £90 twin or double. Weekend breaks £55.00 per person per night, includes dinner, bed and breakfast. Open all year.

NORMANTON PARK HOTEL

Normanton Park, Rutland Water South Shore, Leicestershire LE15 8RP

Telephone: (0780) 720315 *Fax: 0780 721086*

London 101, Stamford 5, Nottingham 31, Peterborough 16, Oakham 6

R & R licence; 16 bedrooms (2 for disabled) 14 en suite, all with direct dial telephone, TV; room service; baby listening; night service; last orders dinner 9.45 p.m.; bar meals; special diets; children welcome; dogs accepted by arrangement; conferences max 60; bird watching; cycling; sailing & boating; shooting & fishing; windsurfing; golf 2 miles; riding 3 miles; all credit cards accepted.

Normanton Park is owned and run by Mr and Mrs Chamberlain, and their daughters. This contributes to the hotel's warm and comfortable family atmosphere. The hotel is situated overlooking Rutland Water, in four acres of beautiful gardens. Visitors have the exclusive privilege of direct access to the lake. The original Normanton Park was demolished in 1925, leaving only the stable block and the old coach house. These have been converted into the present Normanton Park by the Chamberlain family, whose hard work has made the hotel what it is today. All the bedrooms are different, offering single, double, triple and family accommodation, and there are two rooms adapted for the use of disabled guests. All are furnished to impeccable standards of comfort, and feature beau duvets fashioned in fabrics made exclusively for Normanton Park. The restaurant enjoys lovely views over the lake. Here, one can sample dishes from extensive à la carte and table d'hôte menus, prepared by Mr David Eddy, their talented young chef, whose training included the Dorchester in London, and hotels in Paris and New York. Light meals are available in the coach house coffee lounge, famous for its amazing selection of ice-creams. Afternoon tea is also served. The hotel's innovative entertainments include providing tandems for guests to cycle the 27 miles round the Water. Room and breakfast from £46.00 (single), £66.00 (twin). Open all year.

ST. MICHAEL'S MANOR
St. Albans, Hertfordshire AL3 4RY

Telephone: (0727) 864444 *Telex: 917647* *Fax: 0727 48909*

London 20, Luton 8, Heathrow 35, Gatwick 60

F licence; 26 en suite rooms, all with telephone, radio, TV; night service; late meals to 9.00 p.m.; dogs by arrangement; conferences welcome; golf nearby; tennis 1 mile; Visa, Diners, Amex and Master Card accepted.

It was a delightful surprise to discover this manor house, which has just celebrated over 400 years of history, in 5 acres of beautiful grounds at the heart of Roman Verulamium, offering guests complete tranquillity. The comforts, character and quality of the house combine the best of old and new in a way which has won praise from leading commentators on British Tourism, including an award from a 'Grounds for Delight' competition. They noted, as we did, the influence of Mr. and Mrs. Newling Ward, who have owned and lived on the premises for over 25 years. They are assisted by a very professional team, led by Residential Director, Mr. Martin Richardson, and his manager Mr. Andrew Billington. All the staff are very proud of their hotel, and take great pains to ensure their guests have a happy stay. The restaurant, with its Victorian style conservatory, enjoys lovely views over the gardens. Head Chef, Mr. Juett, provides delicious à la carte and table d'hôte menus, with a special Chef's Recommendation Menu in the evening. On Sunday evenings, there is also a very popular buffet supper. I noticed too, that everything was cooked traditionally, using fresh herbs from the garden. The bedrooms are interesting, as they are all so different, with picturesque views, and all have recently refurbished bathrooms. Room and breakfast from £76.00 single, £88.00 double. Always open except 27th–30th December.

BOSCUNDLE MANOR

Tregrehan, St. Austell, Cornwall PL25 3RL

Telephone: (072681) 3557 *Fax: 072681 4997*

London 232, Truro 15, Fowey 6, Newquay Airport 18

R & R licence; 10 bedrooms, all with en suite bathroom, telephone and TV; room service; last orders for dinner 8.30 p.m.; special diets; children welcome; dogs by prior arrangement; croquet lawn; outdoor heated swimming pool; gymnasium; 2-hole practice course; squash and tennis courts, sea bathing, sailing and boating nearby; riding 5 miles; fishing 6 miles; hotel closed mid October–mid April; Visa and Access cards welcome.

Boscundle Manor looks and feels like a private house that just happens to be a very special hotel. Mary and Andrew Flint run this hotel efficiently, yet informally, and I felt instantly at home. The house is mainly 18th century with later additions, filled with lovely antiques and paintings of Cornish scenes, by Fred Yates, a family friend. Together they have created an intriguing and original garden, which includes an outdoor heated swimming pool, croquet lawn, practice golf area and many secluded corners for quiet relaxation. Mary has gained many awards for her superlative cooking, and Andrew is extremely knowledgeable about wines, as can be seen by the extensive and reasonable wine list. A fixed price three course dinner menu (including coffee) is offered with several choices for each course. There are two bedrooms in the garden cottage, one in the garden pavilion and seven in the Manor, some with antique furniture, some with jacuzzi baths. All have en suite facilities, direct dial telephones and remote control television. A small exercise room offers a rowing machine, bicycle and other equipment. Boscundle Manor is in Tregrehan which is signposted off the Liskeard road out of St. Austell. A lovely and highly original hotel. Room and breakfast from £52.50 single, £80.00 double, including service and VAT.

CARLYON BAY HOTEL

Nr. St. Austell, Cornwall PL25 3RD

Telephone: (072681) 2304 Telex: 42551 Fax: 072681 4938

London 242, Exeter 75, Bodmin 11, Falmouth 25, Bristol 147, Truro 14

F licence; 72 en suite bedrooms, all with telephone, colour TV with satellite channels; full central heating; lift; 24 hour room service; last orders 9.00 p.m.; bar meals (lunch); vegetarian diets; children welcome; baby listening; children's adventure paddock; paddling pool and playroom; dogs at manager's discretion; conferences max. 125; games room; dancing regularly; 2 full size snooker tables; indoor and outdoor heated swimming pools; sauna; solarium; sea bathing; sailing; free golf available to residents on hotel's 18-hole golf course; 9-hole approach course also in hotel grounds; 2 tennis courts; many other sports locally; helipad; Access, Amex, Diners, Visa credit cards accepted.

Carlyon Bay Hotel, which 50 years ago was called St. Austell Bay Hotel, featured in the first edition of *Signpost* in 1935, and was described as "A perfectly equipped, splendidly conducted and entirely modern Hotel . . . magnificent site overlooking fine sands . . . de luxe hotel atmosphere allied with first rate cuisine and a wide choice of indoor and outdoor sports". Today it is even better for it has been charged with new ideas, energy and attractions, under the efficient and expert ownership of the Brend family. Here indeed is a place with character, luxury and an atmosphere of well being. The public rooms are elegant, well furnished with pleasant décor and a lift to all floors takes you to the comfortable and well appointed bedrooms. In the attractive dining room you can be assured of delicious food that is cooked and presented with skill and imagination. The wine list is well chosen and extensive. Carlyon is a sportsman's paradise for there is a wide range of sporting activities to pursue, and is especially recommended for Golf Society meetings. But it is, above all, recommended for a superb family holiday throughout the year. Room and breakfast from £56.00 single, £52.00 double per person including VAT. Other terms on application. See Bargain Breaks section. Open all year. A member of the family run Brend Group of Hotels, see page 381.

THE BOLT HEAD HOTEL

Salcombe, South Devon TQ8 8LL

Telephone: (054 884) 3751 *Fax: 054 884 3060*

London 214, Kingsbridge 7, Totnes 19, Exeter 43, Plymouth 26

F licence; 29 en suite bedrooms (4 ground floor), all with direct dial telephones, colour TV, radio, tea/coffee making facilities; full central heating; meals to 9 p.m.; diets; children welcome, baby listening; dogs at Manager's discretion; games room; outdoor heated swimming pool; sailing, boating, private moorings; sea fishing; tennis ¼ mile; riding 7 miles; golf 8 miles; major credit cards accepted.

Blessed with a climate that is said to be the mildest in Devon, and set amid imposing scenery that ends with the fantastically shaped black rocks of mighty Bolt Head, this most southerly hotel in Devon commands a marvellous view of the Salcombe Estuary and coastline, and overlooks the sheltered golden cove of South Sands Beach. There are always yachts and fishing boats to be seen in this unspoilt estuary. The hotel has recently been completely refurbished to a very high standard under the ownership of Mr. Colin Smith. A sun terrace leads off the main lounge. The bedrooms are also very comfortable and equipped as one would expect of this well run hotel. The hotel is renowned for its warm welcome and friendly service and the staff are courteous, attentive and cheerful. The table d'hôte menu with specialities, is interesting and provides a splendid choice, carefully served, in an attractive restaurant which has panoramic views of the estuary. In spite of all that is offered at this first class establishment, it also provides peace and quiet with lovely walks in the National Trust property adjoining the grounds. Dinner, room and breakfast from £48.00 per person per night inclusive of VAT, including Getaway Breaks. Closed mid November to mid March, but office open. A Best Western Hotel.

THE MARINE HOTEL

Salcombe, South Devon TQ8 8JH

Telephone: (054 884) 2251 *Fax: 054 884 3109*

London 214, Bristol 120, Exeter 43, Plymouth 25, Totnes 18

R and R licence; 51 en suite bedrooms, all with remote control colour television, radio, direct dial telephone; full central heating; lift; night service; late meals to 9.30 p.m.; diets; children welcome; baby listening; conferences up to 60 in winter; sauna; solarium, beauty and massage salon, hairdressing; billiards; games room; indoor swimming pool, sea bathing; own slipway and boat mooring; golf 4 miles; tennis 100 yards; squash, badminton, riding 6 miles; fishing; Access, Amex, Visa, Diners credit cards accepted.

The Marine Hotel, under the professional management of Mr. Tim Pettifer, by whom I was warmly welcomed, commands an unrivalled and incomparable position on the beautiful Salcombe Estuary. This hotel offers the highest standards of comfort and personal service, and extensive refurbishing has recently taken place. Most bedrooms have balconies facing the sea and are very well equipped. The hotel is beautifully appointed, and has an attractive lounge, library, cocktail bar and restaurant all on the same floor. Many members of the staff have been with the hotel for several years and all are efficient and courteous. The excellent leisure complex offers a plunge pool, solarium, small gymnasium, spa bath, sauna, massage, a beautician, and hairdressing facilities. There is a large indoor pool and sunbathing terraces. The restaurant offers the highest standard of cuisine and a fine and comprehensive wine list. The connoisseur may enjoy rare bottles of wine, and for those interested in haute cuisine an Epicurean menu is provided. Lunches and snacks can be served either in the restaurant or in the Brasserie or at the Poolside. Room and full English breakfast from £63.00, demi-pension from £162.00 (three nights) or £378.00 weekly. Open all year.

TIDES REACH HOTEL

South Sands, Salcombe, South Devon TQ8 8LJ

Telephone: (054 884) 3466 *Fax: 054 884 3954*

London 214, Kingsbridge 7, Totnes 19, Exeter 43, Plymouth 26

F licence; 40 en suite bedrooms with col. TV, radio, direct dial telephone; some family suites; lift; children welcome over 8; games room; snooker room; some diets available; conference facilities; dogs by arrangement; indoor heated pool; solarium; sauna; Hydro Spa Bath; squash; indoor and outdoor water gardens; drying room; golf, tennis, riding nearby; sea bathing; boating; fishing, wind surfing, water sports from own boathouse.

The position of Tides Reach is perfect – a beautiful secluded sandy cove. The quiet luxury of the hotel strikes you as you enter the conservatory-style hall with its indoor water garden and the flower garden lounge-hall so full of sunshine, scented blooms and unusual colours. The indoor heated swimming pool, around which has been built a new bar and coffee shop, is as glamorous as a Hollywood film set – there is an outdoor sun patio and sun deck leading off and below a new hairdressing and beauty salon including multi gym., sunbed, Scandi Whirlpool Spa bath, sauna, steam baths and slendertone. In addition to the new facilities the dining room has been extended and the bedrooms and public rooms have been re-furnished throughout in a most comfortable and luxurious manner. The food is superb, both à la carte and table d'hôte dishes being really first class. Dinner, room and breakfast from £50.00 to £85.00 per person including VAT, and a continental breakfast can be served in the bedrooms. Closed December–February inclusive. Resident Proprietor Roy Edwards FHCI.

SOAR MILL COVE HOTEL

Soar Mill Cove, Nr. Salcombe, South Devon TQ7 3DS

Telephone: (0548) 561566 *Fax: 0548 561223*

Plymouth 22, Kingsbridge 7, Exeter 40

R & R licence; 16 bedrooms, all ground floor (8 for disabled) all with en suite bathroom; telephone and television; room and limited night service; baby listening; last orders for dinner 9.30 p.m.; bar meals; diets; children welcome; dogs by arrangement; games room; outdoor and indoor heated swimming pools; sea bathing; leisure centre in Kingsbridge; tennis (grass court); golf and riding by arrangement; hotel open all year except January; Access and Visa cards accepted.

The village of Soar, and subsequently Soar Mill Cove Hotel, are signposted from Marlborough just outside Salcombe. The hotel stands idyllically at the top of a sandy cove with glorious views of the bay. Five acres of beautiful grounds include facilities for putting and lawn tennis, as well as a swimming pool and paddock for the hotel's pet donkeys. There is also a wonderful indoor pool, kept at a constant temperature of 88°F, which is supplied from a spring, and treated and filtered without chlorine. The hotel is all on ground floor level, and all bedrooms have patio doors opening onto their own private sun terraces, with lovely views of the gardens and sea. The lounges are attractively decorated and furnished, with comfort in mind, and the bedrooms are large, with every conceivable luxury. The restaurant has wonderful views of the bay, and the cuisine is simply superlative, using the freshest garden produce, game and meat. Crab and lobster caught in the bay also feature on the hotel's menu. Patisserie and chocolate are a speciality of the house. The wine list covers all prices and ranges, and is very comprehensive. Children's meals are provided before the adult evening dinner. The Makepeace family cherish their lovely home and their concern for the comfort of their guests is very evident. This is a hotel that truly combines warmth and professionalism. Room and breakfast from £54.00, or half-board weekly from £350.00.

OLD HALL HOTEL

Newcastle Road, Sandbach, Cheshire CW11 0AL

Telephone: (0270) 761221 *Fax: 0270 762551*

Crewe 5, Manchester 15, Birmingham 50

F licence; 15 bedrooms (3 ground floor), including several rooms with four poster beds, all with en suite bathroom, and some with whirlpool bath; room colour TV and telephone; hair dryers and trouser presses; last orders for dinner 9.00 p.m.; special diets; children welcome; dogs by arrangement; conferences up to 25; local leisure centre; golf 2 miles; hotel open all year; Visa, Amex and Master Card accepted.

Recently taken over by new owners, The Old Hall Hotel has been immensely improved. There have been extensive alterations and it is now well furnished and decorated. Much has been made of the wealth of beams and panelling, yet all modern conveniences have been installed, making comfort the keynote. The warmth of this lovely old building, the friendly and efficient staff and the excellent food, all go to make a stay here a memorable one. One of my favourite rooms is one of the downstairs bedrooms, with its own door to the well-tended gardens. Here, it is more like staying in your own country cottage than being in an hotel! Sandbach is a delightful, ancient little town in which the old hall is centrally placed. It is literally only minutes from the M6 motorway and it is thus an ideal stopping off place for those journeying from north to south or vice versa. The hotel also has a conference room, which makes it an excellent venue for those on business to meet colleagues. If any *Signpost* readers are trying to find an historic hotel offering good food, warmth and comfort, all at a very reasonable price, then they need look no further. Room and breakfast from £52.00 including VAT. For special rates, see Bargain Breaks section.

HAVEN HOTEL

Sandbanks, Poole, Dorset BH13 7QL

Telephone: (0202) 707333 *Fax: 0202 708796*

London 105, Southampton 28

F licence; 96 bedrooms all with en suite bathroom; telephone and TV; room and night service; baby listening; lift; last orders 8.30 p.m.; special diets on request; no dogs; conferences up to 150; conference/business centre; indoor/outdoor heated swimming pool; leisure centre; sauna, spa pool and solarium; jacuzzi and gymnasium; squash court; sea bathing, sailing and boating; golf 2 miles; tennis 3 miles; riding 4 miles; shooting and fishing 10 miles; hotel open all year; major credit cards accepted.

The Haven Hotel at Sandbanks must occupy one of the finest positions of any hotel on the south coast of England. It is situated on the deep water entrance to Poole Harbour where marine activity abounds. All 96 rooms are sophisticated, and décor reaches new heights in excellence. All public rooms, bars, sun lounge and Sea View Restaurant are tastefully presented, creating an aura of sophistication throughout, with friendly attentive service by a professional team of staff. The luxury of relaxing on leather sofas prevails in the Marconi Lounge from where Guglielmo Marconi sent his first wireless messages. The "message" transmitted today is of a first class hotel. The Sea View Restaurant's cuisine is supervised by an excellent French chef who provides a buffet and carvery luncheon, and in the evenings discerning diners can savour culinary delights from the table d'hôte and gourmet selected menus. Wines, champagne and cheeses, are kept in temperature controlled Chambrair cabinets, pleasing to the palate of any connoisseur. The new, purpose built Business Centre, has individual suites and seminar rooms to cater for all requirements. The numerous facilities of the Leisure Centre are also superb. The ultimate luxury must be to charter the hotel's own yacht, for a cruise around the bay. All in all this is a first class hotel, room and breakfast from £50.00 per night, and from £420 per week, full board.

SANDBANKS HOTEL

Banks Road, Sandbanks, Poole, Dorset BH13 7PS

Telephone: (0202) 707377 *Fax: 0202 708885*

London 105, Bournemouth 5, Wareham 10

F licence; 105 bedrooms, all with en suite bathroom; telephone and TV; room and night service; baby listening; lift; last orders for dinner 8.30 p.m.; special diets on request; children welcome; no dogs; conferences up to 200; in house disco/ballroom; indoor heated swimming pool; leisure centre; sauna, steam room, solarium and spa pool; trimnasium; sea bathing, sailing and boating; golf 2 miles; tennis 3 miles; riding 4 miles; hotel open all year; major credit cards accepted.

The Sandbanks Hotel, owned by the FJB Hotel Group has a longstanding tradition for being a first class family hotel. Superb frontage onto the European Blue Flag Beach of Sandbanks provides this hotel with the ideal situation for both family holidays and conferences. Most rooms command a view over the coastline of Poole Bay, while others enjoy an open aspect across Poole harbour, with shallow water anchorage in the foreground, and busy marine activities beyond. All contain the comforts required by today's traveller. Children are catered for exceptionally well. There is a children's restaurant, as well as nursery, play galleon and comprehensive play facilities. There is also a children's entertainer, who is welcomed by parents wishing to relax at this friendly hotel. Public rooms are spacious and tastefully decorated. The attractive restaurant overlooking Poole Bay is in a delightful setting in which to enjoy varied menus and friendly service. A superb atmosphere is created in the ballroom/bar. Stylish detail, the clever use of mirrors, and sophisticated disco lighting systems hint at the full entertainment potential of the Ballroom Suite. Individual or group conference meetings can be well provided for in the newly appointed modern Wessex Suites. You can relax after a busy day in any of the hotel's many leisure and sporting facilities. Room and breakfast from £40.00 per night, £330 per week full board.

THE SAUNTON SANDS HOTEL

Saunton Sands, Nr. Braunton, Devon EX31 1LQ

Telephone: (0271) 890212 *Telex: 42557* *Fax: 0271 890145*

London 203, Barnstaple 8, Ilfracombe 9, Bideford 17, Exeter 48

F licence; 92 en suite bedrooms, all with telephone, colour TV, tea/coffee making facilities; full central heating; lift; 24 hour room service; last orders 9.30 p.m.; bar meals (lunch); afternoon teas; vegetarian and vegan diets; children welcome; baby listening; dogs by arrangement only; conferences max. 200; games room; dancing frequently; full size snooker table; children's paddling pool; heated indoor swimming pool; sauna; solarium; hairdressing salon; mini cinema; 5 miles of beach below hotel; sailing; golf nearby; tennis; squash; riding; shooting; fishing; helipad; Access, Amex, Diners, Visa credit cards accepted.

Lots of sun, miles of golden sands and tiered silvery waves advancing eagerly up the beach is what you look down on from the warm and luxurious rooms of the Saunton Sands Hotel, a member of the Brend Group of Exclusive Hotels. The hotel is light and sunny for most of the rooms face the south, the sea and the sands and there are panoramic views from most. All the staff are efficient, friendly and attentive, creating an air of warmth and friendliness. The furnishings are elegant and comfortable and the bedrooms have all the modern facilities that you could want. Food is of a very high standard and the wine list is well chosen. This splendid hotel provides a truly outstanding holiday for all the family, all the year round. Room and breakfast from £56.00 single, £52.00 per person double, all inclusive of VAT. Other seafront hotels in the Brend Group include Carlyon Bay, near St. Austell, Victoria Hotel, Sidmouth, see pages 214, 231. This splendid hotel provides a truly outstanding holiday for all the family, all the year round. There is a Christmas and New Year programme. See Bargain Breaks section. Open all year.

THE BRICKWALL HOTEL

Sedlescombe, Nr. Battle, East Sussex TN33 0QA

Telephone: (0424870) 253 *Fax: 0424870 785*

London 55, Battle 3, Hastings 7, Eastbourne 20, Rye 10, Dover 47

R and R licence; 24 en suite bedrooms (15 ground floor), all with colour TV, radio, alarm, telephone and tea/coffee making facilities; four four poster bedrooms; private car park; children welcome; dinner until 9.00 p.m.; sea bathing and boating 6 miles; riding 2 miles; heated swimming pool from April to October; credit cards accepted.

Two acres of delightful gardens adjoining the Village Green and its surrounding charm create an outstanding setting for this 16th century Hotel. Retaining all its basic Tudor features, both outside and within, it still offers every modern comfort. Good food, served quietly but efficiently is presented in the oak-beamed dining room, there is a well-stocked cellar, and drinks are served from an attractive bar. The constant care and individual attention given by Mr. and Mrs. Pollio and their staff creates an atmosphere of welcome and the feeling that the comfort of their guests is their first consideration. The ground-floor rooms, often hard to come by, are in very constant demand and the generous provision of three fine lounges makes for unusual freedom. The heated swimming pool is a great asset, and there is a wealth of other garden features allowing each their own kind of pleasure. The splendid Sussex countryside is all around, with its kaleidoscope of beauty and interest inviting exploration. Room and full English breakfast from £40.00 (single) and £55.00 (twin) including VAT. Mini breaks available all year. Always open.

FALCON MANOR

Settle, North Yorkshire BD24 9BD

Telephone: (0729) 823814 *Fax: 0729 822087*

Settle station ¼, Giggleswick station 1, Skipton 14, Kendal 26, Leeds 40, Blackpool 45

F licence, 20 en suite bedrooms (1 room with wheelchair access and 1 suite on ground floor), all with direct dial telephone, radio, TV; full central heating; late meals to 9.30 p.m.; buttery; diets; children welcome, baby listening; dogs by arrangement; conferences up to 40; golf 1 mile, tennis and squash by arrangement, shooting by arrangement; riding, bowling crown green; 2 acres gardens; Access, Diners, Visa credit cards accepted.

Built in 1840 for the first Vicar of Settle, Falcon Manor is an impressive country house skilfully converted to form an excellent hotel with all the comforts demanded by today's traveller or holiday maker. It is run by Mr and Mrs Riley and their daughter, who have earned a well justified reputation for their hospitality and wonderful food. However, it is the location of the hotel which sets it above so many others. Situated on the edge of Settle, a picturesque market town, beside the famed Carlisle–Settle railway, it nestles under Castleberg Crag on the Craven fault and is thus a delight to geologists. With the Lake District, Herriot Country, the Trough of Bowland, Malham Tarn and Malham Cove within easy reach, it has a magnetic attraction for potholers, walkers, botanists, and anyone who loves nature and the outdoor life. Room and breakfast from £45.00 single and £66.00 (twin). Bargain breaks available. Open all year.

CHARLTON HOUSE HOTEL

Charlton Road, Shepton Mallet, Somerset BA4 4PR

Telephone: (0749) 342008 *Fax: 0749 346362*

Wells 6, Glastonbury 8, Bath 18, Bristol 20, Weston-Super-Mare 25, Yeovil 17

R & R licence; 19 bedrooms all with en suite bathroom; telephone and television; room service; baby listening; last orders for dinner 9.30 p.m.; bar meals; special diets; children welcome; dogs allowed; conferences up to 90; indoor heated swimming pool; sauna; tennis; squash courts ½ mile; golf 2 miles; riding 5 miles; hotel open all year; credit cards accepted.

This Georgian-style Manor House dates from the late 1600's and is just outside Shepton Mallet on the road to Frome. It is listed as being of architectural and historical interest. There are six acres of lawns, woods and gardens alongside the River Sheppey, with a beautiful 200 year old copper beech tree and small trout lake. There are facilities for private helicopter arrivals. Each bedroom is furnished and decorated in a different style and all are most attractive. The restaurant, decorated in dusty pink and very well set out, extends into the conservatory, where guests can take their coffee, overlooking the lovely gardens. The imaginative menu is complemented by an extensive choice of interesting wines. The lounge too is very attractive, providing a quiet retreat to sit and dream, or read for a time. Wookey Hole, The Cheddar Gorge, Longleat House and Safari Park, as well as the cities of Bath and Wells are all within easy driving distance for guests to explore. Tariff on application. Open all year.

THE EASTBURY HOTEL

Long Street, Sherborne, Dorset DT9 3BY

Telephone: (0935) 813131 *Telex: 46644 Eastby* *Fax: 0935 817296*

Yeovil 4, Dorchester 13, Salisbury 20

F licence; 15 en suite bedrooms, all with telephone, colour TV, tea/coffee making facilities, hairdryer, trouser press, full central heating; night service; last orders 9.30 p.m.; diets; children welcome; baby listening; conferences max. 80; golf, tennis, squash, badminton, riding, shooting, fishing all nearby; Access, Visa credit cards accepted.

The Eastbury Hotel was built in 1740 during the reign of George II and was originally an elegant town house. It has been beautifully converted into an hotel and throughout the recent refurbishment its Georgian character has been carefully preserved. The Hotel is situated in a quiet street of the lovely old town of Sherborne, famous for its fine 8th century abbey and two castles. It is ideally placed for exploring the lovely Dorset countryside and there are many places of interest to visit. The public rooms are beautifully furnished and include a library of antiquarian books which emphasises the feeling of being in an elegant private house. The bedrooms are all named after English garden flowers and are charmingly decorated to match. They all have all the modern amenities expected today including hairdryer and trouser press. The restaurant has been extended into a most attractive conservatory, prettily tented with a delightful view of the secluded gardens and provides a very popular venue for wedding receptions in the spring and summer months. A high standard of traditional English cooking is offered with local Dorset produce much in evidence and there is an excellent and extensive international wine list. Room and breakfast from £62.50 single, £80.00 double. Hotel open all year.

HAWKSTONE PARK HOTEL

Weston-under-Redcastle, Shrewsbury,
Shropshire SY4 5UY

Telephone: (093924) 611 *Telex: 35793* *Fax: 0939 24311*

Shrewsbury 14, Birmingham 50, Manchester 55, Chester 28, London 160, Motorway M54 Exit 4 – 14 miles main A49 Shrewsbury to Whitchurch road.

F licence; 59 bedrooms (2 suites), including 16 annexe rooms, all with private bathroom and shower, colour TV, radio, direct dial telephone, baby listening, tea/coffee making facilities; full central heating; night porter service; late meals to 10.00 p.m., restaurant; diets; children welcome; guide dogs only; business meetings – 7 suites up to 200; speciality weekends; full size billiard table; sauna; solarium and trimnasium; games room; outdoor swimming pool (open May–September); tennis; croquet; two eighteen hole golf courses; helipad; riding and fishing (coarse) nearby also clay shooting by prior arrangement; all major credit cards accepted.

Hawkstone Park, a ''golfer's paradise'', has been associated with golf since the 1930's and is famed for its two fine 18 hole golf courses and a large estate where Sandy Lyle, the 1985 Open Champion and Master's Champion 1988, learned his game. But it has a lot more to offer. I can highly recommend this sports-oriented country house hotel throughout the year, although during the months of May, June and September, the hotel is very much a golfing enthusiast's 'Mecca'. Set in 300 acres of parkland in the quiet serenity of Shropshire, Hawkstone Park, with its many facilities, is a very comfortable hotel. The hotel continues to prosper under the expert direction of Mr. Kevin Brazier, who has run the establishment under various ownerships, since 1978. It is renowned for good food, and the menus are imaginative and interesting with a traditional English flavour. A selective wine list features good value house wines. For lighter meals in less formal surroundings, I found the Restaurant provided an excellent Bill of Fayre, at reasonable rates. Bed and breakfast from £60.00 per person (standard single) inc. VAT. Other terms, including Speciality Weekends (see Bargain Break section) on application. Always open. A member of Best Western Hotels.

THE BELMONT HOTEL

Sidmouth, Devon EX10 8RX

Telephone: (0395) 512555 *Fax: 0395 79154*

London 161, Birmingham 159, Bristol 70, Exeter 15, Honiton 9, Lyme Regis 16

F licence; 55 en suite bedrooms, all with telephone, colour TV, tea/coffee making facilities; full central heating; lift; 24 hour room service; last orders 9.00 p.m.; bar meals (lunch); diets and vegetarians catered for; children welcome; baby listening; dogs by arrangement only; conferences max. 80; dancing weekly; indoor and outdoor heated swimming pools, sauna, solarium, hairdressing salon all at Victoria Hotel next door; sea bathing; windsurfing, sailing, golf, tennis, riding, fishing all nearby; Access, Amex, Diners, Visa credit cards accepted.

Over 150 years ago, the Belmont was built on the seafront of this Regency resort and has provided gracious living for several generations. Enjoying an idyllic position with views of the esplanade, bay and beach, it became a first-class hotel in 1920 and is now owned and personally supervised by the Brend family, who also own the adjacent Victoria Hotel (see page 231), Carlyon Bay (see page 214), the Royal Duchy (see page 95), the Saunton Sands Hotel (see page 222) and others. The Belmont offers a traditionally warm welcome with the luxurious atmosphere of a bygone era. Public rooms are distinctive and well proportioned, with elegant furnishings. All the bedrooms are comfortably furnished; the majority have panoramic seaviews and many have balconies. There are a number of Deluxe bedrooms and there are also a number of communicating rooms which are ideal for family holidays. Personal and attentive service has always been the hallmark of Brend Hotels and nowhere is this better seen than in the restaurant where you can enjoy first class continental and English cuisine and choose from a carefully selected wine list. Sidmouth and the surrounding area offers a wealth of activities for all the family, and for those wanting an energetic break or wishing for peace and relaxation. Room and breakfast from £60.00 single, £46.00 double per person, including VAT. Other terms on application. Open all year.

HOTEL RIVIERA

The Esplanade, Sidmouth, Devon EX10 8AY

Telephone: (0395) 515201 *Fax: 0395 577775*

London 164, Birmingham 141, Bristol 68, Exeter 15, Honiton 9, Torquay 38

F licence; 34 en suite bedrooms (2 for disabled), TV and telephone; 24 hour room service; night service; baby listening; lift; last orders for dinner 9.00 p.m.; bar and table d'hôte luncheons; special diets; children welcome; dogs by arrangement; conferences up to 80; ballroom; piano bar; bowls, tennis, fishing, riding, windsurfing, sea bathing, sailing and boating nearby; golf at Sidmouth Golf Club; pheasant and duck shooting on 7 nearby estates by arrangement; Master Card, Visa, Amex and Diners accepted, open all year.

Originally part of a terrace of elegantly bow fronted Regency houses, The Riviera Hotel stands centrally on Sidmouth Esplanade overlooking Lyme Bay, with sea bathing direct from the hotel. The Riviera is privately owned by Mr. and Mrs. Wharton and managed by their son, Peter. Staff are exceptionally courteous and efficient, some of them having worked at the hotel for many years. Bedrooms are tastefully furnished, the majority with glorious sea views, and naturally have been equipped with every modern comfort. The dining room is attractively decorated in pastel shades, with impressionist style paintings and splendid chandeliers. I enjoyed an excellent meal there; table d'hôte and à la carte menus are offered, with a wide selection of wines to complement your choice of food. The lounge is sumptuously furnished in lovely warm coloured velvets, with many excellent paintings adorning the walls. Leading from here is the Regency Bar, with a pianist for your enjoyment. Functions of all types and sizes are well catered for in the Cavalier Room and Ballroom. All public rooms are fully air conditioned and parking is available at the rear. A comfortable and well run hotel which I can thoroughly recommend. Room and English breakfast from £41.00 to £57.00 or £47.00 to £63.00 for dinner, bed and English breakfast, all inclusive of VAT.

THE ROYAL GLEN HOTEL

Sidmouth, Devon EX10 8RW

Telephone: (0395) 513221

London 161, Torquay 35, Birmingham 159

R & R licence; 35 bedrooms, 34 with bathroom/shower, 3 on ground floor; all have colour TV, telephone and full central heating; last orders 8.00 p.m.; children from 8 years; dogs allowed; indoor heated swimming pool; sea bathing; golf nearby; tennis 1 mile; Access and Visa cards accepted.

Originally built in 1700 as a farmhouse, the Royal Glen Hotel has been managed by a member of the Crane family for over 100 years. This historic and lovely hotel stands in its own grounds, 200 yards from the sea-front at Sidmouth. The cricket club is nearby as well as the golf course and shopping centre. Overlooking the cricket club is the Royal Glen's sister hotel, The Torbay, managed by Mr. and Mrs. Martin Caldwell, daughter and son-in-law of the Cranes. Mr. Orson Crane proudly showed me around his lovely hotel, with its wonderful antique furniture and memorabilia from the time of Queen Victoria, whose family, the Kents, used it as a holiday cottage until the untimely death of the Duke. During the course of the young Victoria's stay, she came close to death when an apprentice boy who was shooting at birds in the garden, hit a window in the nursery, narrowly missing the future Queen. The hotel has a great deal of old world charm; the upstairs drawing room is oval with period furniture, and the dining room of the same shape houses an intriguing collection of period chairs. The food is excellent, including a superlative pudding trolley and an extensive wine list. It is possible for visitors to the hotel to stay in a Royal bedroom or Princess Victoria's nursery. The hotel also has a wonderfully up-to-date swimming pool. Prices start at £31.50 per night, and from £348.20 weekly. Open all year.

THE VICTORIA HOTEL

Sidmouth, Devon EX10 8RY

Telephone: (0395) 512651 *Fax: 0395 579154*
Telex: 42551 EXONIA G ref BREND 2

London 161, Birmingham 159, Bristol 70, Exeter 15, Honiton 9, Torquay 35

F licence; 61 en suite bedrooms, all with radio, telephone, col. TV; full central heating; lift; night service; meals to 9.30 p.m.; diets and vegetarian menus; children welcome; dogs accepted at discretion of management; conferences up to 100; hairdressing salon; games room; entertainment; billiards; indoor heated swimming pool; sauna; solarium; spa bath; outdoor heated swimming pool and lido; two 18 hole putting courses; sea bathing; sailing; golf; fishing by arrangement; squash, badminton and riding all nearby; major credit cards accepted.

Sidmouth was discovered as a resort by the affluent in Queen Victoria's day – hence the name of this imposing hotel which dominates the west end of the promenade, with an uninterrupted view of the wide sweeping bay. The Victoria is owned by the Brend family who own other luxurious hotels, including the Royal Duchy, Falmouth (see page 95), Carlyon Bay, St. Austell (see page 214), the Saunton Sands Hotel, Saunton Sands (see page 222), and the Belmont Hotel, Sidmouth (see page 228). Mr. John Brend, Managing Director, is very much in evidence looking after the needs of the guests with the help of his efficient and attentive staff. The ground floor creates an impression of space and good taste; everything is planned for your comfort and well being. The Restaurant has a first class reputation for good food, the table d'hôte and à la carte menus reaching high levels in quality, presentation and service. The wine list is comprehensive and well chosen. Upstairs, the well appointed bedrooms are comfortable and pleasantly furnished. Set in 5 acres of landscaped gardens, with many outside attractions, I can recommend the Victoria to all ages. Open all year. Room and breakfast from £60.00 single, £50.00 double per person (including VAT). Other terms on application, including special Out of Season breaks.

THE SKINBURNESS HOTEL

Silloth-on-Solway, Cumbria CA5 4QY

Telephone: (06973) 32332 *Fax: 06973 32549*

Carlisle 23, Keswick 30, M6 Exit 41 30 miles

F licence; 25 bedrooms (1 for disabled), all with en suite bathroom, telephone, TV; baby listening; last orders for dinner 9.30 p.m.; bar meals; special diets; children welcome; dogs accepted; conferences up to 36; snooker and billiards; sauna, solarium and gymnasium; indoor heated swimming pool, golf 1 mile; tennis and squash 2 miles; riding 2½ miles; sea fishing nearby; hotel open all year; major credit cards accepted.

I have known this hotel for many years, and have always felt that with refurbishment it could be marvellous. It has recently had that refurbishment, and it is once again all that one could ask for in a country house hotel. With its tasteful décor, comfortable furnishings and warm, friendly atmosphere, it is a delight. Meals, served in the attractive dining room, from an interesting and varied menu, are delicious, and there is an imaginative wine list from which to choose the accompaniment. You could not have a more restful end to the day than to retire to your bedroom after dinner, and find all the devices that we now expect of a modern hotel, such as hairdryers, telephone and remote control TV awaiting you, along with a comfortable bed. I can think of no other hotel on the whole of the Cumbrian coast to match The Skinburness and, if you are looking for peace and quiet, then few hotels in the north can compare with this. Should you wish to be energetic, there are lovely walks along the coast (designated an area of outstanding natural beauty), starting at the very door of the hotel, and there are numerous leisure facilities, both on the premises, and at the Solway Village, a holiday and golfing complex associated with the hotel, located a mile or so away. Golfing holidays are a speciality of The Skinburness. Tariff on application.

BOTLEY PARK HOTEL

Boorley Green, Botley, Southampton, Hants SO3 2UA

Telephone: (0489) 780888 *Fax: 0489 789242*

Southampton 7, Soton Airport 5, Portsmouth 10, Mainlink BR 5

F licence; 100 en suite bedrooms (2 for disabled), all with TV and telephone; room and night service; baby listening; last orders for dinner 10.00 p.m.; bar meals; special diets; children welcome; dogs by arrangement; conferences max. 240; games room, snooker/billiards; petanque, croquet; indoor heated swimming pool; leisure centre; sauna, solarium and spa pool; gym; squash, tennis; golf; riding 3 miles by arrangement; sailing, boating, shooting and fishing 5 miles by arrangement; hotel open all year; credit cards accepted.

The new development of the Botley Park Hotel and Country Club is situated north west of the picturesque old village centre of Botley, on the B3354 Winchester Road. Classical style, quality of service, tasteful decoration and thoughtful attention to detail highlight the sophistication behind the development of this superb Hotel and first class Golf and Leisure Club. The 100 bedrooms and suites provide guests with the highest standards of facilities and comfort. Superb cuisine can be savoured in the elegant restaurant, where service is discreet but attentive. Hotel residents have exclusive access to the Botley Park Golf and Leisure Club. A purpose-designed, challenging 18-hole golf course blends into the general landscaping of the surrounding grounds. The focal point from most of the public rooms and lounges is the beautiful indoor pool complex. Facilities such as aerobics, hairdressing and beauty salon add to the impressive selection of leisure opportunities at the Botley Park. Conferences of up to 250 delegates can be catered for with the resident conference manager arranging and assuring success in individual business and conference events. A truly first class hotel, ideal for a relaxing break in Hampshire, and superb for conference and leisure attractions. Tariff on application.

BRIGGENS HOUSE HOTEL

Stanstead Abbots, Nr. Ware, Hertfordshire SG12 8LD

Telephone: (027979) 2416 *Telex: 817906* *Fax: 027979 3685*

London 25, Ware 3, Hertford 6, on A414

F licence; 54 en suite bedrooms, all with direct dial telephone, radio, TV, hairdryer, mini-bar, tea/coffee making facilities and trouser press; full central heating; lift; night service; late meals to 10.00 p.m.; diets; children welcome, baby listening; conferences; heated outdoor swimming pool; 9 hole golf course, croquet, boules, tennis, fishing; Mastercard, Amex, Diners, Visa credit cards accepted.

Briggens House is a magnificent 300 year old mansion, set amongst 80 acres of rolling Hertfordshire countryside, complete with its own Arboretum featuring several rare specimen trees. Previously the home of Lord Aldenham, the house has been painstakingly restored to its former glory. The 54 bedrooms are all individually designed in the style which reflects the period of the house and all are fully equipped with private facilities. The Bridgeman Restaurant, named after the man who designed the charming gardens, provides the perfect backdrop for a taste of country living and offers a unique blend of classical and modern cuisine. The adjoining lounge area, complete with log fire, board games and books is an ideal setting for guests to enjoy a traditional afternoon tea. Briggens can also boast its own professional Golf Club, complete with full time Pro. The 9 hole course has a par 31, and a yardage of 2095 (9 holes). The P.G.A. approved Pro-shop offers a comprehensive range of equipment as well as providing corporate golfing days, tournaments and tuition. Additional on site activities are tennis, boules, croquet, fishing and clay shooting. Nearby sports facilities include horseriding, gliding, karting and a dry ski slope. Tariff on application.

GABRIEL COURT HOTEL

Stoke Gabriel, Nr. Totnes, South Devon TQ9 6SF

Telephone: (080428) 206/207/267

London 198, Paignton Station 4, Totnes 4, Kingswear 7, Torquay 6

R and R licence; 20 bedrooms (2 ground floor), 19 with private bath, 1 with shower and W.C., colour TV, telephone, radio; hairdryers; tea/coffee making facilities; baby listening; full central heating; TV lounge; diets; children welcome; small dogs accepted; guests' laundry facilities; outdoor heated swimming pool; croquet; sea and river bathing; fishing; riding nearby; golf (Churston 3 miles). Peace and tranquillity. Open all year except February.

This lovely old Manor House dating back to 1487, is situated in the picturesque village of Stoke Gabriel, on the River Dart, equidistant from Totnes and Paignton, and in 3 acres of beautifully kept grounds, with yew archways, box hedges and magnolia trees. Owned by Michael and Eryl Beacom, very experienced and wonderful hosts, and assisted by an attentive, cheerful and courteous staff, the hotel is extremely comfortable and furnished in very good taste. The bedrooms are well appointed and nicely furnished, and include three family suites. Gabriel Court has always had an excellent reputation for its food, the very best of English cooking. Most of the vegetables are freshly picked from the kitchen garden. Game is often available as are Exmoor venison and Brixham scallops. Dinner, room and full English breakfast from £50.00 per person, inclusive of VAT. A very pleasant atmosphere and as peaceful and popular out of season as it is in summer.

THE STONEHOUSE COURT HOTEL

Bristol Road, Stonehouse, Gloucestershire GL10 3RA

Telephone: (0453) 825155 *Fax: 0453 824611*

Gloucester 9, Stroud 3, London 111

F licence; 37 en suite bedrooms (8 ground floor), all with telephone, colour TV, full central heating; night service; last orders 9.30 p.m.; diets; children welcome; baby listening; dogs not accepted; conferences max. 120; fishing; croquet; golf, riding, gliding and Slimbridge Wildfowl Trust nearby; Visa and Access credit cards accepted.

I had a warm welcome to this charming stone court house, set in six acres of secluded gardens. The oak panelling, soft lighting and beautiful fresh flowers all add to the relaxed atmosphere, perfect for those on holiday and business executives too. The cocktail bar and restaurant have open fireplaces, which provide a fine backdrop for the enjoyment of excellent cuisine, using the best local produce accompanied by good wines from an extensive wine list. The bedrooms are all individually furnished in impeccable taste with all modern amenities. The grounds to the hotel are quite superb, offering the opportunity to fish, watch the local wild life and study the many unusual and rare plants and shrubs. As Stonehouse Court is only 1 mile from the M5 at Junction 13 it would be an ideal place to stop over on a long journey north or south as well as being a good centre from which to explore the Cotswolds and visit local attractions such as the famous Slimbridge Wildfowl Trust and the Severn Valley Railway. Room and breakfast from £67.50 single, £80.00 double. Hotel open all year.

WYCK HILL HOUSE

Burford Road, Stow-on-the-Wold, Gloucestershire GL54 1HY

Telephone: (0451) 31936 *Fax: 0451 32243*

Broadway 15, Oxford 18, London 70, Stratford 18, Cheltenham 15

F licence; 30 bedrooms all with en suite bathrooms, TV and telephone; room and night service; baby listening; lift; last orders for dinner 9.30 p.m.; light lunches; special diets; children welcome; dogs by arrangement; conferences up to 20; croquet; clay pigeon shooting; riding 2 miles; golf 15 miles; hotel open all year; major credit cards accepted.

Wyck Hill House is situated high on a hill on the A424 Burford to Stow-on-the-Wold road. It lies, well-secluded, in a hundred acres of woodland. The hotel is set amid landscaped grounds, with terraced lawns and enjoys panoramic views of the Windrush Valley. The house which was built in the 1700s and has been enlarged over the centuries, is now one of the finest hotels in the Cotswolds. The elegant dining room overlooks the gardens and is the ideal setting in which to enjoy the wide selection of food, superbly created by the resident chef. There is a sunny little Garden Room which is perfect for intimate parties and light luncheons, and the larger Heythrop Room is available for weddings and conferences. All the rooms are impressively furnished, and the staff, under the supervision of Peter Robinson are unobtrusive yet very attentive. In recent years the old Coach Houses have been renovated and altered to accommodate nine more bedrooms, some with exceptionally spacious bathrooms, and each individually designed to offer every convenience to the guest. The Orangery too has been converted into a further five ground-floor bedrooms, all of which overlook the surrounding countryside. Wyck Hill House is within easy reach of Stratford upon Avon, Oxford and Cheltenham and boasts a wealth of beautiful locations close by for you to discover and explore for yourself. Single room from £75.00, double room from £90.00.

STRATFORD HOUSE HOTEL

Sheep Street, Stratford-Upon-Avon,
Warwickshire CV37 6EF

Telephone: (0789) 68288 *Telex: 311612*

Birmingham 24, London 95, Oxford 40, Warwick 6, Gloucester 39

R & R licence; 10 en suite bedrooms (3 ground floor), all with telephone, colour TV; full central heating; night service till midnight; last orders 9.30 p.m. but pre theatre dinners arranged; diets by arrangement; children welcome; baby sitting arranged; no dogs; small meetings; credit cards accepted. Theatre tickets arranged.

You cannot walk down Sheep Street at lunch time without stopping for a delicious meal in ''SHEPHERDS'', situated up a sunny little pathway just behind the main building of the Stratford House Hotel. It is a modern restaurant with a bright conservatory filled with comfortable cane chairs and pretty tables. I was there recently for dinner with some friends, and had the most memorable meal; a warm salad of Smoked Bacon Lardons, Chicken, Avocado and Wild Mushrooms followed by Noisettes of Dorset Spring Lamb, served on a Chervil, Parsley and Chive Butter Sauce. Although not a pudding person myself, one of the party had a bitter chocolate mousse with white chocolate ice cream and fresh raspberries which I certainly helped to eat! Chef Michael Quinn, seems to have no trouble maintaining his high standard of cuisine. Much money has been spent refurnishing the bedrooms, and although not large, they include all the comforts demanded by today's guest. At the top of the house there is a large family suite, just right for four guests, but beware of the beams! Privately owned by Sylvia Adcock who has filled the house with her antique china and pictures, the hotel runs smoothly in the capable hands of Jennifer and Peter Ashen. The Stratford House creates a home-from-home atmosphere, providing an ideal place to stay whilst touring the Heart of England, and the nearby Royal Shakespeare Theatre is just one of a multitude of exciting places to visit. Bed and full English Breakfast from £55.00 single and £32.00 double, including VAT.

WELCOMBE HOTEL AND GOLF COURSE

Stratford-upon-Avon, Warwickshire CV37 0NR

Telephone: (0789) 295252 *Telex: 31347* *Fax: 0789 414666*

London 92, Banbury 20, Birmingham 24, Coventry 19, Oxford 40, Warwick 6

F licence; 76 en suite bedrooms (7 ground floor) all with showers, hairdryers, radio, TV, telephone & minibars; full central heating; night service; children welcome, baby listening by arrangement; dogs accepted in bedrooms; diets by arrangement; golf; 2 hard all-weather tennis courts; conferences; credit cards accepted.

On the Warwick Road, only a couple of miles out of Stratford-upon-Avon, famous for Shakespeare's birthplace, you will find the Welcombe Hotel set in 157 acres of parkland. At the end of a winding drive lies this large country house hotel which was once the home of the famous historian Sir George Trevelyan and is now in the capable hands of General Manager, Brian Miller. During the last three years, Venice Simplon Orient-Express Hotels have spent two and a half million pounds refurbishing the entire place. The bedrooms vary from the high ceilinged spacious ones in the old house to those with twin beds in the modern Garden wing; all are now of an exceptionally high standard and the décor is truly unsurpassed. There are now 35 bathrooms all with Italian marble fittings. The restaurant overlooks the formal gardens and offers the best of French and English cuisine and the food is well complemented by an excellent wine list. Facilities include an 18-hole golf course (6202 yards, par 70) surrounding the hotel with a new Club House and also two all-weather tennis courts. Theatre tickets can be booked in advance through the hotel, and there is a garage serving petrol. Room and full English breakfast from £90.00 single, £125.00 double including VAT at 15%. Open all year.

BILLESLEY MANOR

Alcester, Nr. Stratford-upon-Avon, Warwickshire B49 6NF

Telephone: (0789) 400888 *Telex: 312599* *Fax: 0789 764145*

Stratford-upon-Avon 4, Birmingham 23, Oxford 23, London 95

F licence; 41 en suite bedrooms (9 ground floor), all with telephone and colour TV, full central heating; night service, last orders 9.30 p.m.; diets; children welcome; baby listening by arrangement; conferences; indoor heated indoor swimming pool; tennis; croquet; pitch & putt; riding, shooting, fishing by arrangement; Access, Amex, Visa, Diners and Mastercharge cards accepted.

Billesley Manor is situated just off the A422 in the heart of England and it would be difficult to find a more agreeable place in the midst of Shakespeare country. Here you will come across the old blending with the new. There is a large oak panelled bar with a carved fireplace, usually burning logs in the winter months. The dining room is also panelled and I thoroughly enjoyed the Sunday table d'hôte lunch which was very well priced. A good wine list complements the excellent cuisine. All the public rooms are lavishly furnished and very comfortable. There is a superb indoor swimming pool with sun patio, as well as tennis courts, croquet and pitch and putt in the grounds. Also amongst the 11 acres of grounds you will find a well maintained topiary garden. The bedrooms, whether you choose a modern suite or one with a four poster bed, are all of the highest quality. Peter Henderson, General Manager, oversees his staff well and you can be assured of a warm welcome. The hotel is an ideal base for visiting the Royal Shakespeare Theatre and the many other historical sites that Warwickshire has to offer. However, if it is a quiet time that you are looking for, Billesley is a perfect retreat for total relaxation. Twin or double room and English breakfast from £105.00. Weekend breaks and Christmas programme available. Open all year.

THE SWAN DIPLOMAT

Streatley-on-Thames, Berkshire RG8 9HR

Telephone: (0491) 873737 *Telex: 848259* *Fax: 0491 872554*

London 50, Reading 9, Oxford 20, Newbury 13, Windsor 30, Henley 20

F licence; 46 en suite bedrooms, all with telephone, colour TV and full central heating; night service; last orders 9.30 p.m.; bar meals; diets; children welcome, baby listening; dogs by arrangement; conferences up to 100; indoor, heated fit-pool; sauna and solarium; leisure centre; golf, tennis and fishing ½ mile; shooting 1 mile; riding 5 miles; sailing and boating can be arranged; Amex, Diners', Barclaycard and Access accepted.

This centuries old hotel, recently extended and refurbished, is set in 23 acres of grounds on the bank of the River Thames – a really delightful location. The spacious bedrooms, some with balconies, are individually designed and furnished and many look on to the river or have views to the Streatley hills. The comfortable lounge overlooks the river and the hotel's own island. The Riverside Restaurant enjoys an enviable reputation for its classical French cuisine, wine list and high standard of service under the direction of Head Chef, Christopher Cleveland. Other facilities include the Reflexions Leisure Club (free membership for hotel guests) and the rebuilt 19th-century Magdalen College barge – a wonderful venue for meetings or private functions. There are many short walks around the hotel, a number of National Trust properties and stately homes within easy reach and arrangements can be made for golf at local courses or the hire of a river cruiser. To sum up, this is a luxurious hotel in a marvellous setting which offers plenty to do and see – or you can even just relax by the river! Bed and full English breakfast from £81.00. No service charge. Open all year.

THE AMBERLEY INN

Amberley, Nr. Stroud,
Gloucestershire GL5 5AF

Telephone: (0453) 872565 and 872777 *Fax: 0453 872738*

London 104, Stroud Station 3, Cirencester 10, Cheltenham 16, Bristol 32, Gloucester 12

F licence; 14 en suite bedrooms, all with colour TV, radio and telephone; children welcome; bar meals; late meals; diets; drying room; golf and riding nearby.

Scenically the Amberley Inn enjoys one of the finest views in the Cotswolds, for it is perched on the very edge of a wold. It is a splendid base for the walker, artist or photographer, for, at this southern end of the Cotswolds, the wolds are much more abrupt and curious than those in the north. For the golfer, Minchinhampton's old course adjoins the Inn with its 18-hole new course 3 miles distant. The atmosphere of the Inn is one of complete informality. The lounge bar is adjacent to The Country Bar that is a popular meeting place for local people. The bedrooms are comfortable and spotlessly clean. A very pretty Garden House has four bedrooms, which are secluded and peaceful. The dining room has recently been extended with a lovely new bedroom above, but without detracting from the Cotswold character of the Inn. There are normally three menus available which is a good idea as people often just pop in for a quick bite and can order a steak or something similar in the bar. Room and breakfast from £52.00 single, £64.00 double, dinner from £13.50, inclusive of VAT and service. Always open. Owned by the Price family of the Hare & Hounds just a few miles away (see page 249). A member of Best Western Hotels.

MANOR HOUSE HOTEL

Studland Bay, Nr. Swanage,
Dorset BH19 3AU
Telephone: (092944) 288

London 113, Swanage 3, Bournemouth 8, Dorchester 26, Corfe Castle 6

R & R licence; 18 en suite bedrooms, all with colour TV, radio, tea/coffee making facilities, telephone and full central heating; last orders for dinner 8.30 p.m.; bar lunches; vegetarian diets; children over 5 welcome; dogs allowed; sea bathing 3 miles, with sandy beach, sailing and boating; 2 tennis courts (hard); riding; golf within 2 miles; Access and Visa cards accepted.

The Manor House Hotel is set in 16 acres of secluded gardens and grounds overlooking the sea. The site is mentioned in the Domesday Book and parts of the present rambling Gothic house date back to 1750. It is full of character and its Medieval carvings are said to have come from the residential quarters of Corfe Castle, home of the famous Mary Banks, who defended it so bravely against Cromwell's troops. In the early 1800s, George Henry Banks MP made many additions to create a suitable sea-side residence for his wife and fourteen children. The bedrooms all have their own individual style and character. Four have four poster beds, most have glorious views of the sea and Old Harry Rocks. The Westminster Bedroom is particularly attractive, and unusual with its four poster bed and lovely wall carvings, reputed to be from the old Palace of Westminster, circa 1636. Studland is a conservation area with lovely sandy beaches, and it is renowned for the variety and richness of its flora and fauna. It is also a perfect base from which to explore different nature trails, or go birdwatching. The nature reserves of Studland Heath, Brownsea Island, Arne (RSPB), and Morden Heath are all within easy reach. The comfortably furnished reception rooms overlooking the lawns and sea have some lovely old panelling. There is a good choice on the menu and fresh local produce, including delicious Studland lobster is used whenever possible. Dinner, room and breakfast from £41.00–£55.00. Weekly rates from £225.00–£300.00. Hotel closed Christmas and January.

KNOLL HOUSE HOTEL

Studland Bay,
Dorset BH19 2AH

Telephone: Studland (092 944) 251

London 113, Swanage 3, Bournemouth 8, Studland 1, Corfe Castle 6, Kingston Lacy 12

C licence; 79 bedrooms (many ground floor), comprising 30 family suites, 29 single, 20 twin bedded rooms; 57 private bathrooms; 5 lounges; children's dining room; self-service laundry; 3 games rooms; solarium; children's disco in season; colour TV room; 9 acre golf course; 2 hard tennis courts, playground, outdoor swimming and paddling pools; full leisure centre; adjoins clean sandy beach, safe bathing; Isle of Purbeck Golf Club 2 miles, 2 courses; no credit cards.

This delightful hotel is situated on the finest stretch of Dorset heritage coastline, surrounded by some of the prettiest countryside in the West and it is well worth a visit. It is within a National Trust Reserve and overlooks three miles of golden beach with first class swimming, fishing, boating and wind-surfing. Knoll House is an independent country house hotel under the personal management of its family owners and is set in pine trees with the most attractive gardens where you can relax away from the cares of everyday life. The sporting facilities are numerous – tennis courts, a nine-hole par 3 golf course and outdoor heated swimming pool. For relaxation there is a sauna, steam-room, Jacuzzi, plunge-pool, solarium and gym set in a marvellous health hydro complex with fruit juice and coffee bar. Many of the bedrooms are arranged as suites, ideal for families. Log fires and an attractive cocktail bar add to the unique atmosphere of this extremely efficiently run hotel. The quality, choice and presentation of the menus is excellent. At lunchtime a superb hors d'oeuvres selection and buffet table laden with cold meats, pies and salads is a speciality, followed by delicious puddings and a good English cheeseboard. Young children are catered for in their own dining room and there are many and varied facilities to keep them amused all day. Sandbanks and Bournemouth are easily reached by the nearby car ferry, with Dorchester, Corfe Castle and the picturesque villages of Dorset only a short drive away. The hotel is open from April to October. Half board from £45.00 daily, or full board (weekly) £316.00 (April, October) – £408.00 (August). Generous full board terms for five nights out of season.

Old Harry rocks and Studland Bay.

↓ K.H.

← K.H.

MOOR HALL HOTEL

Moor Hall Drive, Sutton Coldfield,
West Midlands B75 6LN

Telephone: (021) 308 3751 *Telex: 335127* *Fax: 021 308 8974*

Birmingham International Airport and N.E.C. 11, Birmingham 7, Lichfield 6, Sutton Park (2,400 acres of parkland) 1½, Four Oaks Railway Station 1½

F licence; 75 bedrooms (30 ground floor), all with private bathroom and shower, colour TV, telephone, radio, baby listening, tea/coffee making facilities, hairdryer, trouser press, mini-bar/drinks tray; night service; late meals to 10.30 p.m.; diets; children welcome; dogs by arrangement only; conferences, 6 rooms up to 200; receptions, wedding and banquets up to 250 welcome; fitness centre with gymnasium, steam room, sauna, solarium and relaxation lounge; golf, two championship courses nearby; tennis, squash, badminton, riding all nearby; all credit cards accepted.

Moor Hall, a gracious country house, is owned and personally cared for by Michael and Jean Webb and Gerry Coletti, General Manager. Gerry and his team always make sure of a warm, friendly welcome for their guests. The elegant oak panelled restaurant offers à la carte and an imaginative Bill of Fayre, whilst Jake's American-style Winer Diner offers home made burgers and crispy salads in a fun atmosphere. Moor Hall is a particularly ideal venue for conferences, as it is situated in the heart of the motorway system and is thus convenient for delegates travelling from any part of the country. There is a professionally supervised Fitness Centre, exercise in the gym, or you can relax in the sauna, steam room or solarium or relax in the lounge. Conference and banqueting facilities for up to 250 are available in the superb new Charter Suite, with its own conservatory overlooking the sunken garden and golf course. The executive bedrooms include 2 Four Poster Rooms and a bedroom with a whirlpool spa bath actually in the room. These luxuriously appointed bedrooms all overlook the sunken garden. Further facilities include an indoor swimming pool and beauty salon, planned to open January 1991. Available to residents. Rates on application. Always open.

BLUNSDON HOUSE HOTEL

Blunsdon, Nr. Swindon, Wiltshire SN2 4AD

Telephone: (0793) 721701 *Fax: 0793 721056*

London 91, Oxford 29, Reading 40, Bristol 41, Southampton 64, Birmingham 80

F licence; 88 en suite rooms (29 ground floor), all with telephone, radio, TV; lift; night service; late meals to 10.00 p.m., coffee shop to 10.30 p.m.; diets; children welcome, baby listening; no dogs; conferences; sauna, solarium, spa bath, gym, massage/beauty treatment; billiard room, games room; dancing by arrangement; hairdresser; heated indoor swimming pool; squash; tennis; petanque; 1 mile woodland walk; major credit cards accepted.

Blunsdon House stands in 70 acres of grounds off the A419, just north of Swindon. During the last thirty years, the Clifford family have worked hard, making this hotel the fine, modern, four-star establishment it is today. In spite of the size of the hotel, the emphasis is still on personal service, starting with the courteous hall porter who escorts you to your room and explains the location and operation of the many facilities. All the accommodation is spacious and comfortable, and there is no extra charge for children sharing their parents' room. The Ridge Restaurant offers a high standard of food, English and Continental dishes, from daily fixed price or à la carte menus. I found the dinner and service excellent. For a more informal meal, try Carrie's Carverie, where there is a good choice from a fixed price menu. Three bars provide a choice of venue for your pre-lunch or dinner drink. The hotel is 7 miles from junction 15 on M4 and on the link road to the M5. On the edge of the Cotswolds, an ideal centre for Bath, Longleat, Stonehenge, Salisbury and many other interesting places. Room and full English breakfast from £75.00; twin/double £85.00 inclusive of VAT and service. Getaway Breaks and Honeymoon Breaks available. Open all year.

CRICKLADE HOTEL AND COUNTRY CLUB

Cricklade, Nr. Swindon, Wiltshire SN6 6HA

Telephone: (0793) 750751 *Fax: 0793 751767*

London 87, Swindon 8, Cirencester 8

F licence; 2 suites and 42 bedrooms (24 ground floor) all with private bath, radio, colour TV, telephone, hairdryer, trouser-press and tea/coffee making facilities; full central heating; late meals to 10.00 p.m.; diets; conferences; 9 hole golf course; snooker; indoor swimming pool; steam baths, spa bath, gym, solarium; 1 all-weather tennis court; live entertainment Friday and Saturday; riding and skeet shooting by arrangement; helicopter pad; Visa, Access, Amex credit cards accepted.

Built at the turn of the century in a style of traditional English architecture this privately owned hotel stands in 25 acres of secluded grounds at the heart of rural Wiltshire. The old house has been carefully and tastefully restored and offers a warm friendly welcome, tranquillity and comfort, with open fires. Doves restaurant has a fine outlook and offers, in most pleasant surroundings, à la carte and set menus with a good choice of dishes. 24 bedrooms are in the main house, the remainder are in the adjacent wing, all of which provide all that you require in the way of comfort with most pleasant décor and furnishings. As can be seen above, the hotel has a wide range of activities to offer the keen sportsman or woman and all resident guests are made honorary members of the Club, without additional cost, for the duration of their stay. Bed and full English breakfast, midweek from £72.00 (single), £82.00 (double) inclusive of VAT. No service charge. Weekend breaks throughout the year. The hotel is not suitable for children under the age of 14. Open all year.

HARE AND HOUNDS

Westonbirt, Nr. Tetbury, Gloucestershire GL8 8QL

Telephone: (066 688) 233 *Telex: 940 122 42* *Fax: 066 688 241*

London 100, Bath 19, Birmingham 78, Bristol 25, Cheltenham 26, Cirencester 13, Gloucester 22, Severn Wild Fowl Trust 15

F licence; 30 en suite bedrooms, all with colour TV, radio and direct dial telephones; tennis; squash; snooker; croquet in summer; table tennis; golf 1 mile; children welcome; dogs welcome; drying room; conference rooms; large garden; snacks; diets; Duke of Beaufort's Hunt Country.

This most attractive Cotswold stone Country House has been owned by the Price family for over thirty eight years, and the two brothers, Martin and Jeremy, now run the hotel. The house, set in ten acres of garden and woodland, stands well back from the A433 which runs from the A40 near Burford towards Bath and Bristol. There are beautiful fresh flowers everywhere, arranged by Mrs Price, which add a lovely personal touch to this elegant hotel. The spacious lounges are comfortable and relaxing, with views of the garden, and in the winter there are welcoming log fires as well as full central heating. The bedrooms are attractive and well furnished, with some particularly pleasant rooms in the adjacent garden cottage, including two on the ground floor. The restaurant offers daily menus with a good choice of varied and original dishes as well as à la carte. There is also Jack Hare's bar which serves excellent hot and cold food at lunchtime – and remember Westonbirt is the site of Britain's most famous arboretum and one of the country's best-known girls' schools, apart from the Hare & Hounds! Single room from £52.00, doubles from £70.00. Dinner from £16.50. Always open. The family also owns the Amberley Inn, just a few miles away (see page 242). A member of Best Western Hotels.

THE SPREAD EAGLE HOTEL

Thame, Oxfordshire OX9 2BW

Telephone: (0844) 213661 *Telex: 83343 SEH* *Fax: 0844 261380*

Oxford 13, Aylesbury 10, High Wycombe 15

F licence; 33 en suite bedrooms, including 2 suites and 12 ground floor rooms, all with telephone, colour TV and thermostatically controlled central heating; night service; last orders 10.00 p.m. (Sunday 9.00 p.m.); bar meals; diets; children welcome; baby listening; dogs in bar only; conferences up to 200; dancing in December; hotel open throughout winter except 28th–30th December.

A country market town in the heart of Oxfordshire, Thame is accessible from London by the M40 and from the North and Midlands by the M1 and M25. The Spread Eagle is situated centrally in the town, and is a traditional coaching Inn, made famous in the '20's by its owner, an eccentric named John Fothergill. Fothergill's innovative cuisine attracted a distinguished clientele such as Augustus John, Shaw, H. G. Wells and Evelyn Waugh, and his unusual management is chronicled in his well known book "An Innkeeper's Diary". His name lives on within the hotel, for instance the restaurant is called after him. A daily house menu is available and you can also make up your own from the set choices of Three Inns Selection and Fothergill's Choice. Vegetarian and Children's Menus are also offered. David Barrington is particularly proud of his wine list, which features over 130 wines. The hotel provides a warm welcome, and great comfort with the bedrooms being recently refurbished. The Tudor Wing is the most luxurious. Banqueting facilities for up to 200 are available in the hotel. At Christmas, the hotel hosts a house party, and at Easter a weekend break package includes visiting the Hotel's own Antiques Fair and others in the locality. Thame is central for visiting many places of interest, such as Blenheim Palace, the manors of Hughenden and Claydon, the gardens at Waterperry and Mattocks Rose Nursery at Nuneham Courtney. Mr. and Mrs. Barrington are proud of their hotel, their motto being "hospitality is our speciality". Tariff on application, with weekend break terms available and special interest packages offered.

THORNBURY CASTLE

Thornbury, Nr. Bristol, Avon BS12 1HH

Telephone: (0454) 418511 *Telex: 449986 Castle G* *Fax: 0454 416188*

London 120, Bristol 15, Bath 20

F licence; 18 bedchambers (4 ground floor) all with en suite facilities, telephone, colour TV; full central heating; diets; children over 12 welcome; conferences max. 25; clay pigeon shooting; golf, tennis, squash, badminton, riding, fishing all nearby; all major credit cards accepted.

Although the owner, Mr Maurice Taylor, lived in North America for 18 years, he is very much an English gentleman in his castle. Thornbury Castle is both a most beautiful building and very interesting historically, for Henry VIII once owned the Castle, and in 1535 stayed here with Anne Boleyn. Today, with all the luxuries of a modern age, Thornbury Castle still retains the splendour and majesty of castle life, and is the only Tudor castle in England to be operated as an hotel. The 18 bedchambers are all beautifully appointed (some with four posters and beautiful oriel windows which overlook the Tudor gardens and vineyard). My bedroom was in the south tower and had a Tudor fireplace, four poster bed and, to my amusement, the key was a huge old-fashioned lock key as would fit any castle door! There would be no question of leaving Thornbury with this key in your pocket. Dinner was quite superb as the food is an outstanding feature that would delight any gourmet. The staff are friendly and helpful and although one is living in a castle we were made to feel most welcome and at home. Other charming features included homemade canapes with our pre-dinner drinks and delicious hand-made chocolates which were served after dinner. Apart from the fun of staying in a castle, Thornbury is ideally placed for touring the West Country, the Cotswolds and Wales. It is close to Bristol and Bath and only 5 miles from the Severn Bridge and the junctions of the M5 and M4. Double room and breakfast from £90 per night. Closed 10 days during January.

DEVONSHIRE HOTEL
Torquay, Devon TQ1 2DY

Telephone: (0803) 291123 Telex: 42988 AB Code DEVPRI Fax: 0803 29170

London 192, Exeter 22, Dartmouth 11, Plymouth 31

F licence; 71 en suite bedrooms (18 ground floor), all with colour TV, radio, tea/coffee making facilities, direct dial telephones, intercom and baby listening; annexe 12 suites (6 ground floor), with private bath; night service; late meals; lunchtime bar snacks; conferences; colour TV lounge; full sized snooker table; children and dogs welcome; dancing; cabaret; heated outdoor swimming pool; hard tennis court; riding, golf, squash, boating, fishing, sea bathing all nearby; beach chalet.

The Devonshire and nearby Princes Hotel are owned by the experienced hotelier, Mr. Michael Gardiner. They are situated near the remarkable "Daddy Hole" headland. The ground floor rooms are spacious, comfortable and pleasantly decorated and the recently extended lounge and dining-room overlook the garden and swimming pool. Good food and well chosen wines are served in the dining-room where dancing takes place three times a week during the season, and an occasional cabaret and other forms of entertainment are provided for the guests. The bedrooms are pleasantly furnished and well-appointed. There are twelve suites in the comfortable, modern annexe. Mr. and Mrs. David Phillips as hotel managers create a friendly, cheerful atmosphere which is reflected by the attentive courteous staff. The sheltered outdoor heated swimming pool is set in an attractive terrace providing an excellent sun-trap for the relaxation of guests. Tariff on request. Special winter breaks are available on application. Open all year.

THE GLENEAGLES HOTEL

Wellswood, Torquay, Devon TQ1 2QS

Telephone: (0803) 293637 *Fax: 0803 295106*

London 192, Birmingham 185, Exeter 22, Plymouth 30, Bristol 98

R and R licence; 41 en suite bedrooms (5 ground floor), all with telephone, colour TV; last orders 8.30 p.m.; bar meals; diets; children welcome; baby listening; dogs accepted; conferences max. 100; games room; entertainment 4 nights a week; games room; heated outdoor swimming pool; solarium; sea bathing, sea fishing, sailing, golf, tennis, squash, badminton all nearby; Visa, Access, Amex, Diners credit cards accepted.

Set in the secluded district of Wellswood, the Gleneagles Hotel is far enough away from all the traffic noise and bustle of a busy resort to be quiet and restful, yet it is still within easy reach of all Torquay's amenities by walking, bus or car, and has its own path down to the beach. The new resident proprietors, Messrs. Shiers and Brandon, run this attractive modern hotel with efficiency and imagination and they have many ideas for yet further improvements in the future. The open-plan main lounge has a cocktail bar and dance floor, with views across the gardens to Anstey's Cove. There is also a quiet lounge for those who prefer to relax in a peaceful, tranquil atmosphere. Most of the well-appointed, comfortable bedrooms have sea views, and all have their own sun balcony on which to enjoy Torquay's enviable warm climate. For this reason, the solar heated swimming pool and glazed sun patio are very popular with guests. The menu is interesting and varied, with a well-chosen wine list. However long your stay at Gleneagles, you will return to everyday life refreshed and invigorated, determined to repeat the experience. Room and breakfast from £23.00 per person, weekly from £185.00, inclusive of VAT. Other rates on application. Open all year.

IMPERIAL HOTEL

Torquay, Devon TQ1 2DG

Telephone: (0803) 294301 *Telex: 42849* *Fax: 0803 298293*

London 200, Birmingham 200, Bristol 100, Exeter 22, Plymouth 30

F licence; 167 en suite bedrooms, including 17 suites, all with telephone, colour TV, video; full central heating; lift; 24 hour room service; light bar meals; diets; children welcome; baby listening; dogs accepted; conferences max. 350; receptions and functions welcome; dancing nightly Monday to Saturday; Mariners Night Club, Friday and Saturday; indoor heated swimming pool; leisure centre – solarium, sauna, gymnasium, massage, spa bath, slimming therapy; outdoor heated swimming pool; tennis; squash; croquet; mini golf; sea bathing; sailing; golf, riding, shooting, including clay pigeon, fishing – fresh and deep sea – all by arrangement; all major credit cards accepted.

With its commanding cliff-top position, The Imperial offers superb panoramic views of Torbay and is set within five acres of beautifully tended sub-tropical gardens. The Prince of Wales – later King Edward VII – made numerous visits as have other Royalty through the years. Managed by Mr. Harry Murray, the Executive Director, The Imperial provides a peaceful haven for those wishing to relax, and the opportunity for the more active to sample many sporting activities in the hotel's own leisure centre. With a long and renowned tradition for its cuisine, The Imperial is the venue for the famous "Gastronomic Weekends" when world famous chefs present their own and regional specialities, accompanied by well-chosen wines. As you would expect, all the public rooms and bedrooms are spacious and luxuriously furnished, and most of the bedrooms have balconies. Many of the staff have given years of service and you can be assured of a warm and friendly welcome to this excellent hotel. Tariff on application. Open all year. A Trusthouse Forte Hotel.

THE PALACE HOTEL

Babbacombe Road, Torquay,
Devon TQ1 3TG

Telephone: (0803) 200200 *Telex: 42606* *Fax: 0803 299899*

London 192, Birmingham 185, Exeter 22, Plymouth 31, Dartmouth 11, Bristol 98, Exeter Airport 25, M5 Motorway 9, Torquay Railway Station 1½

F licence; 141 en suite bedrooms, inc. 6 luxury suites, all with colour TV, telephone, tea/coffee making facilities, supplementing 24 hour room service; full central heating; 2 lifts; night service; light meals and refreshment available in lounges; meals to 9.15 p.m.; diets; children welcome; baby listening; children's nanny; conferences up to 600; entertainment 6 nights a week; hairdressing salons; games room; billiards room – 2 full size tables; indoor heated swimming pool; sauna; 2 indoor tennis courts; 2 squash courts; outdoor heated swimming pool; 4 outdoor tennis courts; 9 hole golf course; putting green; croquet lawn; sea bathing, sailing, boating, fishing and riding all nearby; credit cards accepted except Amex.

This privately owned hotel, standing in 25 acres of well kept grounds close to Anstey's Cove, is one of Britain's most remarkable and successful hotels. Its present majestic and baronial proportions bear little similarity to the original building known as the Bishop's Summer Palace. It was, in fact, the residence of the Bishop of Exeter – Bishop Phillpot. The Hotel's rise to prosperity and popularity is greatly due to the marvellous leisure facilities offered to all ages. Anyone can find somewhere, something that suits the mood. Inside the Palace, you will find that the public rooms and the bedrooms are spacious and elegant with soft colour schemes and comfortable furnishings. The Restaurant provides dishes that are interesting, admirably cooked and well presented. The wine list is comprehensive and well chosen. During a recent visit I was delighted to find Denis Eldergill in charge of the bar. Finally, the fact that there are no extras – the charges include all games, sports and entertainments – is a great consideration. Dinner, room and breakfast from £55.00 per person, inclusive of VAT. Special discount on stays of 7 nights or more. Further terms on application. Garage and parking space for 200 cars (approx.). Open all year.

THE PRINCES HOTEL

Parkhill Road, Torquay, Devon TQ1 2DU

Telephone: (0803) 291803 Telex: 42988 DEVPRI Fax: 0803 291710

London 192, Birmingham 185, Exeter 22, Plymouth 30, Bristol 98

F licence; 54 bedrooms (11 ground floor) all with private baths, telephone, col. TV and tea/coffee making facilities; full central heating; night service; last orders 8.45 p.m.; bar meals (lunch); diets; children welcome; baby listening; dogs accepted; conferences max. 100; games room; dancing 3/4 nights per week in season; outdoor heated swimming pool; sea bathing; sailing; golf, tennis, squash, fishing all nearby; all major credit cards accepted.

The Princes Hotel was built as the elegant home of a Victorian gentleman and overlooks Torbay, the pride of Devon's seaside resorts. Today it is a luxurious family hotel, offering complete relaxation in congenial surroundings, attended by a courteous, efficient and friendly staff. Michael Gardiner owns both this hotel and the Devonshire Hotel (see page 252) and with David Phillips as General Manager you are assured of a warm welcome and a friendly atmosphere. Princes has recently been completely renovated and the furnishings are attractive with cheerful colour schemes. The ground floor rooms are spacious and comfortable, with a cocktail bar and lounges that all have views over the bay, and you can enjoy Torquay's excellent climate on the delightful sun patio. Traditional English dishes are prepared using fresh local produce, complemented by a full wine list. Tariff on application. Open all year.

ORESTONE MANOR HOUSE

Maidencombe, Nr. Torquay, Devon TQ1 4SX

Telephone: (0803) 328098/99

London 190, Birmingham 183, Bristol 96, Exeter 20, Plymouth 33, Torquay 3

R and R licence; 20 en suite bedrooms, all with direct dial telephone, colour TV, radio, baby listening, tea/coffee making facilities; part central heating; late meals to 8.30 p.m.; vegetarian diets; children welcome; dogs by prior arrangement; conferences up to 30 welcome; games room; outdoor heated swimming pool; riding by arrangement; sea bathing, sailing and boating ½ mile; fishing, golf, tennis, squash 2 miles; most major credit cards accepted.

Orestone, originally a Georgian country lodge, with a sub-tropical garden, is now a warm and inviting country Manor House situated on the fringe of Torbay. Peace, tranquillity and the lovely sheltered gardens, set off with many unusual and fine shrubs, still remain in this area of natural beauty which has extensive views of sea and coast line. The Manor House, full of character and charm, is owned and personally cared for by Mark and Sara Cleaver; their scrupulous attention to detail makes your stay very comfortable, there is an atmosphere of a most hospitable country home. The décor and furnishings are of the highest standard, the bedrooms being individually furnished and well appointed. The attractive restaurant offers an excellent table d'hôte menu, supplemented by a specialized menu, which changes on a seasonal basis. The food is carefully prepared under the supervision of head chef Stewart Mallen, who makes good use of local produce and home grown vegetables. I enjoyed an excellent dinner, which was interesting and superbly cooked, complemented by a wine list that is comprehensive and carefully chosen. Dinner, room and breakfast from £36.00 per person, weekly from £210.00 inclusive of VAT. 'Castaway' breaks (2 days) early and late season £60.00 per person, additional days pro rata. A member of Inter Hotels. Ample parking. Open all year.

THE OLD RECTORY COUNTRY HOUSE HOTEL

Torver, Coniston, Cumbria LA21 8AX

Telephone: (05394) 41353

Kendal 15, Coniston 2, Ambleside 8, Windermere 10

R & R licence; 7 bedrooms, 3 with bath, 4 with shower, all with TV, mini bar, hairdryer and tea making facilities; last orders for dinner 7.30 p.m.; special diets; children by arrangement; no dogs; sailing cruiser for daily hire; sailing and boating; walking, riding and fishing locally; shooting by arrangement; credit cards not accepted.

I am sure the owners of this lovely house, Mr. and Mrs. Fletcher will forgive me for writing that here is a country house for the simple life. It is isolated in three acres of wooded grounds, set amidst miles of peaceful, sylvan countryside. The area is noted for its literary associations, particularly Ruskin, Arthur Ransome and Beatrix Potter. However, if you must be energetic, there are marvellous walks around Lake Coniston, there is fell walking and all the other activities for which the Lakes are famous. Back to the house – I hesitate to call it an hotel, such is the atmosphere of the Rectory. It was built in 1868 and has been sympathetically brought up to date without detracting from its original charm and warmth. Downstairs, the particularly pleasant and comfortable public rooms have lovely views over the countryside, providing a relaxing setting to enjoy the imaginative four course dinners created by Mrs. Fletcher. To accompany the menu is a short, but well chosen wine list. To sum up, The Old Rectory is a haven for those seeking relaxation, a superb venue for those of an artistic nature and an ideal centre for those partaking in more energetic activities. Let the latter be warned, however, for I think they could well succumb to the gentler way of life here. Dinner, room and breakfast from £35.00, weekly from £227.50.

THE PENDLEY MANOR HOTEL

Tring, Hertfordshire HP23 5QY

Telephone: (0442) 891891 *Fax: 0442 890687*

M1 10 (junction 8), M25 13 (junction 20), London 35

F licence; 70 en suite bedrooms; telephone; television; room and night service; lift; dinner till 9.30 p.m.; drawing room light snacks; diets; children welcome; dogs accepted; conferences up to 180; 30 acres of gardens; Shakespeare Festival, outdoor production 10th–18th August; games room; snooker; sauna and solarium; spa pool; leisure centre and gymnasium; indoor heated swimming pool (opens late 1990); 2 floodlit tennis courts; squash courts 1 mile; riding 2 miles; golf, shooting and fishing 3 miles; motorized polo 3 miles; gliding 4 miles; war games close by; credit cards accepted; hotel open all year round.

Pendley Manor is situated in 35 acres of wooded parkland and it is so peaceful that you forget you are not far from the major motorways. The Manor's history dates back to the Domesday Book and at the beginning of the nineteenth century it was burnt down, and re-built in 1872. In 1989 this Tudor style house, after major renovation was returned to its former glory, and transformed to the hotel it is today. The entrance, with its original floor, leads into an impressive Hall with a welcome-fire burning. A magnificent staircase takes you to the comfortable bedrooms, which are all individual in character, and have views over the beautifully landscaped gardens. The main dining room, with its fine oak panelling, fireplace and high ceiling, is a very pleasant and peaceful room in which to relax and dine. The food is excellent, serving a Businessman's Lunch, and an à la carte menu, specialising in English and European cuisine, accompanied by an extensive selection of wines. The Verney Room is ideal for small conferences or parties. There is also the main conference facility, which includes a banqueting hall. Both are served by their own kitchens. The hotel is superbly run by a very efficient and enthusiastic team who always make you feel welcome. Single room and breakfast from £100.00, double from £125.00.

ALEXANDER HOUSE
Turners Hill, West Sussex RH10 4QD

Telephone: (0342) 714914 *Telex: 95611* *Fax: 0342 717328*

London 35, Brighton 25, Gatwick 9, East Grinstead 3, M23 6

F licence; 13 en suite bedrooms (1 on ground floor), all with colour TV, telephone and full central heating; lift; night service; last orders 9.30 p.m. (Sundays 9.00 p.m.); bar meals; diets; conferences up to 50 for day sessions, 12 residential; billiards, tennis; fishing 1 mile; golf 4 miles; Amex, Diners, Visa and Access accepted.

Alexander House lies on the B2110 road between Turners Hill and East Grinstead, 6 miles from Junction 10 on the M23 motorway. This lovely mansion is set in a secluded park, deep in the Sussex countryside, yet is only 9 miles from Gatwick airport; it is also one of the most luxurious hotels in England. Exquisite paintings adorn well-proportioned, beautifully furnished rooms, where guests can relax in total comfort. The hotel maintains the highest standards of discreet service and personal care. Only the freshest foods are served, and imaginatively presented, the most delicious classic French and English dishes, accompanied by truly fine wines. The bedrooms have en suite bathrooms, and some also include sitting rooms. All are superbly decorated with the intricate detail that hallmarks fine country house hotels; fresh flowers, magazines, and so on. Apart from the glorious grounds and surrounding countryside, there is a tennis court and a croquet lawn, as well as golfing, horse-riding and trout-fishing nearby. Sussex is well known for the many places of interest there are to visit, Glyndebourne and Brighton, to name but two; both are only half an hour away. Open all year, prices start at £90.00, inclusive of VAT. The hotel's Daimler limousine and chauffeur may be hired at competitive rates. There are weekend breaks on application.

SHARROW BAY COUNTRY HOUSE HOTEL

Ullswater, Penrith, Cumbria CA10 2LZ

Telephone: (07684) 86301 or 86483 *Fax: 07684 86349*

On the Howtown Road

London 289, Penrith 7, Kendal 33, Keswick 20, Windermere 25

R and R licence; 30 bedrooms; 26 with private bath and/or shower, including 6 cottage suites; TV; radio; antiques; peace; golf locally; lake bathing; boating; riding; fishing; small conference facilities.

Away from the bustle of the holiday rush, in the most envied position in the Lake District, Francis Coulson and Brian Sack must be congratulated on their 43rd year of service to the gourmets of the world, providing the most exquisite food and wines in the most comfortable of atmospheres. Reputed to be the first Country House Hotel in this country and to be approved by the Relais et Chateaux, only sixteen being so included in Great Britain, is surely recommendation enough, but speak to anyone who has stayed here and you will hear nothing but superlatives as the owners believe in creating a home from home. The décor is superb, the service impeccable and the overall effect the product of these two brilliant hoteliers. Add to all this the beauty of the Lake and mountains and you have total perfection. I should add there is now a beautiful converted farmhouse called Bank House, about a mile from Sharrow, which has seven superbly furnished bedrooms, all with private bathrooms and lake views. Breakfast is served in the magnificent Refectory dining room, which was converted from the seventeenth century barn. It has a striking Portland stone fireplace and overmantle, which came from Warwick Castle. It also has incredible English silk damask curtains, old English furniture and an especially made carpet, being a copy of that in the Royal Opera House. Lunch and Dinner are served at Sharrow Bay. Tariff on application. Please note that the hotel is closed for part of December, January and February.

THE FALCON HOTEL

Uppingham, Rutland, Leicestershire LE15 9PY

Telephone: (0572) 823535 *Fax: 0572 821621*

Oakham 6, Rutland Water 6, Peterborough 18, Leicester 16, M1 motorway 18, A1 road 14

F licence; 27 bedrooms, all with en suite bathroom, TV and telephone; room and night service; baby listening; last orders for dinner 10.00 p.m.; bar meals; special diets; children welcome; dogs allowed; conferences up to 120; sauna and solarium; gymnasium; squash, golf, tennis, riding, shooting, fishing, sailing and boating all by arrangement; Visa, Amex, Diners and Master Card welcome.

The Falcon Hotel is situated in the centre of the lovely old market town of Uppingham, which recently won an award for its profusion of flowers. As soon as I entered this hotel, I knew it was under new ownership, as the most wonderful improvements have been made. The main lounge has been completely opened up, creating a lovely, airy room, decorated with beautiful country flowers. There are comfortable, elegant chairs, where one can relax over a morning coffee, or enjoy an excellent lunch or afternoon tea – all these are specialities of the Hotel. The Brasserie Bar has been re-designed, and now adjoins the lounge, and there is a wide selection from the Brasserie Menu or the Daily Specials. Meals can also be taken in the pretty courtyard garden, abundant with flower. The pleasant Garden Room Restaurant features a covered outdoor terrace. There are extensive table d'hôte and à la carte menus. The Falcon was originally a Coaching Inn, and all rooms are full of character, including the Banqueting Rooms, which also serve for functions and conferences. Bedrooms are individual and very comfortable, and all are beautifully decorated. The Apple Suite has a sitting room downstairs, and a bedroom and bathroom upstairs. Special nights are offered to Honeymoon couples, and there are exciting ideas for weekend breaks throughout the year. Room and breakfast from £55.00 single, £65.00 double.

WHITE LION HOTEL

High Street, Upton-upon-Severn, Worcester WR8 0HJ

Telephone: (06846) 2551

Malvern 7, Tewkesbury 7, Pershore 7, Worcester 10, 3 Counties Showground 4½

F licence; 10 bedrooms with en suite bathroom/shower, telephone and TV; room service; night service till 12.00; last orders for dinner 9.15 p.m.; bar meals (ex. Saturday evening); special diets; children welcome; dogs allowed; conferences up to 10; golf and riding nearby; hotel open all year, ex. Christmas Day and Boxing Day. Credit cards accepted.

As my journey took me through Malvern, towards the Cotswolds, I passed Upton upon Severn, which in turn led me to the White Lion. This is a former coaching Inn and in Fielding's famous story, 'Tom Jones' (1749), he refers to the Hotel's Wild Goose Room and the Rose Room. Both of these have been preserved with the utmost care to combine old and new. The Rose Room has a four poster bed, and all rooms are well furnished and comfortable, providing the guest with all modern facilities. The oak beamed restaurant is well laid out and the 'Tom Jones Bill of Fayre', changed regularly, has a good selection of dishes. There is also an à la carte menu. Sunday lunch is extremely well priced, and is a must if you are passing by. Fresh snacks and sandwiches are served daily in the friendly bar. The owners, Robert and Bridget Withey are both experienced hoteliers, and immediately make guests feel at home. Upton is a picturesque village within easy distance of the Malvern Hills. An ideal place to stay for the Three Counties Show, but do book early! It is also not far from the beautiful Wye Valley, Hereford and the Cotswolds. Room and breakfast from £46.00 single, £62.00 double. Extended 2 day breaks are also offered.

THE NARE HOTEL

Carne Beach, Veryan, Cornwall TR2 5PF

Telephone: (0872) 501279 *Fax: 0872 501856*

London 261, Truro 14, St. Austell 14, St. Mawes 5

R & R licence; 39 en suite bedrooms (7 ground floor) all with remote control TV, telephone, tea/coffee making facilities; family suites; last orders 9.30 p.m.; light luncheons; diets; children welcome; dogs accepted; very warm outdoor swimming pool; sauna and solarium; gymnasium; billiards; games room; sea bathing 50 yards; hotel boat, windsurfing, sailing, all weather tennis court. Free golf, fishing and riding all nearby; credit cards accepted; trains met at Truro station (free of charge) by prior arrangement.

The Nare Hotel is superbly situated in about 4 acres of grounds about 50 yards from the sea, just above the mile-long golden sands of Carne Beach, and is surrounded by National Trust Land. This highly recommended hotel faces south, and enjoys the balmy climate of the Roseland peninsula, where winters are mild and summers are long and warm. The owners are Mr. and Mrs. Gray, and it is personally managed by Mrs. Daphne Burt, the Resident Director. There are three comfortable lounges elegantly furnished with antiques and an abundance of fresh flowers, with log fires for cooler days and an attractive Cocktail Bar, which leads onto the well kept terraces and gardens. The energetic can use the heated swimming pool – even toddlers have their own paddling pool. The dining room overlooks the gardens and sea, and the food is carefully prepared and presented, using local Cornish delicacies and sea food, and there is a wide choice. The wine list is well chosen and interesting. Most of the well appointed bedrooms have sea views and many have balconies or patios. The aim is to give that increasingly rare but unobtrusive old fashioned service, where the guests' comfort really comes first. There are some lovely walks along the coastal path adjoining the hotel and through the surrounding countryside. Room and full English breakfast from £39.00 per person, including VAT. Other rates on application. Open all year. Christmas and New Year festivities. Please write for colour brochure.

ST. MORITZ HOTEL

Trebetherick, Nr. Wadebridge, Cornwall PL27 6SD

Telephone: (0208) 862242 *Fax: 0208 862262*

Wadebridge 7, Falmouth 39, Padstow 14, Newquay 23, Bodmin 14, Truro 31

R & R licence; 30 en suite bedrooms, all with direct dial telephone, colour TV, radio and full central heating; meals until 9.30 p.m.; diets; children welcome, baby listening; dogs allowed; ladies' hairdressing & beauty salon; sea bathing; sailing, golf, sea and river fishing all nearby; riding by arrangement; major credit cards accepted.

The St. Moritz Hotel, located on the B3314 from Wadebridge, stands on 8 acres of land overlooking the Camel estuary. It is an area of outstanding natural beauty, much beloved by the Poet Laureate John Betjeman, who now rests in the pretty little church of St. Enodoc. This highly recommended hotel is owned by Stephen Rushworth and his mother, and their partner Brad J. Trethewey. All the bedrooms are en suite and well appointed, whilst downstairs, the new and attractive dining rooms and lounges are comfortable and restful. Due to be completed by the summer of 1991 is a leisure centre, including indoor swimming pool, and hotel guests will automatically become members during their stay. Plans for the future include self-catering villas, more hotel bedrooms, an outdoor pool, badminton and squash courts and a bowling green. The building will be completed over 2 winter phases. Thanks to the expertise of Brad Trethewey, St. Moritz has a fine reputation for good food. Great care and consideration are taken in the preparation of English and Continental dishes, using local sea-food and garden produce whenever possible. A well chosen and selective wine list is offered to complete a delicious meal. There are three beaches nearby, offering safe bathing, canoeing, surfing and sailing. For golfers, St. Enodoc Golf Club is ideally situated ½ mile away, with a choice of two 18 hole courses, and only a few miles away, the newly built Bowood Park Golf Course offers a full 18-hole course designed by Bob Sandow. The hotel is closed from November to March 31st, but the office is open for enquiries. Room and breakfast from £32.00 per person, including VAT. Other terms on application.

KEMPS COUNTRY HOUSE HOTEL AND RESTAURANT

East Stoke, Nr. Wareham, Dorset BH20 6AL

Telephone: (0929) 462563 *Fax: 0929 405287*

Wareham 2, Poole 10, Bournemouth 15, Dorchester 15, London 110

R & R licence; 15 bedrooms (8 ground floor) 14 en suite, 1 with own bathroom, all with telephone and colour TV; full central heating; last orders 9.30 p.m.; diets; children welcome; baby listening; no dogs; conference room for up to 120, also suitable for weddings and banquets; Leisure centre with indoor pool, squash & tennis 1½ miles; 3 golf courses nearby, nearest 2 miles; seabathing, riding & fishing within 5 miles, sailing & boating 10 miles; Visa, Master Card, Diners, Amex accepted.

Originally a Victorian rectory, Kemps Hotel and Restaurant has been carefully extended, and without loss of its character, turned into a charming hotel. Overlooking the lovely Purbeck Hills, it is ideally situated for the exploration of Thomas Hardy country and the beautiful Dorset coast. Under the personal direction of the present proprietors, Paul and Jill Warren, you will receive a warm welcome in a relaxed country house atmosphere. The public rooms are comfortably furnished in soft, muted colours, and there is an interesting bar which was once fitted on board a ship! The restaurant, with its victorian conservatory is highly thought of, and has a great many regular visitors. Wherever possible the food is prepared from fresh, local ingredients and bread is baked twice daily. The table d'hôte menu is well thought out, changed daily. An à la carte menu is also available. The bedrooms are attractively decorated. In the new wing, the rooms have views over the Purbecks and are particularly spacious and there is a special honeymoon suite with four-poster bed and whirlpool bath and another room with half-tester bed and whirlpool bath. Small conferences and seminars are well catered for in the new conference rooms. Single room and breakfast from £45.00, weekly double occupancy, half board from £255.00. Open all year.

THE GLEBE AT BARFORD

Barford, Warwick, Warwickshire CV35 8BS

Telephone: (0926) 624218 *Fax: 0926 624625*

Birmingham Airport/NEC 18, Coventry 12, Stratford-upon-Avon 7, London 98, Warwick 2, Royal Showground Stoneleigh 6.

F licence; 36 bedrooms, all with en suite bathroom, all with telephone, colour TV; satellite TV; full central heating; last orders 9.30 p.m.; bar meals; diets; children welcome; baby listening; conferences max. 130; leisure centre; credit cards accepted.

What a transformation in The Glebe! This hotel has been recommended by *Signpost* for some years, and it has now been refurbished and a very impressive extension added. One can now walk from the original building into the new bar, with its marble floors, palms and cane furniture. It looks out onto a small internal courtyard, in the centre of which there is a beautiful fountain. On the far side, you will find the "Director's Room", so called because of its lovely mahogany boardroom-type table. There is a most pleasantly appointed conference/private party room, and a leisure centre containing an indoor swimming pool, sauna and steam room, sun beds and a mini gymnasium. In addition to this, the bedrooms have now been tripled in quantity, yet maintain the same high standards of décor and furnishings. The conservatory, with its graceful arches, leads to the restaurant, which is a very popular venue for both luncheon and dinner. This is evidenced in the fact that a good friend of mine eats here regularly. Barford is a small village situated on the A429 just south of Warwick and close to the new junction of the M40. It is an ideal location both for those there on business, and for visitors who plan to explore historical Stratford-upon-Avon, Warwick and nearby Kenilworth. The National Exhibition Centre and the Royal Agricultural Showground are also within easy reach. Tariff on application.

MOONFLEET MANOR HOTEL AND COUNTRY CLUB

Nr. Weymouth, Dorset DT3 4ED

Telephone: (0305) 786948 *Fax: 0305 774395*

Weymouth 5, Dorchester 9, London 125

F licence; 38 bedrooms all en suite with telephone; TV; central heating; lift; night service; last orders 10.30 p.m.; conservatory terrace for light meals and bar snacks, diets; children welcome; baby check system; no dogs; conferences 20–30 persons; dancing in cellar discotheque; full size snooker table room; adjacent country club, 4 indoor bowls rinks; 2 squash courts, 2 tennis courts, swimming pool complete with gymnasium; sauna; solarium; table tennis; toddlers indoor play area.

The origins of the romantically named Moonfleet Manor Hotel go back to 1564 when it was the seat of the Mohun family. It was featured in the exciting 'Moonfleet' story of smugglers and adventure on the Dorset coast and the Summer House mentioned can still be found in the grounds. Although just a short drive from Weymouth, Moonfleet Manor is in a lovely secluded position overlooking Chesil Beach, ideally situated for bird watching and nature trailing. Bruce and Jan Hemingway, the resident proprietors for seventeen years, have made a speciality of their sporting facilities; these are exceptional and include a four rink indoor bowling green with a resident coach. There are also tennis and squash courts and an indoor swimming pool complex with sauna, sunbeds and multi-gym. Children are well catered for with cots, high chairs and early suppers and a large safe garden with huge sandpit and play equipment; a special paddling pool section of the swimming pool is provided. Room and breakfast from £30.50 per person, weekly from £235.00 per person, dinner, bed and breakfast. See Bargain Break Section. Always open.

THE SHIREBURN ARMS

Hurst Green, Nr. Whalley,
Lancashire BB6 9QJ

Telephone: (025486) 518

Blackpool 20, Preston 10, Lake District 60, Newcastle 110, London 219

F licence; 16 en suite bedrooms (2 on ground floor), all with radio, telephone, TV; full central heating; meals to 9.30 p.m.; diets; children welcome; baby listening; dogs welcome; conferences up to 80; fishing; golf within 10 miles; local riding; shooting by arrangement; Access and Visa credit cards welcome.

After a day spent exploring the beautiful surrounding countryside, or as a welcome break from a long journey, it is a pleasure to enter The Shireburn Arms in the peaceful village of Hurst Green. The village itself is set at the heart of the Ribble Valley and only a few miles from the M6. The hotel is situated opposite the gates of Stoneyhurst College on the edge of the forest of Bowland. The owners, Mr. and Mrs. Atkinson, have transformed the hotel. It still retains the warmth and ambience from before the alterations, but now there is a more spacious and airy atmosphere. The view from the new dining room window, over the Ribble Valley is stunning. Couple this with excellent food and a superb wine list, and you have the perfect venue from which to conduct a business trip to Manchester (only 45 minutes away), or from which to tour such accessible places as Yorkshire, the Lake District, Blackpool, the famous Trough of Bowland and the Ribble Valley. Open all year. Room and breakfast from £39.50 single, £55.00 double, weekly rates on application.

WOODHAYES COUNTRY HOUSE HOTEL

Whimple, Nr. Exeter, Devon EX5 2TD

Telephone: (0404) 822237

Exeter 8, M5 motorway 8, Exeter Airport 5

R & R licence; 8 bedrooms, all with en suite bathroom, TV, telephone; room and night service; late dinners; bar meals, special diets; children over 12 welcome; very small dogs accepted; croquet; tennis; hotel open all year; major credit cards accepted.

The warm and friendly personalities of Katherine and Frank Rendle, and their son Michael, resident proprietors of this small, Georgian Country House Hotel, ensure a pleasant visit, and I know you will return again and again. The village of Whimple is clearly marked on the A30 between Exeter and Honiton, and is only 8 miles from the M5. The hotel stands in large and peaceful grounds, complete with croquet lawn and tennis court. The surrounding countryside is ideal for quiet walks and the sea is only 11 miles away. Nearby coastal resorts include Torquay, Sidmouth, Seaton, Beer, Exmouth and Lyme Regis. There are 8 spacious bedrooms, all having en suite facilities, direct dial telephones, TV, radio and hair dryer. All are beautifully decorated. Both lounges are elegant, yet supremely comfortable; there is a bar and a charming dining room with sun terrace. Katherine provides fine English and French cuisine to a very high standard. The wine list is thoughtfully chosen and well explained. The comfort of their guests is important to the Rendle family, and this is very evident. Tariff on application.

WHITWELL HALL COUNTRY HOUSE HOTEL

Whitwell on the Hill, York YO6 7JJ

Telephone: (065381) 551 *Fax: 065381 554*

London 222, York 12, Scarborough 29

R & R licence; 23 en suite bedrooms, all with radio, telephone and TV; no children; dogs by arrangement, but not in bedrooms; sauna; indoor heated swimming pool; tennis; very beautiful gardens; Master Card, Barclaycard and Amex accepted.

Set on a hill overlooking the Vale of York, Whitwell Hall offers magnificent views. The House itself is an imposing mansion, beautifully decorated and furnished with fine antiques and pictures. There is a superb indoor heated swimming pool.From the Orangery next door sliding doors open on to the terrace and the views. Lunch is served in the Orangery. The Coach House has further bedrooms with modern furniture and décor. The Conference Room, for prestigious meetings, occupies the old family chapel in this block. The food here is excellent and dinner is served from a table d'hôte menu in the delightful dining room, making a stay here a most memorable occasion. The owners, Peter and Sally Milner, have thought of everything to make their guests comfortable. Even bicycles are provided for the energetic who wish to explore this historic and lovely area, famous for its stately homes and abbeys. The Yorkshire Moors are easily accessible; Scarborough, and Whitby are within 30 miles, and York itself is only 12 miles away. Closer at hand are the beautiful and well kept gardens in which guests can stroll. Whitwell Hall is a country house of character and style, run with efficiency and flair, yet it is a warm and relaxing place to stay. Room and breakfast from £50.00 single, £69.00 double. Weekly tariff on application. Open all year.

GILPIN LODGE

Crook Road, Windermere, Cumbria LA23 3NE

Telephone: (09662) 88818 *Fax: 09662 88058*

London 280, Kendal 6, Windermere 2, Manchester 75

R & R licence; 9 bedrooms, all with en suite bathroom, telephone and TV; room service; last orders for dinner 9.00 p.m.; special diets; children of 9 and above welcome; no dogs; conferences up to 20; croquet and gardens; golf opposite hotel; sailing, boating, tennis, riding, shooting and fishing 2 miles; hotel open all year; all major credit cards accepted.

Gilpin Lodge is to me the epitome of the Country House. This is not the huge, luxurious establishment that one so often equates with country house hotels, but it is small, superbly comfortable, offering a quiet, relaxing atmosphere, complemented by excellent food and a list of 150 bins of thoughtfully chosen wines. Three large bedrooms have recently been added and these, along with the original rooms, are all individually and beautifully decorated. The hotel is run by Mr. and Mrs. Cunliffe and the personal touch is evident in the welcome on arrival, the abundance of fresh flowers and the attentive service in general. Dinner is a five course feast with many interesting choices and all the dishes are prepared from the best of ingredients, and are superbly cooked and presented. Gilpin Lodge is not on the Lake itself, being a mile away from Windermere, and so avoids the bustle of so many of these lakeside hotels. It is situated in four acres of well tended gardens and is in a particularly bucolic corner of the Lake District. It therefore offers the peace and tranquillity that is becoming increasingly difficult to find in this beautiful part of England. This is one of the few hotels highly recommended by the English Tourist Board, an accolade much sought after and rarely attained. Room and breakfast from £30.00 shared/double; dinner, bed and breakfast from £210.00 weekly.

THE LAKESIDE HOTEL

Newby Bridge, On Windermere, Cumbria LA12 8AT

Telephone: (05395) 31207 *Telex: 65149* *Fax: 05395 31699*

M6 (Junction 36) 20 minutes, Manchester 84 miles

F licence; 80 en suite bedrooms (11 ground floor), 7 with patio doors, all with telephone, colour TV; lift; last orders 9.30 p.m.; coffee shop; bar meals; special diets; children welcome, baby listening; dogs by arrangement; conferences up to 100; shooting; lake bathing, fishing, sailing and boating; boat launching and mooring; tennis, squash and riding nearby; golf within 10 miles (4 courses); all credit cards accepted.

As its name implies, the hotel stands on the beautiful shores of Lake Windermere, and its gardens run down to the water's edge. Nearby, at the pierside, steamers wait to take you on a cruise through some of the most superb scenery in England, culminating perhaps, in a nostalgic ride on the old steam railway from Lakeside to Haverthwaite and back. The hotel itself has been completely refurbished over the last year, and whilst still retaining its Victorian/Edwardian ambience, it now offers all the comfort and facilities of a modern hotel. Most of the rooms enjoy delightful views over the water to the hills beyond, and some have four poster beds. Other rooms are designed with disabled guests particularly in mind. The new conservatory allows one to sit in luxury, and watch the activities of those participating in the many watersports offered by the hotel. To complete your day, a meal in the elegantly redecorated restaurant overlooking Lake Windermere, chosen from an excellent menu, changed daily and which uses fresh local produce and complemented by a wine from the well chosen list, is a must. Conferences are a speciality here, but the hotel is also an ideal venue for tourists, holiday makers, and particularly, boat minded people. It can be easily reached from the M6 with the home of Beatrix Potter, 'Hilltop', only seven miles away with the picturesque village of Hawkshead nearby. Tariff on application.

LANGDALE CHASE HOTEL
Windermere, Cumbria LA23 1LW

Telephone: (05394) 32201 *Fax: 05394 32604*

London 283, Windermere 3½, Ambleside 2½

F licence; 33 bedrooms, 32 private baths; colour TV, telephones, tea/coffee making facilities in all rooms; radio; late meals by arrangement; diets available; most beautiful grounds; tennis; boating; fishing; riding near; night service.

As the Langdale Chase Hotel is renowned for its excellence by connoisseurs all over the country and by all in the Lake District, just ask any 'local' and he will direct you to the gates on the Windermere to Ambleside Road. Then turn in at the drive and note the stately trees and immaculately mown and edged lawns, and park in peace outside the front door. Note, too, the splendid lakeside view with the unique skyline of the Langdales in the distance. Inside, parts of the hotel suggest a baronial atmosphere; others are more modern and this particularly refers to the picture windowed restaurant with its garden and lake views. Food is properly understood here and is enjoyed all the more for the setting in which it's served, and you're treated as a human being and not just as a bedroom number. Some of the staff have been here for years and will probably remember your name. Upstairs you'll be intrigued by some of the bedrooms which grow small offshoots in the turrets. A Lakeland stone bungalow offers six superb new bedrooms with bathrooms so that a guest, although enjoying all the facilities of the hotel, virtually has his own flat to which he can drive his car directly. Room and breakfast from £45.00 including service charge and VAT.

THE MORTAL MAN HOTEL
Troutbeck, Nr. Windermere,
Cumbria LA23 1PL

Telephone: Ambleside (05394) 33193. Visitors 32610

London 283, Windermere Station 3, Kirkstone Summit 3, Patterdale 9

F licence; 12 en suite bedrooms, all with TV; diets available; dogs welcome; no children under 5 years old.

Up on the hills on the long rise from Windermere to the summit of the Kirkstone Pass you'll spy a freshly painted, gabled, black and cream house a few hundred yards west. A sign at the entrance to a lane points the way to the Mortal Man, a hotel with a long, romantic and honourable history. It's just the place for a go-as-you-please holiday exploring the fells, lakes and passes. Now under the capable management of Annette and Christopher Poulsom the hotel maintains the reputation that it has always enjoyed. As with so many hotels in the area, peace is the main attribute but with the Mortal Man this is accentuated by the fact that it stands on a little-used side road and even in the height of the season one can relax in comfort. Dinner, bed and breakfast from £45.00 single, £90.00 twin. Closed mid-November to mid-February.

WILD BOAR HOTEL

Crook, Nr. Windermere, Cumbria LA23 3NF

Telephone: (09662) 5225 *Telex: 65464* *Fax: 09662 2498*

Bowness 3, Ambleside 7, Grasmere 11, Kendal 6, Blackpool 50, Manchester 75

F licence; 36 en suite bedrooms (6 ground floor), including 2 luxury suites, all with direct dial telephone, remote control TV; fresh fruit, welcoming sherry; last orders 8.45 p.m.; special diets; children welcome; baby listening; conferences max. 40; dinner dances from mid-October to Easter; Windermere 18 hole golf course 1 mile away, guests enjoy discounted green fees; fishing 3 miles, complimentary permits; Access, Amex, Diners, Visa credit cards accepted.

Whether on a business trip or touring, the position of the Wild Boar makes it invaluable to the traveller. It is close to the M6, on the B5284 Bowness-on-Windermere to Kendal road, and only three miles from the shores of Lake Windermere. The air-conditioned Gilpin Room has been specially designed and built for conferences of up to forty people, with all the visual aids etc. necessary for a meeting. There is plenty of parking space. The hotel is situated in the most rural of settings in the beautiful Gilpin Valley; it is a former 19th century coaching inn, outside the doors of which, it is said, that the last feral wild boar in England was slain. On entering you will find cosy public rooms with low oak beams, open log fires and chintzy furnishings. The bedrooms are all beautifully decorated and have every modern facility. In the attractive candle-lit dining room, with a natural outcrop of rock at one end, you can choose delicious dishes, including the house speciality fresh wild boar, from either the menu of the day or from the à la carte. A well selected wine list, which has itself gained an enviable reputation, gives you the final excuse to make your stay an extended one. Your host, Mr. Douglas Dale, looks forward to your company, and to looking after you during your visit. The Wild Boar is a member of Best Western Hotels. Room and breakfast from £40.00, half board rate for a week from £41.00 per guest, daily. Open all year.

ROYAL OAK INN

Winsford, Exmoor National Park, Somerset TA24 7JE

Telephone: (064385) 455 *Telex: 46529 Ref Roak* *Fax: 064385 388*

London 200, Taunton 28, Exeter 35, Minehead 16, Bristol 65, Tiverton 30

F licence; 14 en suite bedrooms (8 in the Inn, 6 in the ground floor annexe), all with colour TV; full central heating; night service to 9.30 p.m.; dinner – last orders 9 p.m.; diets on request; children welcome; golf, tennis, squash at Minehead and Tiverton; riding; fishing; shooting by arrangement; credit cards accepted.

The Royal Oak is an attractive 15th century thatched Inn situated in Winsford, a pretty village near Dunster and Dulverton, on the River Exe. Owned and personally cared for by Mr. and Mrs. Charles Steven, there is always a warm welcome, and great attention is paid to good food, service and comfort. The bedrooms are luxurious, spacious and well appointed. There is one suite, a very fine apartment, of character and quality. The two bars and lounge areas are comfortable and well furnished; the Dining Room, tables nicely laid up with silver and good glass, has a reputation for high quality food. The à la carte and table d'hôte menus were outstanding – a good choice of delicious dishes produced with imagination and artistry. The wine list is selective and well chosen. I can thoroughly recommend the Royal Oak Inn throughout the year and especially so in the summer months. The surrounding countryside is full of interesting places and varied walks, whilst the coast is only 15/20 minutes drive. Dinner, room and breakfast from £50.00 per person, inclusive of VAT. Other terms and special breaks on application. Open all year. RAC***, English Tourist Board ****.

THE OLD VICARAGE COUNTRY HOUSE HOTEL

Witherslack, Cumbria LA11 6RS

Telephone: (05395) 52381 *Fax: 05395 52373*

M6 Junction 36 10 mins., Sea 4, Kendal 8, Lake Windermere 6

R & R licence; 9 en suite bedrooms and 5 in the Orchard House, all with telephone, colour TV, full central heating; dinner 7.30 p.m. for 8.00 p.m.; diets; children by arrangement; dogs by arrangement; all weather tennis court for guests' use; sea bathing, sailing, golf, squash, badminton, riding, shooting, fishing all nearby; Visa, Amex, Access, Diners credit cards accepted.

The Old Vicarage was recommended to me by one of the country's top hoteliers – and how right he was to do so. For those wishing to visit the Lake District, to remain in perfect peace and seclusion and yet to sample the art of cooking and service at their best, then here is the venue in which to do so to perfection. The hotel is set in a particularly beautiful valley and it offers the finest of food prepared only from the freshest of ingredients. It is indeed a haven. The atmosphere is of unhurried simplicity but the thought and energy expended to achieve this ambience is, I am sure, immeasurable. Mr. and Mrs. Burrington-Brown and Mr. and Mrs. Reeve have set a standard that many hotels will strive to match but which few will attain. I look forward to visiting this unique hotel again, and especially to staying in the "Celebration Suite", one of the new bedrooms in the Orchard House, with its terraces overlooking unspoilt woodland. Room and breakfast from £35.00 per person, inclusive of VAT. No service charges. Open all year, except for Christmas week.

CANTLEY HOUSE

Milton Road, Wokingham, Berks. RG11 5QG

Telephone: (0734) 789912 *Fax: 0734 774294*

Heathrow Airport 30, Wokingham Station 2, London 38, Reading 8

F licence; 29 bedrooms (1 for disabled) all with en suite bathroom; telephone and colour TV; 24 hour room service; baby listening; night service; last orders 10.00 p.m.; bar meals; vegetarian diets; children welcome; dogs accepted; conferences up to 25 in boardroom, and 70 in theatre; pool; croquet lawn; tennis; golf 5 minutes; riding 10 minutes; shooting ½ hour; credit cards accepted.

Conveniently located only five minutes from the busy centre of Wokingham, and just a few miles from Junction 10 of the M4 motorway, this charming Victorian Mansion is nevertheless pervaded by a sense of rural peace, set back from the A321 towards Henley and Twyford. Forty acres of parkland protect it from the noisiest excesses of modern day living. The tastefully furnished bedrooms have all modern amenities, including direct dial telephones, radio alarm clocks and beverage making facilities. Maryline's Brasserie, the Hotel restaurant, is a beautifully restored 17th century barn, with a large open fire. The menu caters for the most discerning diner, and offers the finest English food, with a French influence. Other facilities at Cantley House include the Ormonde and Pipers Rooms, ideal venues for conferences, weddings and banquets, and adjacent to the restaurant is the Penguin and Vulture pub. Tariff on application, open all year.

THE FEATHERS HOTEL
Woodstock, Oxford OX7 1SX

Telephone: (0993) 812291 *Fax: 0993 813158*

London 59, Stratford-upon-Avon 32, Oxford 8

F licence; 15 bedrooms, including 2 suites, all with private bath, room telephone, TV and radio; full central heating; last orders 9.30 p.m.; diets; children welcome; dogs welcome; conferences; golf, riding, shooting 5 miles; squash, badminton 3 miles; tennis and fishing 1 mile; major credit cards accepted.

Woodstock is a fascinating town in every way. There are many interesting places in the area to visit, including Blenheim Palace, and Oxford is only eight miles away. A visit to the Feathers Hotel will be a lovely surprise – I was tempted to visit by the hotel's beautiful bright display of window boxes and found a correspondingly charming ambience indoors. This 17th century building is privately owned and is furnished throughout with antiques, chintzes and paintings. Fresh flowers greet the eye at every turn and log fires burn during the winter. I took my family to lunch recently and received attentive and courteous service. The delicious food from an innovative menu was thoughtfully presented. In the evenings you may dine by candlelight and in the summer, lunch may be taken in the garden. The fifteen bedrooms are all individually decorated and furnished. I thoroughly recommend this friendly country house hotel for anyone visiting this lovely part of England. The hotel is open all year. Room and breakfast from £90.00 (double) including VAT and service. Special winter terms on application.

WATERSMEET HOTEL

Mortehoe, Woolacombe, Devon EX34 7EB

Telephone: (0271) 870333 *Fax: 0271 870890*

Taunton 62, Bristol 79, Barnstaple 14, Exeter 56

F licence; 26 bedrooms (1 ground floor) all with private bathroom, remote control colour TV; direct dial telephones; children welcome; meals till 8.30 p.m.; light lunches; diets; pool table; games room; outdoor heated swimming pool; grass tennis court; bathing, sandy beach – private steps to seashore, surfing and sailing, boating, sea and river fishing, riding and 3 golf courses all nearby; lovely walks – National Trust; all major credit cards accepted.

Watersmeet , facing south, is wonderfully situated on the water's edge, with its terraced gardens leading to a private access to Combersgate Beach by way of their own steps. This lovely house is owned and personally looked after by Brian and Pat Wheeldon, both very experienced, they have taken great care preserving the comfort and style of a country house. All the public rooms and bedrooms are delightfully furnished with soft colour schemes complemented by lovely fabrics. There are two bars, one an exclusive cocktail bar with comfortable lounges leading off. The recently built Pavilion Restaurant, a most attractive octagonal dining room is designed so that every table enjoys a spectacular view of the sea. It was obvious to me that special pride is taken in the food, the interesting dishes are cooked with imagination and flair. The selection of wines are well chosen. I can thoroughly recommend this well run family hotel, where the service is efficient and conveys a happy atmosphere. Dinner, room and breakfast from £55.00 per person including VAT. Other terms, including special breaks on application. Clay pigeon shooting and painting holidays arranged. Closed December to February but office open for enquiries. Do write for their most attractive and informative brochure.

BILBROUGH MANOR COUNTRY HOUSE HOTEL

Bilbrough, York, Yorkshire YO2 3PH

Telephone: (0937) 834002

York 5, Leeds 22, Harrogate 25, A1 7, London 200, Edinburgh 200

R & R licence; 12 en suite bedrooms, all with telephone, colour TV and full central heating; night butler; last orders 9.30 p.m.; diets; children over 12 welcome; no dogs; executive conferences 12–20 welcome; croquet; golf, riding, shooting and fishing by arrangement; many local race courses; all credit cards accepted.

I am indebted to a noted hotelier of the district for guiding me to this hotel. I had heard glowing accounts of Bilbrough Manor but his praises rang too good to be true. How wrong I was to doubt. In a manor house re-built in 1901, Colin and Susan Bell have sympathetically re-created the country house atmosphere of that period. The visual and physical comfort of all the rooms is superb. The cuisine, prepared by David Deacon and his team of chefs is exceptional and the service in the oak panelled dining room in particular, is a symphony of discretion and friendliness, orchestrated by Antonio Esteve. Seldom does one find an hotel with the comfort and service that Bilbrough affords without that hotel being over formal. Here, a carefree and relaxing aura flows around one, whilst courtesy and service prevail. All this leaves little room to write of the superb situation of Bilbrough. With fine views over the Vale of York, towards distant Ilkley Moor, it has beautifully kept gardens in which to relax, and for the energetic there is riding, shooting, fishing and walking all close by. There are also 10 race courses within an hour's drive. York, with all its famous attractions is only 5 miles away and Yorkshire's historical sites and unsurpassed scenery are within easy motoring distance. Brochure and tariff on application. The hotel is closed over Christmas.

SWALLOW CHASE HOTEL

Tadcaster Road, Dringhouses,
York, Yorkshire YO2 2QQ

Telephone: (0904) 701000

York ½, London 209, Leeds 24, Wetherby 14, Ripon 24

F licence; 112 en suite bedrooms (22 ground floor), all with colour TV, telephone and full central heating; 2 lifts; night service; last orders 10.00 p.m.; coffee shop; bar meals; diets; children welcome, baby listening; dogs allowed; conferences up to 140; indoor heated swimming pool; sauna and solarium; leisure centre; Access, Visa, Amex and Diners cards welcome.

This famous racing hotel has recently been completely updated and refurbished to produce a mix of modern facilities and old fashioned standards of service. The hotel restaurant overlooks the mature gardens, which in turn lead down to York racecourse. There is a leisure centre in which to relax after a strenuous day, perhaps at the races or touring the nearby historic city of York. The bedrooms are bright, pleasantly furnished and decorated, and they have all the modern facilities that we have come to expect of a hotel of this calibre. I can think of few hotels from which such a range of activities can be enjoyed as at the Swallow Chase. All of Yorkshire with its superb sporting facilities, with its abundance of historic houses and its wonderful countryside lies within easy driving distance, and the city itself is unsurpassed as a tourist centre. Open all year, tariff on application.

WALES

THE COUNTRY

Wales is a land of lore and legend, medieval myth and magic, which has a special allure for hundreds of thousands of people, who come from all over the world to discover or recapture its enchantment and beauty.

Wales is a part of Britain but it is also a land apart. Looking at a map it may appear to be simply a geographical extension of England – but nothing could be further from the truth. It is as different from England as Spain is from France and you soon realize this when you cross 'the border'.

You will hear the Welsh language used daily, spoken on the streets, on television and radio, and you'll also see many tongue twisting Welsh place names – but phrase books aren't necessary as the Welsh speakers are all bilingual!

But it's not just the language which sets Wales apart – the country has its own unique culture, heritage and traditions. The friendliness of the Welsh people is another essential ingredient which ensures a stay in Wales will be a memorable one.

Wales is a country of outstanding natural beauty, a land of endless scenic variety and dramatic contrasts, and it is this combination which serves to offer visitors an experience of a lifetime.

Although only a small country – less than 200 miles from north to south and just over 8000 square miles – Wales has a tremendous amount to offer. It is a land of wide open spaces, with vast tracts of moorland, moody mountain ranges and deep forests where you are never far from the mountains or the coast.

There are three national parks covering a staggering 1,600 square miles, and five acres officially designated as being of outstanding natural beauty. There are also numerous country parks and nature reserves, mile after mile of quiet country lanes to explore, meandering salmon-rich rivers, natural lakes, vast reservoirs and tranquil canals.

The Welsh coastline covers more than 700 miles, boasting vast stretches of golden sands, tiny coves, craggy cliffs, rocky outcrops, as well as busy, bustling resorts, picturesque harbours, and quaint fishing villages.

There are islands to explore by boat, fishing trips to enjoy – shark fishing is a speciality in some areas – and an abundance of wildlife and birdlife to observe.

Wales has something to offer all ages and all tastes. Those in search of the heritage of Wales, her stately homes and her magnificent castles, and those who come to learn about the country's unique culture and traditions, will not be disappointed.

ENTERTAINMENT AND CULTURE

Yet those who yearn for the bright lights, the sophistication of the cities, the good shops and restaurants, theatre, opera, night clubs and entertainment are also catered for.

Wales is known as a land of castles, and that description is fitting, as there are more castles per square mile here than in any other European country. They stand as strong, solid, stone monuments to a turbulent past.

They dominate many a landscape along the coastline or guard the strategic inland gateways to Wales, a haunting reminder of a dramatic chapter in Welsh history. There are a host of exciting events staged in many castles throughout the year, ranging from dramatic re-enactments of ancient battles, to open air Shakespearian plays.

You can also travel back in time and sample a medieval banquet at one of the castles and enjoy an evening of traditional entertainment with good food, wine and mead.

The country's religious heritage can be traced through visiting old abbeys, monasteries cathedrals and the palaces of the prelates as well as superb little Norman churches.

Literature, poetry, music and song play an important part in the cultural heritage of Wales, which is celebrated each year at the National Eisteddfod, a Welsh speaking festival where the cream of the country's singers, musicians and poets, old and young, gather to compete and to listen and learn.

There is also an International Eisteddfod which is held at Llangollen each year, attracting dancers, singers and musicians from all over the world. This small town becomes a vibrant colourful cosmos, a place where international friendships are forged annually.

Apart from these two big cultural events, there are always a host of smaller festivals and events held in towns and villages in Wales throughout the year where visitors are encouraged to join in the fun.

Each age has left its mark on Wales, from the Romans through to the Industrial Revolution, and this heritage is evident from the amazing number of museums which specialize in capturing the past for us to enjoy in the present.

In the south at Caerleon – once the Roman fortress of Isca, visitors can marvel at the completely excavated amphitheatre in Britain. The elaborate fortress baths and the only Roman barrack block are also on view. Many of the interesting finds unearthed on the site are displayed in the museum.

There are ancient cromlechs – burial grounds of Neolithic man, throughout Wales from the Preseli hills in the south – where the stones for Stonehenge were hewn – to the Isle of Anglesey in the north.

The National Folk Museum of Wales, near Cardiff, is a fascinating place, a microcosm of old rural Wales. Here, set in one hundred acres of wooded parkland stand houses, cottages and buildings dating back centuries from all over Wales. They have been saved for posterity and reconstructed stone by stone and furnished according to their period.

The buildings range from a working bakery where visitors can buy hotbaked bread to a smithy where a blacksmith can be seen working at his forge.

Other museums in Wales specialize in a variety of subjects ranging from motorbikes to military and maritime history. There's even a small museum dedicated to Dylan Thomas, Wales's most famous 20th century poet and another to that famous Welsh politician, Lloyd George.

Industries which once brought wealth and employment to Wales now provide visitors with a fascinating insight into a bygone age. There are many excellent interpretive centres to remind visitors of this heritage.

Visitors can take a trip into a gold mine first worked by the Romans, go down into the bowels of a coal mine, visit the slate mines and caverns carved by Victorian miners or marvel at the natural beauty in the largest underground show caves in western Europe, which are situated in the Swansea Valley in the south.

Wales is a mecca for those interested in the arts and crafts, and there are numerous centres where visitors can see traditional skills being used to produce handmade merchandise of the highest quality.

There are many exciting and unusual places to see like the Centre of Alternate Technology near Machynlleth, a 'green' self sufficient village of the future, where energy saving ideas have been developed, and subsequently used worldwide; the world famous magical 'Italianate' village of Portmeirion created by Sir Clough Williams-Ellis; the spa towns of Wales where visitors can still take the waters, or the vast Dinorwig Pumped Storage Power Station concealed inside a mountain in North Wales.

Another 'speciality' of Wales is the narrow gauge railways. The Great Little Trains of Wales offer memorable rides on steam trains through areas of outstanding natural beauty. You can even travel 3,000 feet to the summit of Snowdon – the highest peak in Britain, south of Scotland – on one of these trains.

HOLIDAY COMFORTS

Good food is an essential ingredient of any holiday and the high standard of Welsh cuisine will appeal to the most discerning palates. Given the country's expanse of coastline, seafood is obviously a speciality and diners can enjoy Welsh oysters and lobster, trout and salmon from the rivers, produce from Welsh organic farms and a wide variety of farmhouse cheeses.

The choice of hotel accommodation on offer is wide, ranging from the luxury of a modernised castle, first class modern hotels, beautiful country house hotel and seaside hotels. All accommodation in the Wales Tourist Board brochures has been inspected and verified to ensure high standards.

Wales is easily accessible, with its own airport just outside Cardiff and good road, rail and coach links with the rest of Britain.

THE WALES TOURIST BOARD

For further details about where to go and what to see in Wales contact:

THE WALES TOURIST BOARD,
THE CARDIFF VISITORS' CENTRE,
UNITS 3–6,
BRIDGE STREET,
CARDIFF CF1 2EE
Telephone: (0222) 227281

Or call at the nearest Tourist Information Centre.

TREFEDDIAN HOTEL

Aberdovey, Gwynedd LL35 OSB

Telephone: (065 472) 213

London 215, Birmingham 111, Manchester 110, Dolgellau 24, Barmouth 34, Harlech 45, Machynlleth 11, Talyllyn & Cader Idris 14

F licence; 46 en suite bedrooms, all with colour TV; lift; drying room; children welcome; baby listening; dogs welcome by arrangement but not in public rooms; games room, with badminton court, pool table, table tennis; indoor heated swimming pool and solarium; putting green; tennis court; golf; sea bathing; boating; fishing nearby; garage.

The Trefeddian Hotel stands in its own grounds, away from the main road, and is one mile from the middle of Aberdovey, a town with many attractions and which is becoming a centre where everyone, particularly the young, can pursue many outdoor activities. For example, supervision and special instruction can be arranged for sailing, to mention one of the activities available. The Directors, Mr. and Mrs. John Cave and Mr. Peter Cave, are responsible for the running of this first class family hotel, which has all the amenities that are part of a splendid holiday. The lounges are spacious, relaxing and peaceful. The bedrooms, with views of Cardigan Bay, are comfortable and elegantly decorated. The menus offer a good choice of interesting and nicely presented dishes, complemented by a well chosen wine list. The Trefeddian is in the immediate vicinity of a four mile stretch of sandy beach and overlooks the golf course with the ever changing view of the sea beyond. The courtesy and efficiency of the staff create a happy atmosphere. Dinner, bed and breakfast from £34.00 per person, inclusive of VAT. Weekly terms, mini breaks, reductions for children and golfers, all shown on tariff sent, with brochure, on application. Open 23rd March to 2nd January (including Christmas and New Year), but office always open.

CRAIG-Y-DDERWEN COUNTRY HOUSE HOTEL

Betws-y-Coed, Gwynedd, North Wales LL24 0AS

Telephone: (06902) 293 *Fax: 06902 362*

London 217, Llangollen 20

R & R licence; 18 bedrooms, one adapted for disabled guests, all with en suite bathrooms; telephone and television; room and night service; baby listening; last orders for dinner 8.30 p.m.; special diets; children welcome; dogs allowed; conferences up to 60; golf, riding, shooting and fishing all nearby; hotel open all year except January; Access and Visa accepted.

The Craig-y-Dderwen Country House Hotel is located in five acres of wooded grounds, on the river bank, where the iron bridge crosses the river Conwy in Betws-y-Coed. Built as a private house in 1890 and converted to a hotel in the 1920's, it then became a base for secret operations during the War. The composer Elgar, is known to have relaxed here, on the riverbank. The house has been carefully and sympathetically restored by the proprietors, Mel and Megan Evans, who have retained all the original features of the building. Most rooms have superb views of the river, particularly from the Terrace restaurant. Much thought and care has gone into the bedroom décor; all rooms are spacious and pretty, and have excellent en suite facilities. There are also several attractive four poster suites. Full business facilities are available for small conferences and residential courses. The cuisine is imaginative with seasonal variations from the repertoire of the chef-proprietor, using only the freshest ingredients. I found the menus very original and exciting. Betws-y-Coed is a wonderfully scenic area with many outdoor pursuits, including rock climbing, or you can take a trip on the mountain railway and visit the famous Portmeirion village. Room and breakfast from £35.00, or weekly from £210.00.

GWYDYR HOTEL

Betws-y-Coed, Gwynedd,
North Wales LL24 0AB

Telephone: (069 02) 777, Visitors: 641/642 *Fax: 069 02 777*

London 217, Bangor 21, Caernarfon 23, Colwyn Bay 17, Rhyl 26, Dolgellau 33

F licence; 20 bedrooms all en suite, with telephone, colour TV; full central heating; late meals to 9.00 p.m.; diets; children welcome; dogs accepted; conferences up to 50; sauna, solarium; fishing – hotel controls 20 miles of trout and salmon fishing; golf and riding nearby; Visa and Access credit cards accepted.

Gwydyr Hotel, situated in the village of Betws-y-Coed, is surrounded by some of the most picturesque scenery in North Wales. Full of character and atmosphere, it is owned and run by David and Owen Wainwright, who are very experienced hoteliers. Under the 'Heart of Wales Hotels' the Wainwright family also own the 'Tyn-y-Coed' at Capel Curig, and the 'Eagles Hotel' at Llanrwst, all different but all noted for their hospitality, comfort, friendly atmosphere, excellent food, good wine and willing service. The Gwydyr is particularly well known to people who find their greatest pleasure in fishing. Visitors will be enthralled by the 20 miles of rivers and lakes belonging to the hotel, which are carefully controlled and supervised. The public rooms are attractive, comfortably furnished and well appointed. I can highly recommend Gwydyr for a wonderful holiday in superb surroundings, all the year round. Room and breakfast from £21.00 single, £42.00 twin, inclusive of VAT. Other terms on application. Always open.

SOUGHTON HALL

Northop, Nr. Chester, Clwyd, N. Wales CH7 6AB

Telephone: (035 286) 811 Telex: 61267 SOWTON Fax: 035 286 382

Chester 11, Manchester 45, Liverpool 25

R licence; 12 en suite bedrooms, all with radio, telephone, TV; full central heating; night service; meals to 10.00 p.m.; private executive meetings and conferences up to 20; billiards; games room; golf by arrangement; riding and fishing nearby; hard tennis court in grounds; shooting; squash, badminton, Deeside Leisure Centre, including ice skating, 4 miles; clay pigeon shooting at Shotton Sealand; Access, Visa, Amex credit cards accepted.

Soughton Hall is one of the finest country houses in Britain, standing in parkland at the end of an impressive avenue of trees. It is furnished to perfection with antiques and fabrics sympathetic to the period. There is every modern convenience without any clash of style. Mr. and Mrs. Rodenhurst and their son, Simon, have successfully achieved a high standard of comfort and elegance, while retaining the authenticity and ambience of the Hall. The staff are efficient yet courteous and friendly, and the food is of the finest quality. Words fail to do justice to this delightful hotel which is a haven for the businessman, historian, gourmet or romantic. I defy anyone to drive down the avenue at night, with the soft lights glowing through the magnificent windows of the Hall, and not wish to stay. I could not recommend this Hotel more strongly – suffice to say that in 16 years of inspecting hotels, Soughton Hall ranks very much at the top of my list. Open all year. Room and breakfast from £48.00 plus VAT per person, double occupancy.

HOTEL SEVENTY DEGREES

Penmaenhead, Colwyn Bay, Clwyd LL29 9LD

Telephone: (0492) 516555 *Telex: 61363* *Fax: 0492 515565*

Liverpool 55, Manchester 78, Chester 41, Snowdonia National Park 17, London 221

F licence; 43 en suite bedrooms (22 ground floor) all with colour TV, direct dial telephone, baby listening, trouser press, hairdryer, tea/coffee making facilities; Honeymoon and Executive suites available; central heating; night service, meals to 10.00 p.m.; diets; children welcome; dogs accepted; conferences; dancing Sats.; sea bathing, sailing/boating, golf, tennis, squash, riding, shooting, fishing all nearby; credit cards accepted.

The Hotel Seventy Degrees is a distinctive hotel, situated high on a cliff top with spectacular sea and mountain views. In an excellent location for touring North Wales and seeing Snowdonia, Conwy Castle and the many attractions of the area, the hotel derives its name from the unusual angle at which it was constructed. The warmth of the hotel and the friendliness of the staff will be immediately obvious on your arrival. The comfortable lounge area is ideal for mid-morning coffee, lunchtime bar snacks, afternoon tea or as a place to gather for drinks before dinner. The award-winning Horizon restaurant with its panoramic sea views offers an excellent choice of menu, creative dishes and a wide-ranging wine list. Each of its 43 en suite bedrooms has a sea view and for those wishing for something extra, the hotel also has a luxurious four-poster suite. With easy access to the A55, major centres such as Chester and Manchester, the hotel is ideally placed for your stay in North Wales, providing ample parking, convenient train travel and a C.A.A. approved helipad. Accommodation and breakfast from £49.00 single, £69.00 twin, including VAT. Open all year.

BRON EIFION COUNTRY HOUSE HOTEL

Criccieth, Gwynedd LL52 0SA

Telephone: (0766) 522385 *Fax: 0766 522003*

London 245, Portmadoc 5, Betws-y-Coed 30, Caernarvon 17, Pwllheli 9

R & R licence; 19 bedrooms (1 ground floor) all en suite; all with telephone, col. TV, tea/coffee making facilities; night service; meals till 9.00 p.m.; diets; children welcome; dogs by arrangement; Boardroom conferences and meetings; functions and receptions; golf, tennis, sea and river bathing, fishing and riding all nearby.

Half a mile westward from Criccieth on the A497, a road sign proclaims Bron Eifion Country House Hotel. Set in five acres of beautiful gardens with woodlands and lakes beyond, interlaced with private paths and carriageways, this 19th century estate offers peace, privacy and gentle relaxation. It is indeed a place for all seasons enjoying a mild pleasant climate with all the beauty spots of Snowdonia and the Lleyn Peninsula within very easy reach. Since 1989, Bron Eifion has been the home of Mr. Bob Lilley who has embarked on a restoration and improvement programme for the hotel. I was shown one of the newly refurbished bedrooms which was most attractive and comfortable. The dining room has large windows overlooking the garden and is a very pleasant light and airy room. Mr. Lilley is aiming to create a restaurant that will be one of the foremost in the area and he is already well on the way to achieving his aim. On chilly evenings log fires in the beautiful panelled galleried hall create a cosy atmosphere to enjoy a pre-dinner drink or after dinner coffee. If you require comfort and good food in beautiful surroundings, go to Bron Eifion, you will want to return again in the various seasons. Weekend breaks are available at special winter terms. Room and breakfast from £37.00 single, £30.00 twin per person. Dinner room and breakfast from £42.00 per person inclusive of service and VAT. Traditional Christmas and New Year breaks. Open all year.

GLIFFAES COUNTRY HOUSE HOTEL

Crickhowell, Powys NP8 1RH

Telephone: Bwlch (0874) 730371 *Fax: 0874 730463*

London 153, Crickhowell 3½, Abergavenny 9½, Brecon 10½

F licence; 22 en suite bedrooms all with self dial telephone; baby listening; children welcome; dogs (but not in hotel); late meals by arrangement; diets; TV room; small conferences up to 25; receptions welcome; salmon and trout fishing; tennis; putting; croquet; full size billiards table in traditional surrounding; golf, riding, hang gliding, sailing and boating all nearby; Amex, Access, Diners and Visa accepted.

Gliffaes provides spacious comfort in the true country house tradition. It stands in 29 acres of parkland and well kept gardens with flowering shrubs and trees which are amongst the rarest and most beautiful to be found in this country. The hotel is situated in the lovely valley of the River Usk, midway between the Brecon Beacons and the Black Mountains, and yet only one mile off the main A40 road. Gliffaes Country House Hotel has been family owned since 1948, and is now under the personal care of Nick and Peta Brabner, two wonderful and experienced people who are doing a great job. They are supported by Nick's mother, Jane Brabner who with her husband Major S. G. Brabner created a home that has an atmosphere of friendliness, informality and high standards. Care is taken to maintain the best of country house cooking. My excellent dinner, chosen from the table d'hôte menu, showed imagination and was well served by the efficient staff (an à la carte menu is also available). There is a good selection of wines. The well-appointed bedrooms, all with their own bathroom or shower, are individual in décor and furnishings. The downstairs rooms are elegantly furnished and comfortable and delicious home-made afternoon teas are thoroughly recommended. Most rooms command views of the surrounding hills and the river running through the wooded valley. The Lodge has now been converted into an annexe, equipped for self catering to a degree. It has a family room and two double bedrooms. Fishing for salmon and trout is provided for on the 2½ miles of the Usk, owned by the hotel and reserved primarily for guests. Room and breakfast from £26.40 to £35.20 per person including service and VAT. Short stay and weekly rates on application. Closed 1st January to mid-March.

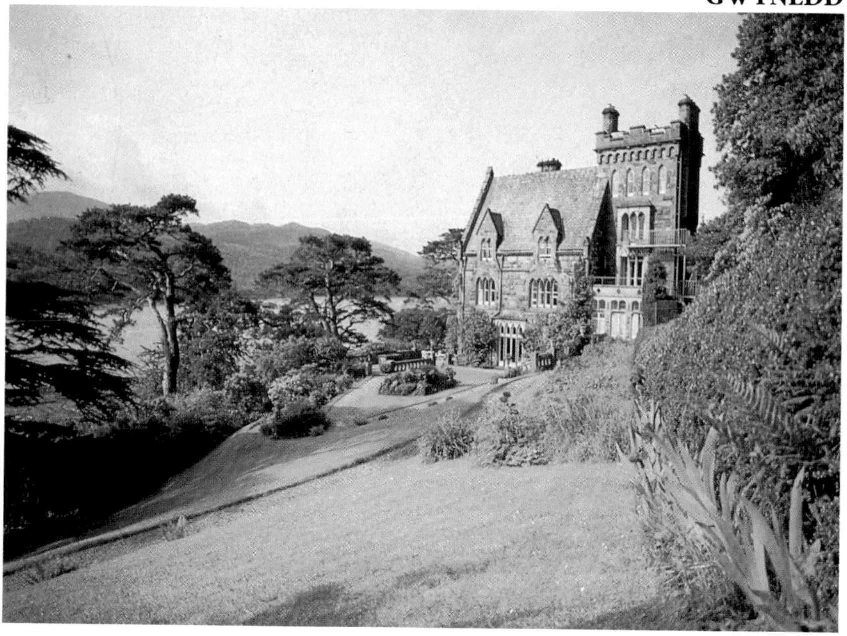

BONTDDU HALL HOTEL

Bontddu, Nr. Dolgellau,
Gwynedd LL40 2SU
Telephone: (0341) 49661 *Fax: 0341 49284*

Barmouth 5, Dolgellau 5, Aberystwyth 35, Caernarfon 50, Birmingham 110, London 235

F licence; 22 en suite bedrooms, all with telephone, colour TV, clock radio, hairdryer, tea/coffee making facilities; central heating; night service to midnight; late meals to 9.30 p.m.; diets; children welcome; dogs welcome; sea bathing, golf and riding all 5 miles; gold mine nearby; Access, Amex, Visa credit cards accepted.

Bontddu Hall, wonderfully situated in 3 acres of landscaped grounds, overlooks fine views of the Mawddach Estuary and famous Cader Idris range of mountains. The unspoilt charm of this attractive Victorian mansion has always made it a favourite of mine, and the owners Margaretta and Michael Ball, know what is good. You will enjoy excellent food from an interesting country house evening dinner menu, dishes are varied and nicely served. Salmon and lobster are a speciality when available. In the Garden Restaurant an appetizing lunch is served and a Special Carvery lunch on Sundays.Here is no hotel atmosphere, for the furniture, pictures, colour schemes and flowers are all reminiscent of a country house and the hotel has been completely refurbished in 1989. All rooms are very comfortable and the ''Princess of Wales'' Bar extends a warm welcome. Nearly all bedrooms are with estuary and mountain views. In the Lodge, above the main drive are some luxurious suites. Space prevents me from telling of the many attractions to be found in the area, I can only recommend a visit, and you will want to come again and again. Room and breakfast from £42.00 (single), £65.00 (twin), inclusive of VAT. Other terms on application. Closed January and February, but office open for enquiries.

GEORGE III HOTEL

Penmaenpool, Nr. Dolgellau, Gwynedd LL40 1YD

Telephone: (0341) 422525 *Fax: 0341 423565*

Shrewsbury 52, Aberdovey 21, Aberystwyth 31, Barmouth via Toll Bridge 7, Betws-y-Coed 36, Chester 56

F licence; 12 bedrooms (5 ground floor) 10 with private bathroom (one with shower only); all with colour TV, tea/coffee making facilities, direct dial telephone, trouser press & hairdryer; limited baby listening (main building only); full central heating; sea bathing 6 miles (Fairbourne); sailing and boating 7 miles; nine hole golf course at Dolgellau, 2 miles; Championship courses at Harlech (16 miles) & Aberdovey (19 miles); fishing outside hotel; tennis, squash, riding all nearby; lovely walks; Visa, Access & Amex cards accepted.

In the shade of Cader Idris (2,929 ft) on the A493 to Tywyn, you will find this 17th-century Inn. The George III Hotel is superbly situated at the head of the magnificent Mawddach Estuary. The main hotel was built circa 1650 and was once two separate buildings. One half was an inn and the other half was a ship's chandler. In the early 1980's, the old Railway Station Master's house, now called the Lodge (some 50 yards from the hotel), was converted into six very comfortable and well appointed bedrooms with private bathrooms. The owner of this splendid hotel, Ms Gail Hall is a charming young lady with a vast amount of experience and good ideas. Four bedrooms in the hotel are now en suite and most attractive, one bedroom has a shower only. The George III maintains its high reputation for good food, specialising in local duck, pheasant, lobster, seatrout and salmon which is beautifully cooked and served well. Bar luncheons are available in the Welsh Dresser Bar and during the summer months, the Cellar Bar provides toasted sandwiches, pizzas and an assortment of salads served buffet-style. All the rooms are comfortable and nicely furnished; in the entrance lounge there is a particularly fine old open fire place. Room and breakfast from £45.00 double per night; there are no single rooms, so single occupancy of a double room without private bathroom from £26.00 per night (plus 10% service). Other terms on application including special winter breaks. Closed Christmas and New Year.

Allt-yr-afon

WOLFSCASTLE COUNTRY HOTEL AND RESTAURANT

Wolfscastle, Nr. Haverfordwest, Dyfed SA62 5LZ

Telephone: (0437 87) 225/688 *Fax: 0437 87 383*

London 270, Cardiff 103, St. Davids 17, Haverfordwest 7, Fishguard 7, Swansea 70

R and R licence; 15 en suite bedrooms, all with colour TV, tea making facilities; central heating; meals to 9.30 p.m.; diets; children welcome; dogs accepted; en-tout-cas all weather tennis court; 2 squash courts; riding 5 miles, 30 horse indoor school; bathing, sailing and golf 7 miles; Amex, Visa and Master Card accepted.

This attractive Country House is situated just off the main A40, Haverfordwest to Fishguard road, at Wolfscastle. It is owned and personally cared for by Andrew and Pauline Stirling, who are both very experienced and efficient. There is a warm and friendly atmosphere about this pleasant house. The downstairs rooms are attractive with a fine dining room and bar and the comfortable residents drawing room is upstairs. The bedrooms have a certain charm and are well appointed. Andrew Stirling has a great reputation for good food and choice wines. The kitchen under the care of Steve Brown produces menus that are interesting and imaginative, food is carefully prepared with traditional, as well as more adventurous dishes and fresh fish caught locally is amongst their specialities. There is now a new marquee style banqueting suite used for Musical, Jazz and Welsh nights and occasional dinner dances. Gourmet Nights are featured every month. Wolfscastle is within easy reach of the sandy bays of Pembrokeshire, the Coast Path, and the lovely Prescelli hills. Room and breakfast from £30.00 single, £50.00 double including VAT. 10% discount on stays of four nights or more. Other terms on application. Open all year.

THE HAND HOTEL

Llanarmon Dyffryn Ceiriog,
Llangollen, Clwyd LL20 7LD

Telephone: Llanarmon D.C. (069 176) 666 *Fax: 069 176 262*

Turn off A5 at Chirk on B4500 for 11 miles to Llanarmon DC
London 184, Chirk 11, Gobowen 13, Oswestry 9½, Wrexham 21

F licence; 14 en suite bedrooms (4 ground floor); children welcome; drying room; TV; radio; full central heating; diets; peace; dogs by arrangement; small conferences; fire certificate; golf course 15 miles; all weather tennis court, pony trekking by arrangement; fishing; shooting parties catered for; Amex, Access, Diners and Barclaycard accepted.

The Hand Hotel at Llanarmon D.C. has recently been acquired by new owners, Melvin and Lilian Brunton. They are very keen to uphold the reputation of this lovely 16th century hotel, situated in a tiny, picturesque village at the head of the Ceiriog Valley, close to the Berwyn Mountains. The bedrooms have all the modern fittings for comfort and luxury, and each has its own private bathroom. There is also a suite for that special weekend, honeymoon or holiday, which has a double-bedded room, private bathroom and its own lounge with colour television. Another new and excellent feature is the attractive Griffin Room, ideal for private parties or small conferences. The hotel has always specialised in very good food; great attention is given to the cooking and presentation, all complemented by a selection of choice wines in the well-stocked cellar. Here, in the heart of the quiet Welsh hills, you can relax in luxury, far away from the bustle of modern life, and enjoy the atmosphere of old-world charm – would that there were more places like this cosy and well-kept hotel. Room and breakfast from £41.00 single, £64.00 double, inclusive of VAT. Other terms on application, including special rates for weekend or mid week breaks. Open mid-March–1st February.

THE WEST ARMS HOTEL

Llanarmon Dyffryn Ceiriog,
Nr. Llangollen, Clwyd LL20 7LD

Telephone: (069 176) 665

Turn off A5 at Chirk on B4500 for 11 miles to Llanarmon DC
Chester 34, Shrewsbury 34, Birmingham 82, Liverpool 62, Manchester 75

F licence; 14 en suite bedrooms (3 ground floor) including 2 suites, colour TV in suites; full central heating; meals till 9.00 p.m.; diets; children welcome; baby listening; dogs accepted; receptions and conferences for 30 welcome; trout fishing; riding by arrangement; shooting parties catered for; tennis nearby; golf: 3 courses ½ hrs drive; major credit cards accepted; lovely walks; wonderful area for painting; National Trust properties in area.

Llanarmon Dyffryn Ceiriog is a small picturesque village of considerable charm situated at the head of one of the loveliest valleys in North Wales, high on the Berwyns, 900 feet above sea level. Owners Tim and Carolyn Alexander have made a really fine job of refurbishing and renovating this comfortable and well run hotel, rediscovering many of the beautiful original beams which the Victorians painstakingly covered up when they modernised it! It is now intelligently revived and pleasantly furnished and there is a warm and friendly atmosphere. The new bedrooms are quite outstanding, charming and well appointed. This is an ideal rendezvous for all ages with a good choice of interesting food, complemented by well chosen wines. Llanarmon DC is a good centre for exploring North and Mid-Wales with many notable National Trust properties and places of interest. There are lovely walks in the beautiful surrounding countryside. Room and breakfast from £45.00 (single), £70.00 (double) including VAT. Other terms on application including short and weekly breaks. Always open.

TYDDYN LLAN COUNTRY HOUSE HOTEL AND RESTAURANT

Llandrillo, Nr. Corwen, Clwyd LL21 0ST

Telephone: (049084) 264 *Fax: 049084 264*

Bala 8, Llangollen 15, Corwen 4½

R & R licence; 10 bedrooms all with en suite bathrooms; direct dial telephone; room and night service; baby listening; last orders for dinner 9.30 p.m.; bar meals; special diets; children welcome; dogs allowed (but not in public rooms); small conferences; private 1½ mile stretch for fishing; shooting can be arranged; riding, sailing & boating nearby; golf in Bala and Llangollen; hotel open all year; Access and Visa accepted.

This elegant Georgian Country House Hotel is situated peacefully on the outskirts of Llandrillo village near Corwen. Tyddyn Llan is a superb hotel efficiently and pleasantly run by the owners, Peter and Bridget Kindred, and nothing is too much trouble for them in adding to the comfort of their guests. Peter's flair for design is very evident, his style and originality make use of many antiques, period furniture and interesting objets d'art. Bedrooms are all very individual, having en suite facilities, and lovely views of the Berwyn Mountains. Croquet may be played in the gardens, and an attractive water garden has recently been added. The hotel has its own private fishing. Bala Lake is close by and enthusiasts can enjoy wind surfing, sailing and canoeing. Riding, golf, guided walks and pony trekking can easily be arranged. There are facilities too, for small executive conferences. Bridget is justifiably proud of the food in the hotel and recently relinquished the cooking to David Barratt, a chef of enormous flair and originality. I cannot praise the meals I had too highly; all were beautifully cooked and presented. The wine list too, was superlative. I know that you will love visiting this hotel as much as I do. Room and breakfast from £30.00 per night, or weekly from £308.00, also including dinner.

GOGARTH ABBEY

West Shore, Llandudno, Gwynedd LL30 2QY

Telephone: (0492) 76211

London 228, Chester 46, Betws-y-Coed 18

F licence; 40 en suite bedrooms all with colour TV, telephone, radio, tea and coffee making facilities; central heating; dinner served to 8.30 p.m.; indoor heated swimming pool, sauna, solarium, games area, outdoor putting and croquet; bathing, boating and riding nearby; most credit cards accepted.

Although set on Llandudno's West Shore, this well appointed hotel really comes into the country house category, standing as it does in its own spacious grounds with unimpaired views of the Snowdonia range, the Conwy estuary and the Isle of Anglesey. It is interesting to note that this imposing house was formerly the summer residence of the Rev. Henry George Liddell in 1862, and it was here that Charles Dodgson, otherwise Lewis Carroll, was inspired to write 'Alice in Wonderland' and 'Alice Through The Looking Glass' for Liddell's daughter. Today, the attractive Liddell Restaurant is the setting for an imaginative cuisine, made even more enjoyable by attentive service. There are four beautifully appointed lounges, where guests may relax and take in the views, and a pleasant cocktail bar. Bedrooms are well equipped and decorated in tasteful style. All have private facilities, colour TV, radio, telephone, minibar and tea/coffee makers. The hotel has a heated indoor swimming pool, with a games area, and within the grounds you will find a putting green and croquet lawn. Within easy reach are a dry-ski slope and two championship golf courses. Mini-breaks, Golfing, Christmas and New Year Breaks are available. Open all year, room and breakfast from £35.00 single, £65.00 twin.

CARREG BRÂN HOTEL

Llanfairpwllgwyngyll, Anglesey, Gwynedd LL61 5YH

Telephone: (0248) 714224 *Telex: 61464 Cabran G* *Fax: 0248 715938*

London 240, Manchester 89, Liverpool 73, Holyhead 20, Birmingham 129

F licence; 33 en suite bedrooms (2 ground floor) all with direct dial telephone, col. TV, hairdryer & trouser press; full central heating; night service; meals to 10 p.m.; bar meals; diets; children welcome; baby listening; dogs accepted; conferences 150 max.; functions & receptions; dancing when required; sea bathing, sailing, boating, golf, tennis, squash, badminton all nearby; riding, shooting & fishing by arrangement; all major credit cards accepted.

This attractive and interesting hotel was introduced to me by friends who enjoy good living and tasteful, comfortable places. An enjoyable, all too short stay confirmed their views. On crossing the Britannia Bridge, over to the Isle of Anglesey, the Carreg Brân is situated immediately left off the slip road, on the outskirts of the village, well known world-wide as 'Llanfairpwllgwyngyllgogerychwyrndrogwlllantysiliogogogoch', no further comment necessary. This friendly hotel with a nice atmosphere is personally cared for by the owners, Captain R. H. and Mrs. N. Edwards, supported by staff who are attentive, efficient and cheerful. Carreg Brân has recently been refurbished to a high standard, the bedrooms are comfortable and well appointed. The attractively decorated restaurant offers excellent food. I enjoyed the table d'hôte menu which offered a wonderful choice of imaginative dishes perfectly cooked and well presented and this was complemented by a fine selection of wines. Nestling close to the banks of the Menai Strait, outside activities are numerous, sailing, windsurfing and golf are all within easy reach as are local places of interest including the castles of Beaumaris, Caernarfon and Conwy. Room and breakfast from £42.00 per person inclusive of VAT. Other terms on application. Open all year.

BODFACH HALL COUNTRY HOUSE HOTEL

Llanfyllin, Powys SY22 5HS

Telephone: (069184) 272

London 3-3½ hrs, Leeds 3-3½ hrs, Liverpool 1½ hrs, West Midlands 1½ hrs

F licence; 9 en suite bedrooms with TV; room service; last orders for dinner 20.45, bar meals; special diets; children welcome; dogs accepted; leisure centre, squash court, golf & tennis nearby; credit cards accepted; open all year.

Bodfach Hall Country House Hotel can be found at the end of the A490 just ¼ mile off the Oswestry to Lake Vyrnwy Road. Four acres of mature and sheltered gardens contain many interesting trees and shrubs. Parts of the house date back to the 17th century, although there has been a building on the site since the 12th century. There are many fine stained glass windows, and all periods of the building are sympathetically interwoven in this lovely old house. The morning room, where Breakfast is served, has a spectacular painted relief ceiling and the drawing room an 18th century moulded ceiling and fine marble fireplaces. The main Dining Room is panelled with oak. There is a sun room with terrace and a large lounge bar. Most bedrooms have wonderful views and all are en suite, with either bath or shower. The dining room is oak panelled and a four course table d'hôte dinner is offered, as well as a wide range of à la carte dishes, with wines being very reasonably priced. There is plenty to see and do, walking, climbing, sketching, and there are three golf courses to choose from, as well as tennis courts and a sports centre in nearby Llanfyllin. The Gray family feel that peace and comfort are important for their guests, and this they easily achieve. Tariff from £27.50. Weekly from £225.00.

THE LAKE COUNTRY HOUSE HOTEL

Llangammarch Wells, Powys LD4 4BS

Telephone: (05912) 202 *Fax: 05912 457*

London 180, Shrewsbury 75, Cardiff 60, Llanwrtyd 5, Builth Wells 8

F licence; 20 en suite bedrooms (including 13 suites), all with direct dial telephone and colour TV; central heating; meals to 8.45 p.m.; diets; children welcome; well behaved dogs welcome; billiards room; own 9 hole golf course; hard tennis court; putting green; 3 acre trout lake; fishing 5½ miles, River Irfon (salmon and trout); clay pigeon shooting; riding nearby; 50 acres of lovely grounds; Barclay, Access and Amex credit cards accepted.

From the rooms of this attractive Hotel, you can look down over terraced lawns to the river Irfon. To the right, bordered by fine trees is the lake – stocked with trout – from which the place derives its name. In a beautiful setting, this peaceful hotel is efficiently run by the owners, Jean Pierre and Jan Mifsud, who have created a warm and friendly atmosphere. The Lake Hotel is a country house of distinction, reflected in its furnishings and appointments, soft and restful colour schemes that are most complementary. Downstairs the rooms are spacious and elegant, and the bedrooms are most luxurious and well appointed. The food is excellent, superbly cooked with imaginative dishes full of individuality and artistry; Jean Pierre has a fine team. The menu is changed daily, and the presentation of each dish is outstanding. The accent is on "home made from fresh produce", and cheerful and efficient service. There is an excellent wine list of around 300 wines with most clarets listed. Light lunches are available. A haven for bird watchers. Room and breakfast from £40.00 per person, inc. VAT and service. Other terms on application including special winter and weekend breaks. Open all year.

F licence; 17 bedrooms, 16 with private bathrooms or showers; full central heating; late meals to 9.00 p.m. or later by arrangement; diets; children welcome; dogs by arrangement; fishing, tennis, sea bathing, sailing, boating, golf and indoor swimming pool all nearby; riding and shooting 6 miles; squash and badminton 8 miles; Barclaycard, Visa and Access credit cards accepted.

THE ANGLESEY ARMS HOTEL

Menai Bridge, Anglesey, Gwynedd LL59 5EA

Telephone: (0248) 712305

Manchester 125, London 250, Birmingham 135, Glasgow 260, Liverpool 60, Edinburgh 300

As I cross over the famous and historic Telford Suspension Bridge, which I have done many times, I have always noticed and admired the Anglesey Arms Hotel, which stands at the gateway to the Isle of Anglesey. The hotel is set in delightful secluded gardens and commands superb views of the Menai Straits, against a backcloth of the Snowdonia Mountain range. It boasts a long history dating back to the days of horse travel with stables adjoining the hotel. Today the hotel offers a high standard of comfort and service, having been refurbished throughout and much thought has been given to little details that matter so much. The Anglesey Arms makes a good stopping off place, if "en route" for the car ferry at Holyhead and thence to Ireland. The public rooms are nicely furnished and comfortable, as are the bedrooms. The Lounge Bar is attractive with a friendly atmosphere, created by the Manager and his staff who give you a warm welcome to this hotel. Room and breakfast from £32.00 (single), £50.00 (double). Other terms on application. Ample car park. Open all year.

THE CROWN AT WHITEBROOK

Whitebrook, Nr. Monmouth, Gwent NP5 4TX

Telephone: (0600) 860254 *Fax: 0600 860607*

Monmouth 5, Wye Valley 1, Tintern 7, Chepstow 12, M4 (Junc. 22) 12

Situated in Whitebrook Valley between A466 and B4239
5 miles south of Monmouth

F licence; 12 bedrooms, all with en suite bathroom, telephone and TV; room service; baby listening; last orders for dinner 9.00 p.m.; bar meals 12.00–2.00 p.m.; special diets; children welcome; dogs accepted; conferences up to 12; tennis, riding, shooting and fishing 2 miles; golf 5 miles; hotel open all year except 2 weeks in January; all major credit cards accepted.

This delightful little hotel is situated in the narrow, wooded Whitebrook valley, on the edge of Tintern Forest. It is ideally placed for fishing on the River Wye, in an area of Outstanding Natural Beauty, and it is just a short drive from the Brecon Beacons National Park. The beautiful and historic town of Monmouth is also nearby to explore for yourself. The Resident Proprietors, Roger and Sandra Bates have created an exceptionally warm and friendly atmosphere and many guests return time after time. The restaurant, specializing in French cuisine, serves many original dishes, with the emphasis on fresh, local ingredients. It enjoys a high reputation over a wide area, so it is always advisable to book well in advance. There is an interesting selection of fine wines from the cellar, with which you can complement your meal. The hotel has twelve comfortable bedrooms, all with en suite bathroom and televisions, and one of the rooms features a four poster bed. Other luxuries, such as radio alarms and hairdryers also prove very useful, whether you are here on business or pleasure. Central heating can be controlled by guests from their own rooms. There is the small, executive Aubry Room which is available for meetings of up to twelve delegates. Tariff on application.

LLYNDIR HALL HOTEL

Llyndir Lane, Rossett, Clwyd LL12 0AY

Telephone: (0244) 571648 *Fax: 0244 571648*

Manchester Airport 40, Chester Railway 5, Mold 10, Wrexham 4

F licence; 38 bedrooms, disabled and non-smoking rooms available, all with en suite bathroom, TV and telephone; room and night service; last orders for dinner 10.00 p.m.; bar meals; no dogs; conferences up to 150; indoor heated swimming pool; steam room, spa pool, and solarium; trymnasium; golf, riding, tennis, shooting and fishing nearby; hotel open all year; all major credit cards accepted.

Ideally situated mid-way between Chester and Wrexham, Llyndir Hall is one of those rare hotels that offers the best of a first class country house, subtly combined with the facilities of a modern international one. For example, the main house has individually decorated, comfortable bedrooms, furnished with antiques and with every convenience, whereas the new wing has, amongst many other amenities, a superb leisure centre. All the public rooms are, again, most tastefully decorated and furnished, an elegant backdrop to the wonderful food served here at Llyndir. The restaurant, which has built up a most deserved reputation for its cuisine, offers a range of dishes prepared from the finest ingredients, perfectly cooked and beautifully presented. Coupled with the excellent service and friendly atmosphere, a meal here is a memorable experence. For anyone visiting this lovely area, or indeed, for anyone considering holding a conference (for which there are special terms), I cannot recommend this hotel too highly. A hotel such as this is not too easily discovered but it is easy to enjoy and very hard to leave. Tariff on application.

ST. NONS HOTEL

St. David's, Dyfed SA62 6RJ

Telephone: (0437) 720239 *Fax: 0437 721839*

London 264, Birmingham 177, Cardigan 38, Carmarthen 45, Fishguard 16, Haverfordwest 16, Pembroke dock 25

F licence; 24 en suite bedrooms (5 ground floor) all with telephone, TV, tea/coffee making facilities, full central heating; meals to 9.00 p.m.; diets available; children welcome; lunch time bar meals; dogs welcome; residents drawing room; drying room; own laundry; sea bathing; boating; riding by arrangement; pony trekking; 9 hole golf course nearby with free golf for hotel residents.

There is a welcoming atmosphere at this friendly hotel, personally supervised by the proprietor, Sandy Falconer who is well versed in the art of good hotel keeping. Situated on the outskirts of St. David's, the hotel is near to St. David's Cathedral and the picturesque ruins of the Bishop's Palace. The bedrooms, overlooking lovely views of the countryside, are pleasant, and include all the necessary appointments. St. Nons is particularly noted for its food and wine. Fresh foods are used with locally caught fish, crab and lobster among their specialities, all complemented by a wine list of over 80 wines. Guests will delight in the area's natural beauty – within easy reach of beaches, island bird sanctuaries such as Skokholm and Ramsey islands, and the coastal path of the Pembrokeshire National Park. Room and breakfast from £29.50 per person, dinner bed and breakfast from £41.00, inclusive of VAT. Other terms on application including out of season breaks, and special programme for Christmas and New Year. Always open.

WARPOOL COURT HOTEL

St. Davids, Pembrokeshire SA62 6BN

Telephone: (0437) 720300 *Fax: 0437 720676*

London 264, Birmingham 177, Bristol 142, Carmarthen 46, Fishguard 16, Haverfordwest 16, Milford Haven 23, Pembroke dock 25

F licence; 25 en suite bedrooms all with telephone, colour TV with built in hotel feature film system, 4 channel radio, room call & baby listening, tea/coffee making facilities; family rooms; full central heating; meals to 9.30 p.m.; diets; children welcome; dogs accepted; Leisure complex consisting of snooker room, table tennis, gymnasium and sauna, pool table, heated covered swimming pool; all weather tennis court; 9 hole golf course nearby; sea bathing; sandy beaches; lovely walks; major credit cards accepted.

The Warpool Court is sited in a wonderful position overlooking the wild Atlantic and within a few minutes walk of the famous St. David's Cathedral. This splendid Country House Hotel, with its unique collection of antique tiles, has been recommended by *Signpost* for a long time. It is owned by Peter Trier and through his expertise you can be assured of good food, gracious living and a warm welcome from him and his staff. The colour schemes are soft and restful and the staff cheerful and efficient. The hotel has a high reputation for good food and a fine selection of well chosen wines. The à la carte and four course table d'hôte menus are excellent and whenever possible local produce is used. The lounge bar provides a relaxed atmosphere for diners and the residents' lounge ensures peace and comfort. Outdoor activities are numerous and interesting. Room and breakfast from £40.00 (single), £70.00 (twin) inclusive of VAT. Other terms on application including 'Country House Breaks'. Full Christmas and New Year packages. Open all year.

TYNYCORNEL HOTEL
Tal-y-llyn, Tywyn, Gwynedd LL36 9AJ

Telephone: (0654) 77282

London 212, Birmingham 110, Chester 72, Cardiff 132

F licence; 15 bedrooms all with en suite bathroom, TV and telephone; room service; baby listening; last orders for dinner 9.30 p.m.; bar meals 12.30–2.00 p.m.; special diets; children welcome; dogs accepted; conferences up to 35–40; outdoor heated swimming pool; sauna and solarium; shooting and fishing; sea bathing within easy reach; leisure centre, squash courts, tennis 10 miles; golf 14 miles; riding by arrangement; hotel open all year; Visa, Master Card, Amex and Diners cards accepted.

The Tynycornel enjoys a delightful situation on the edge of Tal-y-llyn lake where fishing is available to residents at a reduced rate. Lake Bugeilyn and the nearby river Dysynni may also be fished for wild brown trout, sea trout and salmon. Situated in Snowdonia National Park, Tal-y-llyn's 222 acres of natural waters form part of some of the most beautiful scenery in Wales. The hotel owns six quiet motorised boats and provides everything for the fisherman including freezing facilities, tackle hire and expert advice to novice and experienced fisherman alike. A modern heated outdoor swimming pool, sauna and solarium are available to guests. There are fifteen attractively decorated bedrooms, twelve of them on the ground floor. All are en suite, and enjoy magnificent views of the lake and surrounding mountains. The spacious lounge is furnished with antiques, original prints and window seats overlooking the lake. The bars are cosy and quiet. Both table d'hôte and à la carte menus are offered in the restaurant, and the cuisine is excellent, and supported by a well chosen wine list. Room and breakfast from £34.50, weekly rates from £213.50 per person.

FOURCROFT HOTEL

The Croft, Tenby, Dyfed SA70 8AP

Telephone: (0834) 2886 *Fax: 0834 2888*

Carmarthen 27, Swansea 54, London 240

R & R licence; 38 bedrooms all with en suite bathroom; telephone and television; room and night service; baby listening; lift; last orders 8.30 p.m.; bar meals; special diets; children welcome; dogs accepted; games room; snooker and billiards; outdoor heated swimming pool; leisure centre; sauna and spa pool; gymnasium; sea bathing; golf and tennis nearby; riding, shooting and fishing close by; hotel closed in winter; Access and Visa cards accepted.

Fourcroft Hotel was originally three private houses, built in the Regency Period. With stunning views from its cliff top vantage point, it overlooks Carmarthen Bay and the old fishing harbour. It is ideally situated, and has its own private path to the sandy beach, through beautifully kept, terraced gardens. Just a few minutes' walk from the centre of the delightful old walled town of Tenby, Fourcroft is on a quiet no-through-road which is part of the 170 mile Pembrokeshire National Park coastal footpath. Three generations of the Osborne family have run the hotel over a period of 45 years and it is now under the personal supervision of Mr and Mrs Peter Osborne and their friendly and helpful staff. The modern leisure complex is an added attraction with heated swimming pool and pretty sun terrace; the first aerofitness unit in Wales is amongst its many amenities. The bedrooms are comfortable, all have en suite bathrooms, television and tea and coffee machines; many also have lovely views across the bay. The dining room serves a varied menu, which changes daily, making use of fresh ingredients and local Welsh produce. Room and breakfast from £32.00, and weekly dinner, bed and breakfast from £235.00.

CWRT BLEDDYN HOTEL AND COUNTRY CLUB

Tredunnock, Nr. Usk, Gwent NP5 1PG

Telephone: (063349) 521 *Fax: 063349 220*

Cardiff 12, Bristol 25, London 140

F licence; 36 en suite bedrooms (13 ground floor), all with telephone, colour TV and full central heating; 24 hour night service; last orders 10.30 p.m.; coffee shop; bar meals; diets; children welcome, baby listening; no dogs; conferences up to 200; games room; regular dancing; billiards; indoor heated swimming pool; sauna and solarium; steam room and fitness room; leisure centre; 2 tennis courts and squash; golf, riding, fishing, sailing and boating nearby; shooting on request; Master Card, Visa, Diners' and Amex accepted.

The Cwrt Bleddyn is in a lovely location, set in 17 acres of grounds and gardens, amidst the beautiful countryside of Usk. The original manor house, dating from the 17th century has been extended over the years to create a country house hotel, offering traditional hospitality and every modern comfort. There is a lot to do and see in this picturesque part of Wales; Roman ruins, Medieval castles and abbeys and the Brecon Beacons are all within easy reach, waiting to be explored. The excellent, recently opened country club facilities are available to residents, and include an indoor swimming pool, gymnasium, steam room, sauna, solarium, snooker room, tennis and squash courts. Nicholl's Restaurant has a very good reputation in the area, and serves French influenced cuisine, based on fresh local produce, and game when in season. The bedrooms are furnished to a high standard, with everything the discerning guest could wish for, and several have jacuzzi baths and four poster beds. Tariff on application. Open all year.

SCOTLAND

CASTING A SCOTTISH SPELL

It is no wonder that the Scots are so very proud of their country. Whether travelling by road or rail, the scenery is quite breathtaking. Although you may not be able to please yourself exactly where you go, a trip on British Rail's 'West Highlander' or 'Orcadian' is a delight. The former travels up the West Coast to Fort William and Mallaig and the latter right to the very far north of the country to such romantic sounding places as the Kyle of Lochalsh and the Isle of Skye. On board the trains, the service and food is very good indeed and an expert commentator points out to the traveller all the places of interest en route.

The Lothians, Borders and the Kingdom of Fife offer an attractive blend of tangy sea air, rounded Border hills, mellow villages and pleasant farmlands – every scene has its own personality and are within easy reach of Edinburgh, Scotland's capital and a natural focus for visitors, with its unique blend of dramatic skyline and history, culture and entertainment.

Fife's finest golf courses and picturesque villages lie between fields golden in the autumn, and beaches golden all year round. The valley of the Forth saw some of the earliest industrial developments in Scotland and has some fascinating legacies. Beyond East Lothian's endless beaches is green countryside with attractive red-roofed villages and the backdrop of the Lammermuir Hills – the start of the uplands which roll to the Border. The very best of this distinctive scenery lies close to Edinburgh, making it a natural centre for exploring south-east Scotland. A good road network means easy access – while even the Forth Bridges, road and rail, linking the Lothians to Fife, are an attraction particularly impressive from South Queensferry.

The area has a great variety in its towns and villages: St. Andrews and the East Neuk villages with their old European trading links; or Culcross, a restored 18th century burgh. Bo'ness preserves its Victorian heritage and features a recreation of a typical Scottish railway branch line. Beyond Musselburgh, the largest town in East Lothian, visitors will discover many picturesque communities – such as North Berwick, tucked below Berwick Law by the edge of the sea, attracting sailors, golfers and seaside-lovers; or Haddington, which recaptures the spirit of a Georgian burgh in its harmonious architecture. Each of the border towns also has its own personality and traditions, expressed in the Common Riding ceremonies. The unique atmosphere of such towns as Hawick, Galashiels, Selkirk and Montrose, owes much to this blending of the past with present day activities, such as the production of high quality woollen goods.

For sheer excitement, Edinburgh has its own brand of magic. Perhaps it is the unmistakable outline of its castle, perhaps the inspiring positioning of Princes Street, with its airy views across the gardens. It might be the grandeur of its neo-classical architecture or the sense of history in its Old Town. Whatever the reason, the city is an inspiring place, not just at Festival time, but throughout the year.

The Northern Highlands and Islands have good roads and easy communications, making them much closer than you might at first think. The mainland is excellent touring country, with the roads fanning out from Inverness, the Highland capital, like the spokes of a wheel, though there are also roads round the rim – the spectacular coastline to north and west. Reaching the islands is also easy: Aberdeen, Shetland and Scrabster near Thurso and John o' Groats for Orkney. To reach the Outer Hebrides, there is further choice: to Lewis (Stornaway) but way of Ullapool in Western Ross, Harris (Tarbert) by way of Uig on Skye, which is also the departure point for North Uist (Lochmaddy). South Uist (Lochboisdale) and Barra (Castlebay) are reached by way of Oban in Argyll. The nearest island to the mainland is Skye, just a few minutes by way of the Kyle of Lochalsh, or a little longer by way of Mallaig.

There are many castles to visit, and reminders of prehistory, at such places as the fascinating Jarlshof, near Sumburgh in Shetland, or the Standing Stones of Callanish on Lewis. Orkney claims the richest site of prehistory anywhere in Britain, including the extensive Skara Brae.

Inverness, Fort William and Aviemore are in an area of great variety, known to some as the Heart of the Highlands. Contrasting with these three centres is some of the remotest and wildest country in Britain, in distant Knoydart in the west, as well as one of the finest and longest sandy beaches, for example, at Nairn on the coast of the Moray Forth to the east. Some of the most beautiful glens, such as Cannich and Affric, lie west of the deep trench of Loch Ness, while mysterious lochs of the far west, including Loch Morar (deeper than the North Sea), will also fascinate visitors.

The traveller can also discover the romance of the 'Road to the Isles' – a title which in modern times often refers to the A830 Fort William to Mallaig, though it once referred to the old cattle droving roads from Skye. Amid this dramatic scenery were enacted the turbulent scenes of Culloden and Glencoe, and even today, the mighty defences of Fort George are still a reminder of troubled times.

Argyll and the Isles offer the best coastal resorts and the widest choice of islands in a great harmony of ocean and sealoch, forest and mountain, scattered with impressive statistics. About 30 inhabited islands, 3,000 miles of coastline and an incredible 3,900 listed ancient monuments make this a particularly diverse area. Not all of its beauties lie on the coast. It includes some of Scotland's most impressive scenic spectacles. In addition, the warming influence of the Gulf Stream is an added incentive to gardeners and the visitor will find about a dozen major botanical collections – including the tallest tree in Britain (in Strone Gardens near Loch Fyne).

Argyll and the Isles make for holidays with the unexpected. You'll find the smallest professional theatre in Britain on Mull. You can journey deep underground and visit a strange cavern, full of machinery, at the Ben Cruachan Power Station, and you can even drive across the Atlantic (or at least across the Atlantic bridge) on the way to Easdale. It certainly is an area full of surprises.

For details of what to see and where to go in Scotland contact:

THE SCOTTISH TOURIST BOARD
23 Ravelston Terrace
Edinburgh EH4 3EU

Tel: 031 332 2455

LONDON OFFICE:
19 Cockspur Street,
London SW1Y 5BL

Tel: 071 930 8661

Or call at the nearest Tourist Information Centre

INVERCRERAN COUNTRY HOUSE HOTEL

Glen Creran, Appin, Argyll PA38 4BJ

Telephone: (0631 73) 414/456 *Fax: 0631 73 532*

Glasgow 100, Oban 19, Edinburgh 125, Fort William 25

R & R licence; 7 en suite bedrooms, all with telephone. radio, hairdryer, colour TV; full central heating; last orders 8.00 p.m.; à la carte luncheon; diets; children welcome; sauna; sea bathing, sailing, riding, pony trekking, gliding, fishing, walking all nearby; golf, tennis, squash, badminton all in Oban; Master Card and Visa credit cards accepted.

At Invercreran, you can expect hospitality, excellent cuisine, comfort and very high standards of house keeping. It is run informally and very successfully by the Kersley family. The house is set high on the hillside, looking down into the sylvan glen. The building is designed so that every room enjoys the lovely views. Inside the hotel, the contrast of curve, space and line combine with the skilful use of colour, to please the eye. The dining room is circular, featuring an amazing Sutherland painting on the ceiling. With the lace-clad tables, it is a fitting backdrop for Tony Kersley's beautifully cooked and presented meals. His menus offer plenty of choice, and are changed daily. The food includes local fish, meat and game, with seasonal vegetables and fruits. Loving care has gone into the choice of wines, as with everything else here. Public rooms include a downstairs lounge, and a large, elegantly curved drawing room, with windows opening onto a large terrace. The well furbished bedrooms are comfortable and individual and one boasts its own sitting room. In this lovely area there is much to explore; the sea life centre, near Oban is well worth a visit, and for fishermen and sportsmen much can be arranged. Glen Creran is off the A828 about half way between Fort William and Oban. Dinner, bed and breakfast from £55.00 to £85.00 per person per night: Hotel closed mid November to the end of February. A Scottish Tourist Board Four Crown Commended Hotel.

LOCH DUICH HOTEL

Ardelve, Dornie, by Kyle of Lochalsh,
S.W. Ross & Skye IV40 8DY

Telephone: (059985) 213

Inverness 73, Fort William 69, Kyle of Lochalsh and Skye Ferry 7

F licence; 18 bedrooms; full central heating ground floor, convector heaters in bedrooms; meals to 9.00 p.m.; diets; children welcome; dogs accepted; excellent lunches at bar; aromatherapy; pony trekking; sea fishing; river salmon and sea trout fishing can be arranged; sea bathing and boating nearby.

Loch Duich Hotel is wonderfully situated on the "Road to the Isles", at the meeting place of Loch Duich, Loch Long and Loch Alsh. It commands superb views of the historic Eilean Donan Castle on one side, and down Loch Alsh to the Cuillins of Skye on the other. The hotel was a drovers' inn 300 years ago; today thanks to the experienced and much respected owner, Rod Stenson, it has a warm and welcoming atmosphere. Rod pays particular attention to his cuisine and cellar, so you can look forward to an excellent dinner made from local produce – sea food such as wild salmon, prawns and scallops; scotch beef, heather lamb and venison from the hills. Bread and oatcakes are homemade, together with marmalade and preserves from fruits gathered in the garden. Eggs come from the family's chickens and you can look forward to your morning tea arriving with maybe a shortbread added to your tray. It is impossible to do justice to the wild and beautiful landscape, the wonderful mountains, the road to Skye, the beaches, herons and seals at the foot of the garden and the occasional otter – the answer is "go and find out". Geraldine Stenson DTM, MHSP, offers aromatherapy, reflexology and massage to relax away all kinds of aches and pains. Daily exercises and breath practice are available each morning. I thoroughly recommend this good and friendly hotel for long or short stays. This year Mr. Stenson is offering his 20′ sea-going launch for angling or pleasure parties. He has also acquired a loch stocked for trout fishing for his guests. Bed and breakfast from £22.00. Reductions for 3 days or more. Closed November–mid March, but office open for enquiries. Awarded the AA Rosette for cuisine; a Taste of Scotland finalist 1985 and Bolinger Restaurant of the Year finalist 1986.

LOCH MELFORT HOTEL

Arduaine, by Oban, Argyll PA34 4XG

Telephone: (08522) 233 *Fax: 08522 214*

Oban 19, Lochgilphead 18, Glasgow 99, Fort William 67, Perth 111

F licence; 26 en suite bedrooms (10 on ground floor) all with sea view, telephone, TV; tea/coffee making facilities, baby listening; meals to 9.00 p.m.; informal light lunches, in Chart Room Bar, packed lunches, afternoon tea, lunch parties in the dining room on request; special diets; children welcome; dogs accepted in Cedar Wing; sailing; boating and sea bathing; fishing; clay pigeon shooting; riding nearby; Visa and Master Card accepted.

The Loch Melfort Hotel is situated just off the A816, between Lochgilphead and Oban, overlooking Asknish Bay, with magnificent views to the islands of Jura, Shuna and Scarba. Next to the hotel are the famous gardens of Arduaine, and their flowering azealeas and rhododendrons. There are a further 20 gardens within easy driving distance, and there are many places of historic interest to visit, here and on the islands, reached by ferry from Oban and Tarbert. The hotel is now run by resident owners, Rosalind and Philip Lewis and their cheerful and obliging staff. Public rooms are comfortable, including a cocktail bar, with a log fire on cool evenings, a sitting room and the pine panelled library, warmed by a log burning stove. There is a choice of bedrooms, with balconies and patios facing the sea in The Cedar Wing, or in the main house, which also includes two luxury twin bedded rooms. The dining room, with its superb views, offers a daily changing menu, starting from £19.50. Local sea food, especially lobster, oysters and scallops, with seasonal vegetables, is offered. For those with a sweet tooth, a choice of home made desserts is available, together with an extensive cheese board. Philip Lewis is in charge of the kitchens, and I am told that on Sunday evenings, his sea food buffet is very popular. Room and breakfast from £42.50. See also Bargain Breaks. Open March–Jan. inc. Christmas and New Year.

BARJARG TOWER

Auldgirth, Dumfries and Galloway DG2 0TN

Telephone: (0848) 31545 *Fax: 0848 30918*

Edinburgh 64, Glasgow 65, Dumfries 12, Carlisle 47, London 348, Windermere 91, York 156

R & R licence; 9 rooms, all with private bathroom, all with telephone, colour TV and full central heating; vegetarian food available; children by prior arrangement; no dogs; small, executive conferences welcome; riding, shooting and fishing nearby; golf 4 miles; Visa, Master Card, Amex and Diners' cards accepted.

Having found, fallen in love with and purchased Barjarg Tower, Mary and Archie Donaldson decided to undertake the mammoth task of converting 'The Red Hill Top Fort' into a fine hotel. This the Donaldsons have achieved with considerable success. The atmosphere is of a private country house, where the owners offer quality and comfort, with quiet dedication and attention to detail. Barjarg Tower stands in over forty acres with marvellous views over Nithsdale and the Lowther Hills. One of the features of this hotel is the impressive oak panelling, carved during the First World War by Belgian refugees. In the dining room, the daily-changing menu offers as much fresh and local produce as possible, and is complemented by an interesting choice of wines from the well-balanced wine list. All the bedrooms have been individually furnished, with an eye both for detail and attractiveness. Each offers modern amenities like colour television, hairdryer and trouser press. Private fishing is available on the River Nith, and a number of local estates offer shooting; being in Scotland, there are a number of golf courses nearby. Intriguing walks and plenty of places of interest are in the neighbourhood, like the ancestral home of the Dukes of Buccleuch at Drumlanrig Castle. It is not the easiest place to find; approaching from the south you turn left at Auldgirth 8 miles north of Dumfries and follow the road to Penpont. After four miles, when you think you have passed the hotel you will see the entrance gates on the left. Room and breakfast from £50.00 to £75.00 per person, with supplement for single occupancy. Inclusive terms for stays of three nights or more. Open all year except Christmas and early January.

CORROUR HOUSE HOTEL

Inverdruie, Nr. Aviemore, Highland PH22 1QH

Telephone: (0479) 810220

Inverness 30, Perth 85, Glasgow 139, Edinburgh 128

R & R licence; 8 en suite bedrooms all with telephone, colour TV, full central heating; last orders 8.30 p.m.; diets; children welcome; baby listening; dogs accepted; sailing, boating, golf, tennis, squash, riding, shooting & fishing all nearby; credit cards accepted.

Looking for somewhere peaceful from the bustle of Aviemore village, I was fortunate to find Corrour House. Entering the village from Kingussie, take the right hand turn to Coylumbridge (B970) the hotel's sign is about 200 yards on the right. It is an Edwardian country house lovingly cared for by the resident owners David and Sheana Catto. There are 8 airy bedrooms each prettily decorated and with its own bathroom. They all have TV, telephone and tea tray. Downstairs there is a cosy cocktail bar and large comfortable sitting room. In the dining room the home cooked meals are satisfying and nicely presented. The whole house is 'bright as a new pin' with an atmosphere that is at once warm, friendly, slightly formal and very Scottish. There are tennis courts next door and the village is within walking distance; while in the Aviemore Centre there is swimming, curling, skating, family entertainment and a little bit of 'night life' if you want it. In winter, of course, there is skiing, contact the hotel for 5 and 7 night packages. There are walks for those who like to take their exercise on the horizontal or the perpendicular and the bird life is rich and varied. Golf is within easy reach, watersports can be found on nearby lochs, clay pigeon shooting is just down the road and fishing, rough shooting and deer stalking can all be arranged. If all this is too energetic for you, just sit in the garden and contemplate the wonderful views of the Cairngorm Mountains. Room and breakfast from £44.00 (twin), weekly half board from £235.00. Three and five day breaks, prices on application. Closed from November till Christmas, but bookings taken.

BALLACHULISH HOTEL

Ballachulish, Argyll PA39 4JY

Telephone: (08552) 606 *Telex: 94013696* *Fax: 08552 629*

Fort William 10, Glasgow 90, Edinburgh 120, Oban 35, Glencoe 4

F licence; 30 en suite bedrooms, all with colour TV, radio, direct dial telephone, tea/coffee making facilities; central heating; night service; light meals available all day; diets; children welcome; baby listening; dogs welcome; sailing; golf, tennis, riding, shooting and fishing all nearby; hill walking; mountaineering; ski-ing in winter; major credit cards accepted

The Ballachulish Hotel is wonderfully situated standing beside the narrows separating Loch Leven from Loch Linnhe, commanding a key position on the grand highway from Glasgow and the south through Glencoe and on to Fort William or Oban. The Young family have another exceptional hotel, The Lodge On The Loch (Creag Dhu) in Onich, and they are well versed in the art of making people comfortable and at home. The Ballachulish Hotel has a baronial charm and dignity which its furnishing and appointments enhance. A major refurbishment is now completed, colour schemes are soft and restful. Downstairs the rooms are spacious, elegant lounges lead to the attractive Cocktail Bar, and Loch View Restaurant, where you can enjoy dishes that are varied, well chosen and cooked, complemented by a selective and good wine list. Bar meals are available all day in the famous "Ferry Bar", with regular entertainment. You must remember The Ballachulish Hotel in autumn, winter and spring as well as summer, for they have much to offer. Room and breakfast from £39.50 (single), £30.50 (twin) per person inclusive of VAT. Other terms and special breaks on application. Open all year. STB 4 Crown Commended. "Taste of Scotland" commended.

DARROCH LEARG HOTEL

Ballater, Royal Deeside, Aberdeenshire AB3 5UX

Telephone: (03397) 55443 *Fax: 03397 55443*

Aberdeen 42, Braemar 17, Perth 68, London 519

R & R licence; 23 bedrooms (1 ground floor), 20 with private bathrooms, all with direct dial telephone, colour TV, tea and coffee making facilities, full central heating; diets; children welcome, baby listening; dogs accepted; golf, tennis, riding, fishing etc., nearby; Access and Visa credit cards accepted.

The Darroch Learg, just 10 minutes' walk from the centre of Ballater, sits high on the wooded slopes of the Craigendarroch in five acres of grounds, with entrancing views over the golf course, River Dee and Balmoral Estates, to a panorama of wooded hills and more distant mountains. The hotel comprises two beautiful granite-built Scottish country houses, Darroch Learg and Oakhall, restored and furnished with a mixture of modern and antique furniture by the Franks family over the last 25 years. Offering bedrooms with every modern luxury and convenience, the hotel has an atmosphere of peace and relaxation for those wanting a restful holiday in beautiful surroundings, and gives excellent value. Fishing, golfing, walking, exploring the glens and many castles, gardens and other places of interest, are amongst the pleasures to be enjoyed in this lovely part of Scotland, where the Royal Family spend their holiday every year. It goes without saying that Chef Robert Geddes sees that the food is excellent using predominantly local and fresh produce. Room and breakfast from £24.00. Dinner, room and breakfast from £39.50. See bargain breaks section. The hotel, which is closed in November, December, January, has been awarded "4 Crowns Commended" by the Scottish Tourist Board. Brochure and tariff from Mr. and Mrs. N. D. Franks.

THE KILDONAN HOTEL & COUNTRY ESTATE

Barrhill, Ayrshire KA26 0PV

Telephone: (0465) 82360 *Fax: 0465 82292*

Glasgow 60, Troon 33

F licence; 31 bedrooms (2 suitable for disabled), all with en suite bathroom, telephone and TV; room and night service; baby listening; last orders for dinner 9.30 p.m.; bar meals; special diets; children welcome; dogs at discretion of management; conferences up to 80; snooker/billiards; indoor heated swimming pool; leisure centre; sauna and solarium; gymnasium; squash and tennis courts; golf; shooting and fishing; sailing and boating can be arranged - 4 miles; riding by arrangement - 12 miles; hotel open all year; all major credit cards accepted.

It is amazing to think that this substantial luxury hotel was once the holiday home of the Wallace family - and what a holiday home! Designed by Sir Edwin Lutyens and built for his son-in-law Captain David Wallace, a hero of the First World War, today The Kildonan has been converted and totally refurbished into a first class hotel and country club estate. All the furnishings and fittings throughout will appeal to those who appreciate quality and comfort. Bedrooms are very well fitted out and feature all modern amenities, and the one in which I stayed was huge by present day standards. I enjoyed an excellent dinner, which was served with care commensurate to its preparation and some of the bottles on the wine list made my mouth water! Every facility for exercise is provided; the hotel has its own challenging 9 hole golf course and tennis courts, or you can sharpen up with some clay pigeon shooting, prior to a day's driven pheasants. Rough shooting, sailing, windsurfing and canoeing are also available. There is fishing on a choice of lochs or on the banks of the rivers Dunsk and Cree. Indoors, there is a heated swimming pool, sauna, gymnasium and even a squash court, marked out for badminton as well. I enjoyed my stay, as I am sure you will too. Tariff on application.

BRAEMAR LODGE

Braemar, Royal Deeside AB3 5YQ

Telephone: (03397) 41627

Aberdeen 58, Perth 49, Inverness 80, Balmoral 10 minutes, Glenshee Ski Centre 10 minutes

R & R licence; 7 bedrooms, 5 with en suite bathroom; room television; last orders for dinner 8.30 p.m.; special diets; dogs accepted; wildlife; shooting and fishing locally; golf adjacent to hotel; skiing nearby; open all year except November–December; Visa and Master Card welcome.

Braemar Lodge is an intimate venue from which to explore an area of diverse beauty and interest. The hotel offers excellent value, and is run under the personal supervision of Marian and Trevor Campbell. You can be assured of friendly hospitality, excellent food, cosy log fires and a fine variety of books, magazines and games to enjoy. It even has its own rather nice little gift shop. The public rooms and the pretty, well-equipped bedrooms are comfortably furnished in a style that suites The Lodge. In the dining room, the heart of the hotel, they serve imaginative, well cooked and presented fare, using the best of local produce, and featuring 'Taste of Scotland' dishes. The names are often exotic, and they taste wonderful! Accompanying the menu is a carefully chosen wine list. From The Lodge, you can stroll into Braemar village, or down to the site of the famous Highland Gathering. On the outskirts of the village, stands the local castle, which is open to the public. Balmoral Castle and Lochnagar are also close at hand; space precludes a description of the variety of places to go, and things to do, both for the sportsperson and tourist, yet the Campbells have it all at their fingertips. You will find Braemar on the A93 Perth to Aberdeen Road. From the South, the Lodge is on the left hand side going into the village. Room and breakfast from £30.00 per person.

THE ROYAL MARINE HOTEL

Golf Road, Brora, Sutherland KW9 6QS

Telephone: (0408) 21252 *Telex: 76165*

Inverness 50, Perth 165, Edinburgh 200, Dornoch 15

F licence; 11 en suite bedrooms, all with telephone, col. TV videos and big screen; central heating; last orders 9.00 p.m.; bar meals; diets; children welcome; baby listening; dogs accepted; conferences max. 120; High Teas; games room; billiards; indoor heated swimming pool; sauna; leisure centre; sea bathing; sailing; links golf course, tennis, riding, shooting, fishing, badminton and squash nearby; Access, Amex, Barclay and Diners cards accepted.

This hotel was built in 1913 to a design by Sir Robert Lorimer, and was a country mansion until 1939 when it became a hotel. The present owner installed such modern luxuries as a leisure complex, private bathrooms, televisions and telephones. Here you will find a peaceful and comfortable country house atmosphere backed up by sporting facilities par excellence. Manager Robert Powell and his staff give you an hospitable welcome and kind, friendly service. Chef Bill Honeyman produces well-cooked, satisfying fare, thus ensuring that dinner is a happy occasion. Less formal meals are served in the cheery and comfortable cocktail bar and what could be nicer after a busy day than to have tea served in front of a crackling fire. Some of the bedrooms are particularly spacious and one has a four-poster bed, another offers a Jacuzzi. A most exciting opportunity is the 4 lane curling rink (lessons available) housed in the leisure complex. There is also a snooker table, a pool and darts room and a heated indoor pool which has sliding doors onto a lawn. In the garden there is croquet, putting and badminton. For tennis and bowls the local clubs welcome visitors and there is pony trekking locally. For the fisherman, the hotel keeps a boat on Loch Brora and there are excellent salmon rivers. Sea angling can also be arranged. In summer the curling rink is converted to a driving range. The coastline and the countryside inland are all delightful and whether you spend your time playing a sport, exploring or just lazing, this is an excellent venue. To find the hotel, drive through Brora Village and take a right turn where a sign indicates hotels and harbour. Bed and breakfast from £50.00, weekly from £300.00 half board. Hotel is open all year.

COUL HOUSE HOTEL

Contin, By Strathpeffer, Ross-shire IV14 9EY

Telephone: (0997) 21487 *Fax: 0997 21945*

Inverness 16, Dingwall 7, Edinburgh 175, Newcastle-upon-Tyne 285, Carlisle 280,

F licence; 21 bedrooms (4 ground floor), all with telephone, colour TV, central heating, hospitality tray, trouser press/ironing board, hairdryer, clock radio; last orders 9.00 p.m.; bar meals; diets; baby listening; children welcome; dogs accepted; conferences up to 40 welcome; games room; dancing monthly; sea bathing, sailing; large garden; golf, riding, shooting, fishing; open all year; Diners' & Amex accepted.

Coul House stands above the village of Contin, looking across rolling wooded countryside to the mountains beyond. It is in a choice position for exploring both east and west coasts, and Loch Ness and its environs. The old house is now owned and run by Ann Bryan and Martyn Hill, whose hard work has resulted in a most comfortable, hospitable hotel. It was Ann who planned the most individual colour schemes for the cosy, well-equipped bedrooms; I was most grateful for the ironing board, attached to the trouser press. The hotel has The Mackenzie Cocktail Bar, and The Kitchen Bar, which is excellent for bar meals. The kitchens, presided over by chef Chris Bentley, provide very good food, chosen from table d'hôte or à la carte menus (a generous dish of pan fried scallops, flavoured with herbs and garlic, and the accompanying vegetables were delicious, well-cooked and presented). For anglers, the hotel owns salmon and trout fishing, for golfers, five courses are within reach, pony trekking and guided rambling can be arranged. On summer nights every Friday, pipes can be heard in the gardens of the hotel. Travelling from the South, by-pass Inverness, and continue on the A9 over the Moray Firth Bridge. After five miles, turn left at the roundabout onto the A835. Follow to Contin and look for hotel sign on right. Bed and breakfast from £33.00 per person, per night.

THE CRAIGELLACHIE HOTEL

Craigellachie, Speyside, Banffshire AB3 9SS

Telephone: (0340) 881204 *Fax: 0340 881253*

Aberdeen 60, Inverness 50, Elgin 12, Edinburgh 150

F licence; 30 bedrooms all with en suite bathroom, direct dial telephone, and colour TV; room and night service; baby listening; last orders for dinner 9.30 p.m.; bar meals; special diets; children welcome; dogs accepted; conferences up to 30; drawing room and library; snooker/billiards; gymnasium; sauna and solarium; golf, tennis, riding, shooting and fishing; hotel open all year; major credit cards accepted.

The Craigellachie is a peaceful haven ministered by Mr. Tomas Gronager and his cheerful, courteous staff. Furnished with gleaming antique pieces and recently refurbished throughout, it offers guests beautifully appointed bedrooms and elegant public rooms where log fires burn on cooler days. There is a cosy smoking room and library, and a very beautiful function room. Many guests come here to enjoy the outdoor life; there are 15 golf courses nearby, fishing on the loch and river, riding, shooting, ski-ing, walking, etc. Given enough notice, the hotel can arrange almost anything for you. A rod room and drying facilities are provided, and as an alternative to the cocktail bar, there is an informal bar where you can relax before changing. There is also a sauna and solarium for any aches and pains. For those who enjoy indoor sports, there is a magnificent billiards room and Brian Mutch, an award winning young chef, provides the dining room with the best of Scottish cuisine. Standing high on a level site, the hotel overlooks the Spey and the surrounding woodland. The roads lead the explorer on through varied scenery, castles, museums and distilleries. Craigellachie is on the A95 12 miles from Elgin. Room and breakfast from £39.50 per person per night, or £372.00 weekly. Rates on request for master bedrooms with four poster beds.

FERNIE CASTLE HOTEL

Letham, Nr. Cupar, Fife KY7 7RU

Telephone: (033 781)381 *Fax: 033 781 381*

London 464, Perth 22, St. Andrews 10, Dundee 13

F licence; 16 en suite bedrooms (4 on ground floor), all with radio, telephone, satellite TV, hairdryer, trouser press; full central heating; meals to 9.30 p.m.; diets; children welcome; baby listening; conferences; shooting; fishing; credit cards accepted.

Imposing to look at, luxurious to live in, one would never guess that Fernie Castle started its career in the 12th century when it was owned by Duncan, 13th Earl of Fife. Situated west of Cupar in its own secluded grounds, it offers considerable comfort and an atmosphere of quiet ambience. The décor of the Drawing Room upstairs is delightful, and all the bedrooms have every modern facility – including a mini bar. I enjoyed a well prepared, well presented dinner with suitable wine in the elegant Dining Room. The Conference Room, with its own entrance, is suitable for many functions. In the hotel you can see an original lead bath – rather small and uninviting to my mind! Outside there is an excellent example of an ice house, probably one of the best in Scotland. For golfers, Ladybank is two miles away, and the home of golf – St. Andrews – is less than half an hour away by car. Resident owners, Mr. and Mrs Cinnamond will give you a warm welcome, with help from their friendly young staff. A truly pleasing place to stay. Open all year. Room and breakfast from £50.00 single, £65.00 double.

DOLPHINTON HOUSE HOTEL

Dolphinton, Nr. West Linton, Peeblesshire EH46 7AB

Telephone: (0968) 82286 *Fax: 0899 20456*

Edinburgh Airport 21, Glasgow 32

F licence; 12 en suite bedrooms, all with telephone, colour TV and full central heating; night service; last orders 9.00 p.m.; bar meals 12.00–2.00 p.m.; diets; children welcome; dogs accepted in bedroom; conferences up to 14 welcome; tennis and fishing; golf and riding nearby; Diners', American Express, Access and Visa cards welcome.

This old mansion house, set in 186 acres of park and woodland was recently converted into an hotel. Only about 20 miles south west of Edinburgh, Dolphinton House was the home of the McKenzie family for over 400 years. The hotel is operated by Arthur and Susan Bell who are well known for their high quality food by the 'Scottish Gourmet'; a food by post club. Furnished with every modern comfort, including genuine antiques, fine old prints and log fires, these all contribute to provide the high standard of a luxury country house hotel. The restaurant is a special feature where Master Chef, Roy Ellis creates imaginative dishes using Scottish produce, and excels at preparing new menus with a Scottish flavour. Bar snacks are available at midday in the intimate snug bar where you can find and sample many old malt whiskies. I was particularly impressed with the wine list which was very comprehensive, with some real bargains. Indeed, I found the prices cheaper than on most wine lists. All the bedrooms, some with their own sitting-room, have been decorated with skill and taste and include all modern facilities. Supervised by Deborah Graham, the manager, you can be assured of efficient service in comfortable surroundings. Open throughout the year, prices for room and full Scottish breakfast start at £50.00 single, £79.00 double and suites from £95.00 per night, including VAT.

THE OLD MANSION HOUSE HOTEL

Auchterhouse, By Dundee, Angus DD3 0QN

Telephone: (082626) 366 *Fax: 082626 400*

Dundee 7, Edinburgh 45, Perth 22, Coupar Angus 10

F licence; 8 bedrooms with telephone, 7 with colour TV, 6 with private bathroom; central heating; meals to 9.30 p.m.; diets; children welcome; baby listening; dogs accepted; conferences max. 15; private dinner parties max. 40; outdoor heated swimming pool; squash; tennis; croquet; golf at Carnoustie, St. Andrews, Rosemount and Gleneagles all within easy reach; Amex, Access and Diners Club cards accepted.

I liked this lovely 16th century baronial home immensely. Steeped in Scottish history, it is peacefully set amidst the rolling farmlands of Angus, in the delightful village of Auchterhouse. The Old Mansion House is seven miles outside Dundee and just off the A927. This small but excellent hotel has been skilfully converted by the present owners, Nigel and Eva Bell, to a high standard of comfort and taste. It seems almost a pity to call this place an hotel, for it's much more like the country home of a rich man with the love of luxury, sport and culture, and who demands exceptional food and an excellent wine cellar. The 17th century improvements include the ornate plaster work in the original drawing room with its open Jacobean fire, whilst the vaulted entrance hall is reminiscent of an earlier period. The furnishings and décor of all rooms are a delight and most bedrooms have private bathroom, telephone and colour television. Mr Campbell Bruce, the chef, produces dishes that are interesting and imaginative whilst bar lunches and evening snacks are served in the attractive Courtyard Bar. The staff are pleasant and efficient and there are many interesting and attractive features in the 10 acres of beautifully laid out gardens. Room and breakfast from £60.00 (single), £75.00 (twin), £85.00 family suite. Always open except for first week in January.

DUNDONNELL HOTEL

Dundonnell, By Garve, Ross-shire IV23 2QR

Telephone: (085483) 204 *Fax: 085483 366*

Ullapool 25, Gairloch 30, Inverness 60, Edinburgh 215, Glasgow 230

F licence; 24 bedrooms with en suite bathroom; telephone and television; room service; baby listening; last orders 8.30 p.m.;bar meals; special diets; children welcome; dogs accepted; conferences up to 25; sea bathing, sailing and boating nearby; golf 30 miles; riding 26 miles; credit cards accepted; hotel open all year.

Mr. and Mrs. Selbie Florence are justly proud of their 3-Star hotel, indeed it is the only 3-Star establishment in the Ullapool area. Set beside the road as it winds around Little Loch Broom, it has provided rest for weary travellers for hundreds of years. Today's travellers are not so travel-worn, but they still head for this hotel to enjoy the luxurious accommodation that would have amazed their forebears. Mr. and Mrs. Florence and their family are experienced hoteliers and warm and friendly hosts. Their attractively furbished dining room offers table d'hôte and à la carte menus, featuring Scotch beef and local fish. All this is accompanied by a very comprehensive wine list. The bedrooms offer a variety of extremely pleasing views, and beautiful décor. For families, one room is particularly attractive, because it has an adjacent bedroom, containing bunk beds. The hotel has two bars, which harbour a large collection of single malt whiskies, as well as supplying good bar lunches and suppers. Tea, coffee and home made shortbread are available throughout the day. This is a warm and comfortable, relaxing base from which to enjoy the spectacular scenery and lovely gardens, all to be found in this mild corner of Western Ross. You will find the hotel on the A832 at the South Eastern edge of Little Loch Broom. Room and breakfast from £25.00, or weekly rates from £245.00.

STAKIS DUNKELD HOUSE HOTEL

Dunkeld, Perthshire PH8 0HX

Telephone: (03502) 771 *Fax: 03502 8924*

Glasgow 73, Edinburgh 55, Perth 12, Scone Airport 14, Dunkeld Station 2

F licence; 92 bedrooms (2 for disabled), all with en suite bathroom, telephone and colour TV; baby listening; night service; lift; last orders for dinner 9.45 p.m.; sandwiches in bar; diets; children welcome; dogs in kennels only; conferences up to 100; indoor heated swimming pool; leisure centre; sauna and solarium; spa pool; multi gym; 2 all weather tennis courts; croquet; archery; private salmon fishing beat; Shooting Academy; golf and riding nearby; open all year; Master Card, Visa, Amex and Diners cards accepted.

Dunkeld House is an elegant country house, that has become a first class hotel caring for an international clientele. Dunkeld is the perfect place for a highland holiday, an exclusive conference or a quiet fishing or shooting weekend. It is under the personal management of Mr. and Mrs. Andy Burgess who offer the best of Scottish hospitality with their professional team of staff. In 280 acres of private estate, the hotel has a superb range of indoor leisure facilities and outdoors, guests can choose from a wide range of country pursuits and sporting facilities. The Shooting Academy offers every sporting clay target imaginable using the latest equipment with simulation of high pheasants driven over trees, the bolting rabbit, springing teal and quartering quail, and is managed by Ian Marsden, Commonwealth Gold Medalist 1990. The hotel's public rooms feature pine wood panelling, stained glass windows and a welcoming log fire in the Entrance hall. The beautifully appointed bedrooms have 24 hour room service, tea and coffee making facilities, hairdryer and trouser press. Sample the fine selection of malt whiskies available in the cocktail bar before enjoying dinner featuring the best of fresh Scottish produce presented and served with style. The choice of wines has been carefully selected to complement the menus. Dunkeld House is easily accessible by road or rail and within easy access are Distillery tours, woollen mills, castles and nature reserves amongst some of the most spectacular scenery Scotland has to offer. Room and breakfast from £50.00 per person per night.

CALEDONIAN HOTEL
Princes Street, Edinburgh EH1 2AB

Telephone: (031) 225 2433 *Fax: 031 225 6632*

Aberdeen 128, Ayr 74, Inverness 161, Perth 44

F licence; 237 bedrooms (3 for disabled), all with en suite bathroom, TV and telephone; room and night service; lift; last orders for dinner 10.30 p.m.; bar meals; special diets; children welcome; no dogs; conferences up to 300; sauna and solarium, spa pool, gymnasium, squash and tennis 1 mile; indoor heated swimming pool, golf, leisure centre 2 miles; sea bathing 5 miles; sailing and boating 10 miles; riding 12 miles; shooting and fishing 15 miles; hotel open all year. Amex, Visa, Diners and Master Card accepted.

This fine hotel is sure to impress you, with its ambience of luxury and comfort. Situated at the western end of Princes Street, this sandstone building was erected for the Caledonian Railway company and is the premier hotel of Edinburgh. A truly friendly Scottish welcome awaits you as you enjoy afternoon tea in the spacious lounge. The Pompadour Restaurant has a well deserved, excellent reputation for the finest haute cuisine, and it is very well known, locally and farther afield. A meal in this restaurant is an outstanding experience. There is another restaurant called The Gazebo, where you can enjoy a less formal lunch or dinner. I cannot think of a better hotel in which to stay, whilst doing your sightseeing, or shopping in this lovely city of Edinburgh. Room and breakfast from £180.00. Special weekend breaks are available at the hotel.

ROXBURGHE HOTEL
Charlotte Square, Edinburgh, Lothian EH2 4HG

Telephone: 031-225 3921 *Telex: 727054* *Fax: 031 220 2578*

London 373, Glasgow 44, Coldstream 48, Peebles 23, Stirling 37

F licence; 75 en suite bedrooms including 1 suite; night service; children welcome; full central heating; conferences; diets; credit cards accepted.

The Roxburghe is in a splendid Georgian setting overlooking Charlotte Square, designed by Robert Adam and completed in the early 19th century, and just one minute's walk from Princes Street. The hotel has all the atmosphere and elegance of a private house situated in the centre of a city and continues a tradition of style, comfort, fine food and personal service extending back over three generations. All 75 bedrooms including 10 de luxe rooms and 1 suite, are highly individual and very tastefully furnished and each is equipped with colour TV, radio, telephone, trouser press and tea and coffee making facilities. The Cocktail Bar with its buffet counter, and the recently refurbished Consort Restaurant offer international cuisine while the Melrose Room Buttery serves inexpensive meals or snacks. The Roxburghe and Consort Suites provide a lovely setting for private parties, dances, weddings, and conferences up to 200, the rooms being adaptable to the number of guests. Room and breakfast from £55.00 single, £75.00 double (off season rate) with private bath, service and VAT. Other prices on application. Always open. A member of Best Western Consortium of Independent Hotels. A founder member of "Scotland's Heritage Hotels", a new consortium.

THE MANSION HOUSE HOTEL

Elgin, The Haugh, Grampian IV30 1AW

Telephone: (0343) 548811 *Fax: 0343 547916*

Inverness 40, Aberdeen 67, Cullen 22, Perth 134, London 581

F licence; 7 four poster rooms, 2 twin four poster rooms, 9 twin/double-bedded rooms all with trouser press, hairdryer, mini bar, remote control TV, telephone, tea/coffee making facilities, private bathroom with shower; night service; last orders 9.00 p.m.; room service menu to 11.00 p.m.; diets; children welcome; baby listening; no dogs; conferences max. 40; sailing, golf, tennis, squash, riding, shooting, fishing all nearby; Visa and Master Card accepted.

If you are near Elgin, you would be well advised to visit the Mansion House. You will find awaiting you a delightful and friendly welcome from your host Mr. Fernando de Oliveira, who with his young staff and talented chef, John Alexander, has created an hotel that is both professional and warmly personal. Mr. and Mrs. de Oliveira have transformed the Mansion House into a very well appointed hotel. Whether you choose a four poster suite, the executive suite – designed for those who carry their work with them – or a twin or double room, you will be delighted with your choice. The decorations are very pleasing, as is the range of equipment thoughtfully provided for your use. The drawing room and cocktail bar, decorated in muted pinks, are both comfortable and sophisticated and the quiet greens of the dining room are an elegant backdrop for the creative and delicious food presented there. Many new developments include the Country Club which provides free facilities for guests. The swimming pool overlooks the back lawns and includes a jacuzzi, sauna and Turkish bath, with changing facilities and comprehensive gymnasium. A meal or quick snack is always readily available at the Dip Inn, the multi-purpose bistro bar. The Ballroom provides an ideal location for private parties, dinner dances or entertainment provided by the hotel. The Mansion House is tucked away beside the River Lossie, which flows through the quiet gardens at the rear of the hotel, a quarter of a mile from the centre of Elgin. 2 people bed and breakfast in a double/twin room £90.00, one person bed and breakfast £49.00, 2 people bed and breakfast in a four poster room £95.00. Reductions for children up to 12. Other rates on application.

KNOCKOMIE HOTEL

Grantown Road, Forres, Grampian IV36 0SG
Telephone: (0309) 73146 *Fax: 0309 73146*

Elgin 12, Edinburgh 164, Inverness 27, London 569, Aviemore 38, Oban 142

F licence; 7 en suite bedrooms all with telephone, colour TV; full central heating; last orders 9.30 p.m.; bar meals; diets; children welcome; baby listening; dogs accepted; conferences max. 45; croquet, sea bathing, sailing & boating, golf, tennis, squash, riding all nearby; shooting by arrangement; fishing 2 miles; Access and Visa cards accepted.

Advice from a local took me down to the Knockomie Hotel for a night's shelter. They were busy at that time with builders and decorators but I was taken in, given a warm and most attractive bedroom, a refreshing cup of Earl Grey tea, a good dinner and served with cheerful kindliness. The Hotel is run with charm, youthful energy and dedication by Gavin Ellis and his young team. He has already created an hotel to be proud of and has ongoing plans for the future. The ambience here is that of a country house, panelled and chintzy with plenty of books and newspapers around. There is an added sophistication lent by the well stocked (over 60 malts) panelled bar, elegant party or conference rooms and the restaurant, where the tempting menus are created from the best of Scottish fare: Angus steak, fish from sea and loch and local game all feature. The wine list is well chosen and prices are reasonable. Upstairs all of the 7 bedrooms are very pleasing, I particularly liked the soft furnishings. Each has its own bathroom and is equipped with TV, clock radio, direct dial 'phone, tea tray etc. The master bedrooms are particularly spacious. Gavin Ellis has worked out excellent value golfing, fishing and riding packages (there are 14 golf courses within reach) and shooting can also be arranged. The little town of Forres is set near the coast in rolling well wooded farm land. Apart from the usual pine forests, the area is noted for its hard woods, particularly the towering beeches that line many of the roads. You will find the Knockomie Hotel about 1 mile from Forres on the Grantown Road, I strongly recommend it for its value and friendliness. Room and breakfast from £40.00 single, £60.00 double. If you stay two days, including Sunday, and mention *Signpost*, you will receive a bottle of house wine and a box of chocolates! Always open.

CASTLETON HOUSE HOTEL

By Glamis, Forfar, Angus DD8 1SJ

Telephone: (030784) 340 *Fax: 030784 506*

Forfar 8, Dundee 12, Perth 21, Edinburgh 55, Aberdeen 50

F licence; 6 en suite bedrooms all with telephone, remote control colour TV; last orders 9.30 p.m.; bar meals lunchtime (12.00–3.00); diets; children welcome; dogs, but not in hotel, kennels provided; conferences max 15; golf – St. Andrews, Rosemount, Gleneagles all within easy reach; riding, shooting & fishing can be arranged; Glenshee ski slopes 40 mins. drive; Master Card, Amex & Visa accepted.

Castleton House is set beside the A94 halfway between Forfar and Coupar Angus and is but two miles from Glamis Castle. This hotel provides a most comfortable base from which to explore this very lovely area. Of the many interesting and scenic drives that can be taken from here, one of the most spectacular is through Edzell and Fettercairn up into the Grampians, the view from the topmost pass is breathtaking, quite literally on a windy day. Until last year, Castleton House was a private residence, now refurbished to a very high standard and is owned and run by Mr and Mrs Little and their most courteous staff. Mr Little is an excellent Chef and he plans and prepares the interesting menu which is beautifully served in the elegant dining room. The pleasant gardens surrounding the hotel include a flourishing vegetable plot and the chickens scratching cheerfully in their run provide the freshest of eggs for your breakfast. Preserves are often home made and a shortbread with afternoon tea is definitely to be recommended. Single room and breakfast from £45.00, double £75.00 including VAT. Open all year. S.T.B. 4 Crown Highly Commended.

GLENMORISTON ARMS HOTEL

Invermoriston, By Inverness, Highland IV3 6YA

Telephone: (0320) 51206

Inverness 27, Aberdeen 130, Glasgow 170, Edinburgh 170

F licence; 8 bedrooms, all with private bathroom, colour TV, tea/coffee making facilities; last orders 9.00 p.m.; bar meals; diets; children welcome; dogs accepted; residents' sitting room; golf 5 miles; riding and shooting nearby; fishing; Visa and Master Card accepted.

The Glenmoriston Arms has been a popular hostelry for the past two hundred years, originally part of the Glenmoriston Estates, it is now owned and run by Alan, Betty and Paul Draper. Modernized and providing the facilities expected by today's traveller, the old inn is bright and attractive. All the pretty bedrooms are en suite, one boasting a four poster bed and spa bath. The well stocked cocktail bar has 150 malts, including the Glen Moriston Estate's own blend. The dining room offers a nicely varied à la carte menu, ingredients are fresh, well cooked, and presented. Sited next to the car park and across a little foot bridge, is the Glen Moriston Tavern, where those who wish, may enjoy a hearty bar supper. The Inn is popular with sportsmen, providing fishing from its own boats, and the hotel can also arrange shooting and stalking. It is most inviting, set beside the A82 in Invermoriston, at the south-western end of Loch Ness. An ideal position from which to explore the beautiful Glens or visit the West Coast, or Culloden and Inverness. Nearby, there is the spectacular beauty of the Scottish landscape, with wonderful panoramic views to be enjoyed from the little known B862 road, which goes from Fort Augustus, via Whitebridge, to Inverness. Room and breakfast from £32.00 single, £25.00 per person double. Single dinner, bed and breakfast, £45.00. £3.00 per person supplement for four poster bed.

BUNCHREW HOUSE HOTEL

Bunchrew, Inverness IV3 6TA

Telephone: (0463) 234917

Inverness 2, Edinburgh 158

F licence; 6 en suite bedrooms, all with telephone, colour TV; last orders 9.00 p.m.; bar meals; diets; children welcome; baby listening; dogs by prior arrangement; conferences max. 100; dancing monthly; seabathing, boating, golf, tennis, swimming pool all nearby; riding; shooting on estate; free salmon and trout fishing; Master Card, Amex and Visa credit cards accepted.

A visit to Bunchrew House (pronounced 'Bunkrew'), has a sense of occasion. The family that lives here — Alan and Patsy Wilson, are welcoming and attentive hosts, with their daughters, Karen and Kirsten, and two 'aristocats', Tabitha and Chiquita. Their home is a romantic old house set on the shore of the Beauly Firth which has been sympathetically restored and furnished. The bedrooms are delightful, individually decorated to very high standards. Indeed, they are so popular, that another wing will be opened shortly, providing six more suites. Downstairs, the long low drawing room is peaceful and gracious, there is a comfortable cocktail bar, hung with pictures of the Frazer family, whose forebears built the house in 1621. The dining room is elegant, boasting a prize-winning young waiter. In the kitchen, two chefs, also prize-winners, use Scotland's abundance of natural products to inspire their dishes. The wine list has been carefully chosen to suit every taste and pocket. Bunchrew is located on a sheltered shore curving into the delicate and beautiful Firth. This area, ringing the Beauly Firth, and in turn circled by the distant mountains, is both lovely and picturesque. Bunchrew is located on the A862, 1 mile from Inverness. Prices from £50.00 single, £65.00 double, or from £175.00 weekly. Open all year.

KINGSMILLS HOTEL

Culcabock Road, Inverness IV2 3LP

Telephone: (0463) 237166 *Telex: 75566* *Fax: 0463 225208*

Edinburgh 158, Glasgow 170, London 531, Fort William 67, Nairn 16, Aviemore 32

F licence; 84 en suite bedrooms (31 ground floor), including large family rooms, all with colour teletext TV's, telephone, tea/coffee making facilities, hair dryer, trouser press, iron and board, mini-bar, free in-house movies; night service; late meals to 10.00 p.m.; diets; children welcome, baby listening; dogs welcome; conferences up to 40; private dining rooms; 6 self contained luxury Kingsmills Golf Villas adjacent to the Hotel and Golf Course; Leisure Club; sailing, boating, tennis, riding, fishing, shooting by arrangement; all major credit cards accepted.

Kingsmills is a country house type hotel of great charm and elegance, situated in 4 acres of woodland gardens, next to Inverness Golf Club and a mile from the town centre. Inverness, "Capital of the Highlands" is at the head of the Moray Firth, and north-east of the Great Glen and famous Caledonian Canal. The ground floor rooms are comfortable, and are furnished to a high standard. It has a great reputation for excellent food, the menus show imagination, a good choice, and a wine list discerningly chosen. The luxurious bedrooms, with their individual colour schemes, are magnificently appointed, the spacious executive twin rooms with a sitting room area overlooking the gardens are superb, and can very comfortably accommodate up to four persons. A new conservatory, reception area and 46 large luxury bedrooms will be completed by Easter 1991. Mention must be made of the six Golf Villas, conveniently near, but separate from the hotel, consisting of two twin or double bedrooms, a sitting/dining room, a well equipped kitchen, ideal for two couples or a family of four. They are fully serviced each day. A recent addition is the leisure club with indoor heated swimming pool, spa bath, sauna, steam room, fitness room, sunbed, relaxation area and three hole mini golf course. I can thoroughly recommend this outstanding place for all seasons, happy under the management of Mr Peter Atherton and his efficient, cheerful and friendly staff. Room and breakfast from £65.00 single, £88.00 double, inclusive of VAT. Other terms on application. Always open.

ROSEDALE HOTEL

Portree, Isle Of Skye IV51 9DB

Telephone: Portree (0478) 3131

Edinburgh 237, Invermoriston 90, Fort Augustus 97, Kyle of Lochalsh Ferry 34

F licence; 20 en suite bedrooms (7 ground floor) all with television, telephone, radio, tea/coffee making facilities, also 3 attractive twin bedded rooms with private bathrooms available in nearby Beaumont House; full central heating; sea bathing; boating; tennis nearby; good open air parking.

I was advised by friends in Uig to visit the Rosedale Hotel at Portree, and how glad I was to find this most attractive hotel, so well run by the proprietress, Mrs. Andrew and her son, Hugh. It is situated on the loch side facing the harbour and looking out across the Sound of Raasay to the Isle beyond. Mr. Andrew showed me round the hotel and I realised how much time and energy had been put into making this modernised, yet comfortably furnished and brightly decorated, hotel so acceptable. The Andrew family have done a wonderful job. The bedrooms are very well appointed and the public rooms, including the cocktail bar, are attractive and comfortable creating an atmosphere of peace and quiet. I enjoyed my meals very much; the menus, without being extravagant, were good, admirably cooked and well presented. Whilst you are assured of a great welcome at any time, the Andrews do recommend an early visit when the weather is at its best and the Island less busy. Room and breakfast from £28.00 per person, inclusive of VAT. Other terms on application. Closed October to mid-May, but office open for enquiries and advance bookings.

HOTEL EILEAN IARMAIN

Eilean Iarmain, Sleat, Isle of Skye IV43 8RQ

Telephone: (04713) 332 *Fax: 04713 260*

Kyle of Lochalsh 24, Portree 26, Edinburgh 227

F licence; 12 bedrooms (3 suitable for disabled), 10 with en suite bathrooms, all with tea trays and direct dial telephone; room service; baby listening; last orders for dinner 8.30 p.m.; bar meals; special diets; children welcome; dogs accepted; conferences up to 24; sea bathing; stalking, shooting and fishing; golf and riding nearby; hotel open all year; major credit cards accepted.

The Hotel Eilean Iarmain is a traditional Inn where you will find friendly courtesy, charming accommodation and very good food and wines. The romantic name, meaning St. Dermid's Island, gives a clue to its delightful position, standing on the hard in a fishing hamlet, looking out to the island and beyond, over the sea, to the crowding peaks on the mainland. Nearby, the ferry (a small adventure in itself) plies between Ardvasar and Mallaig. Many a convivial evening has passed in the Public Bar, where they have a fine choice of malts and serve good bar meals. Dining guests can enjoy a quiet drink in the sitting room while choosing from the menu and mulling over a wine list of some 53 bins, ranging from the modestly priced, to premier cru clarets. The à la carte menu is small and nicely balanced, with fresh dishes appearing daily. As the Inn gained in popularity, the proprietors converted the shore-side cottage opposite, into more bedrooms, all en suite. Imaginative modernization has not disturbed the timeless quality of the old inn or the cottage. To find this haven of tranquillity, take the main A851 (single track with passing places) from Ardvasar, about 8 miles on locate a sign to the right, and follow the lane over the hump-back bridge, towards the sea. Room and breakfast from £30.00, weekly from £200.00.

UIG HOTEL

Uig, Portree, Isle Of Skye IV51 9YE

Telephone: Uig (047 042) 205. Guests 367 *Fax: 047 042 308*

Edinburgh 252, Portree 15, Kyle of Lochalsh Ferry 49

F licence; 17 en suite bedrooms, direct dial telephone, colour TV; late meals to order; diets by arrangement; drying room; children over 11 welcome; sea, river bathing; boating; fishing; shooting by arrangement; pony trekking; fire certificate; major credit cards accepted.

The Uig Hotel is situated at the northern end of the lovely island of Skye looking down on the little bay and harbour of Uig. Grace Graham and her son David Taylor, the owners, must be justly proud of their attractive and elegantly furnished hotel with its warm and cheerful atmosphere. The furniture, pictures and colour schemes are very pleasant. There are 11 pretty bedrooms in the hotel and at the rear, offering lovely seaviews, the old steading has been converted into 6 attractive bedrooms, one with a sitting room and all with their own bathroom. Next door, Primrose Cottage has been converted into 3 very comfortable self-catering apartments. Fresh vegetables are supplied from the hotel garden. There is an interesting table d'hôte and the dishes are plentiful and skilfully cooked. The excellent wine list is sure to suit all tastes. For lunch there are interesting snacks with very good coffee. The hotel now has a comfortable cocktail bar. You will enjoy your stay and the scenery and peace of the surrounding country, which has strong associations with Prince Charles and Flora MacDonald. Uig is now served by the new roll on, roll off ferry to the Outer Hebrides, *The Hebridean Isles.* Room and breakfast from £30.00 per person inclusive of VAT. Other terms on application. Closed from October to mid-April but office open.

SUNLAWS HOUSE HOTEL
Kelso, Roxburghshire TD5 8JZ

Telephone: (05735) 331 *Telex: 728147 Sunlaw G* *Fax: 05735 611*

Edinburgh 50, Newcastle 60, Berwick 24, Jedburgh 9, Kelso 3, Hawick 20

F licence; 22 en suite bedrooms (9 on ground floor), all with radio, direct dial telephone, colour TV; full central heating; night service; meals to 9.30 p.m.; diets; children welcome; baby listening; dogs welcome; conferences up to 20; tennis; riding; shooting; fishing; golf 3 miles; major credit cards accepted.

Sunlaws House is owned by the Duke of Roxburghe who lives at the impressive Floors Castle (well worth a visit in itself) and who supervised its conversion into an hotel, and continues to take a keen interest in the success of this once family house. The hotel is situated 3 miles south west of Kelso through Heiton on the A698 turning right with a signposted lane. Fishing on its own beat of the river Teviot and shooting in the Roxburghe Estates are both very popular. Leaflets on fishing breaks and shooting breaks are available. Hearty breakfasts are the order of the day and I certainly enjoyed one during my stay. Emphasis is on Scottish cooking and there is a good selection of wines – some of the older wines coming, no doubt, from His Grace's cellar. Accommodation is of a high standard, as you would expect, the bedrooms being comfortable and relaxing. The conservatory, where I enjoyed a pre-dinner drink, is delightful and bar lunches and afternoon teas can be served here. The Roxburghe Suite is available for private parties or conferences. Mr. David Corkill ably manages this small country house hotel of character. Open all year. Tariff on application.

THE HOLLY TREE

Kentallen, Appin, Argyll PA38 4BY

Telephone: (063174) 292 *Fax: 063174 345*

F licence; 12 bedrooms (2 suitable for disabled), 11 with en suite bathroom; all have room TV, telephone; room service; baby listening; last orders for dinner 9.30 p.m.; bar meals 12.30–2.00 p.m.; special diets; children welcome; dogs by arrangement; conferences up to 20; sea bathing, sailing and boating; riding, shooting and fishing nearby; hotel open all year; Master Card, Visa and Amex accepted.

The Holly Tree is a delightful little hotel that started life as a country railway station. Standing on the very shore of Loch Linnhe, it is smart and cheerful, and very clean and comfortable. The idea was conceived by Alisdair and Jane Robertson. Jane has charge of the "front of house", whilst Alisdair "stars" (two red ones!) in the kitchen, his reputation for fine food justly earned. The defunct railway kindly provided a quay where the hotel's three boats, a sailing dinghy, a Canadian canoe and a motor launch are handy for guests wishing to fish or to explore by water. The hotel faces the Loch and its public rooms and most of the bedrooms enjoy the lovely views of water and mountain. Away from the hotel there is much to explore – the drama of Glen Coe, the softer beauty of Eriska or the lanes beside Loch Awe to name but a few. Nearby at Oban, the Sea Life Centre is worth a visit, and there are boat trips to the smaller islands and Mull. The Holly Tree is on the A828 a few miles south of Ballachulish. Terms on application.

TAYCHREGGAN HOTEL

Kilchrenan, By Taynuilt, Argyll PA35 1HQ

Telephone: (08663) 211 *Fax: 08663 244*

Edinburgh 116, Ballachulish 44, Dalmally 21½, Oban 18

F licence; 15 en suite bedrooms and a luxurious suite, all with hair drier, radio and intercom; central heating; TV lounge and Quiet Room; late meals to 9.00 p.m.; diets; children welcome; dogs accepted; loch bathing; trout fishing; boats available; shooting; deer stalking and salmon fishing by arrangement; riding and golf nearby; local forestry walks; credit cards accepted.

The drive down through Glen Nant to Taychreggan is enchanting and the hotel at the end is delightful. Set facing south on the banks of the spectacular Loch Awe (which is never more than a mile wide but 24 miles long), the house has been sympathetically modernised into a country house hotel with a somewhat continental flavour. John and Monica Tyroll, ably assisted by Frances (willing guide dog to happy wanderers) and a courteous and friendly staff maintain the hospitality for which Taychreggan is justly famed. Gail Struthers has charge of the kitchens, and her menus, featuring the best of local fish, beef and game, are carefully planned, and well cooked and presented. The wine list is carefully selected and includes some fine clarets and burgundies. The hotel is built around a sunny courtyard onto which the bar opens, a pleasant venue for a bar lunch or a summer evening drink. There are three elegant lounges where fresh flowers and log fires add to the atmosphere. The bedrooms are very attractive and comfortable, each one individually decorated. The hotel can arrange shooting, deer stalking and fishing. Riding and golf are nearby. It is lovely walking country, quite easy going, in spring the scents of the wild flowers are a joy (I spotted 2 different varieties of wild orchid on my last visit). From Oban, take the A85, turning off to the right at Taynuilt onto the B845; at the end of the road you will find Taychreggan. Dinner, bed and breakfast from £55.00 per person, including VAT. Other terms on application.

KILDRUMMY CASTLE HOTEL

Kildrummy By Alford, Grampian AB3 8RA

Telephone: (09755) 71288 *Telex: 9401 2529* *Fax: 09755-71345*

Aberdeen 35, Alford 7, Inverness 72, Huntly 16, Edinburgh 130, (location A954 Alford to Mossat Road)

F licence; 16 en suite bedrooms, all with telephone, baby listening, colour TV, radio, tea making facilities; central heating; late meals to 10 p.m.; children welcome; dogs accepted; conferences, receptions and private parties; full-size billiard table; river fishing 3½ miles; riding by prior arrangement; golf 20 minutes away; most credit cards accepted.

Kildrummy Castle Hotel is situated in the renowned and very beautiful Kildrummy Castle Gardens overlooking the ruins of the original castle built in 1245. Inside the appointments are elegant and sumptuous with all modern comforts, whilst retaining the real atmosphere of a stately home. The owners, Tom and Mary Hanna, are ably supported by a cheerful and efficient staff. The public rooms are comfortable and pleasant with pieces of lovely antique furniture, as are the bedrooms, some with four poster beds. The menus both table d'hôte and à la carte are imaginative and well presented, supported by an excellent wine list. There is a delicious choice of dishes, many of Scottish traditional fare. Room and breakfast from £49.00 (single) or £84.00 (double), inclusive of VAT, other terms on application, including special short break holidays October to April. Closed January and February. Scottish Tourist Board 4 star Highly Commended Hotel.

THE KINLOCHBERVIE HOTEL

By Lairg, Sutherland IV27 4RP

Telephone: (097182) 275 *Fax: 097182 438*

Inverness 100, Lairg 47, Ullapool 60, Durness 19

F licence; 14 bedrooms all with en suite bathroom; telephone and television; room service; last orders for dinner 8.30 p.m.; bar meals; special diets on request; children welcome; dogs allowed; no conferences; pool table; sea bathing; sea fishing; sailing and boating, riding, shooting and fishing can be arranged; golf nearby; limited winter service; credit cards accepted.

Set in a remote corner of Sutherland, is a very comfortable modern hotel with high standards of hospitality, service and cuisine. It is family run by Rex and Kate Neame who take a warm, personal interest in the well being of their guests. The décor of the hotel is smart and contemporary, with an air of sophistication. Bedrooms are spacious and warm, with sea and harbour views. The Residents' Sitting Room is supplied with books and magazines, and from the Cocktail Bar, it is possible to watch the sun set over the sea. In the elegant restaurant, the imaginative menu makes full use of local products which are well cooked and beautifully presented with a selective wine list to go with them. Kinlochbervie has a busy modern fishing harbour, where you can see the latest catch, or the daily fish auction. There are beaches of golden sand just down the lane at Oldshore More. Smoo Cave is nearby, or you can visit Handa Island Nature Reserve, either by regular ferry or local boat. The same boat is equipped for deep sea fishing. Next door to the hotel is Garbet Lodge, offering simpler, but nonetheless well-appointed rooms with private facilities, particularly well suited to families. You will find Kinlochbervie off the A838 in the top left hand corner of Scotland. Room and breakfast from £50.00 single, £30.00 double.

LOCHALSH HOTEL

Kyle of Lochalsh, Highland IV40 8AF

Telephone: (0599) 4202 *Telex: 75318* *Fax: 0599 4881*

Edinburgh 207, Glasgow 194, Inverness 86, Plockton 5, Achnasheen 40

F licence; 40 en suite bedrooms (3 ground floor), all with telephone, radio and colour TV; baby listening; full central heating; lift; night service; meals to 9.00 p.m.; special diets; children welcome; dogs accepted; conferences and functions by arrangement; riding; shooting and fishing by arrangement; most credit cards accepted.

The Lochalsh was in the 1939 Edition of *Signpost*, then one read 'this L.M.S. Hotel overlooks the romantic crossing to Skye', it still does, but now under the ownership of Crown Hotels who have brought it up to date without losing any of the old standards of service. The hotel is very comfortable and most of its bedrooms and the dining room have views over the sea to the mountains of Skye. The slipway for the ferry is but a few yards away, and a picturesque journey can be made across the Kyle of Skye to Kyleakin in just five minutes. Light lunches are served in the cocktail bar, and the dining room offers table d'hôte and à la carte menus. For residents, there is also a private sitting room where guests are asked not to smoke. Most of the spacious bedrooms are equipped with easy chairs. The manager and his friendly staff will be pleased to help you plan your stay, and a visit to Plockton is a must. There is so much to see that is both dramatic and beautiful, as well as the number of places of historic interest that abound in the area. Room and breakfast from £53.00, other terms on application.

ACHANY HOUSE

By Lairg, Sutherland IV27 4EE

Telephone: (0549) 2172/2272

Edinburgh 218, Ullapool 48, Lairg 4, Inverness 46

5 bedrooms, 3 with private bathrooms; telephone & television; last orders for dinner 8.30 p.m. – later by arrangement; special diets by arrangement; children welcome; no dogs; house parties; golf & riding nearby; shooting & fishing, stalking red & sika deer can be arranged; house closed December 15th–January 15th; credit cards accepted.

Mrs. Havers-Strong has lovingly restored Achany House and now she opens her doors to guests who can enjoy the 'Achany Experience', to quote the Visitors' Book. She offers one single and three double bedrooms and one has a dressing room. For hunting parties, extra bedrooms can be made available. This elegant house, set in its quiet and lovely glen, was, until 1830, the seat of the Clan Munro, and subsequently, the Matheson family, who opened Britain's trade to the Far East. On either side of the hall are twin rooms, the breakfast parlour and the 'Telly and Welly' Room, where guests can come in wearing outdoor gear, warm themselves at the fire and enjoy a good cup of coffee. The twin towers contain the long oval drawing room, and the dining room, where dinner is served in grand style. The speciality of the house is game, much of it caught by Mrs. Havers-Strong, and her guests. Here you can hunt, participate in the varied field sports, or just enjoy the wild and beautiful glens and moors. Achany House makes an ideal base for a touring holiday, with the North, East and West coasts within easy reach. The house is open during the winter, and offers hind stalking holidays. To find Achany House, take the A836 from Bonar Bridge, and turn left at the sign for The Falls of Shin. The House is on the left about 2 miles past The Falls. Room and breakfast from £30.00 per person, nightly, or weekly from £310.00, including dinner.

GLEDDOCH HOUSE

Langbank, Renfrewshire PA14 6YE

Telephone: (047554) 711 *Telex: 779801* *Fax: 047554 201*

Glasgow 12

F licence; 33 en suite bedrooms, all with telephone, TV, trouser press, hairdryer, full central heating; night service; late meals to 10.00 p.m.; coffee shop; diets; children welcome; baby listening; dogs accepted; conferences; sauna; snooker; indoor heated swimming pool; golf, squash, riding; all credit cards accepted.

Once the private family home of the late Sir James Lithgow, this imposing house was converted into an hotel some ten years ago in a most satisfactory and tasteful manner. What impresses me about Gleddoch House is its general air of quality, and I spent a very agreeable overnight stay at this well managed hotel. You can quietly contemplate the interesting menu in the original panelled cocktail bar and then enjoy a well prepared meal in the pleasant atmosphere of the spacious restaurant. A new conservatory has also been recently added. Attractive smaller rooms are available for lunches, dinners or meetings. The 33 bedrooms are comfortable, pleasantly decorated and very well appointed. The Gleddoch Golf and Country Club lies amongst 250 acres of surrounding grounds. There is a par 72 18 hole golf course with a £15.00 green fee, but no charge for hotel guests, club house, sports shop, squash court, sauna and plunge pool. Also in evidence are horses from the riding stables and a field full of jumps. Gleddoch is situated just off the M8 towards Greenock, ten minutes or so drive from Glasgow airport and half an hour from the city. Gleddoch Hotels also own Houstoun House (see page 372). Room and breakfast from £85.00 (single), £62.50 per person (twin). Dinner, bed and breakfast £66.00 per person per night (weekends). Open all year.

BRISBANE HOTEL

Greenock Road, Esplanade, Largs, Strathclyde KA30 8NF

Telephone: (0474) 687200 *Fax: 0475 676295*

Glasgow 30, Edinburgh 75, Ayr 30, Troon 25, Prestwick 28

F licence; 23 bedrooms, all with en suite bathroom, telephone and TV; room service; baby listening; last orders for dinner 9.30 p.m.; bar meals; vegetarian diets; children welcome; no dogs; conferences max. 20–40; sports centre 5 mins.; swimming pool 100 yards; sea bathing nearby; 2 golf courses, tennis in town; riding, shooting and fishing nearby; hotel open all year; credit cards accepted.

The scenic route from England to Scotland, though longer, embraces the lovely coast of Dumfries, Galloway and Ayrshire. For a comfortable hotel let me suggest this Georgian mansion, recently extensively refurbished throughout. The hotel is situated on the A78 Esplanade, overlooking the Firth of Clyde estuary with views of the Isles of Arran and the Kyles of Bute. The first class bedrooms cannot fail to impress, with mahogany and cherry wood furniture, and where colour television, trouser press, hairdryer and minibars are standard. Good food is a feature one can appreciate, with table d'hôte or à la carte dinner menus. Local fresh fish ensures quality and can be recommended. From the varied wine list I am sure you will find a bottle to your liking. Some friends of mine spent a very enjoyable time here on a bowling holiday. Largs is well known for its sailing and water sports, and there are a couple of golf courses nearby. The hotel is under the same management as the Redcliffe Hotel, situated along the road to Skelmorlie (see page 368). Room and breakfast from £45.00 single, £75.00 double/twin, or weekly rates for dinner, bed and breakfast from £420.00 single, £575.00 twin/double.

INCHNADAMPH HOTEL

Loch Assynt, By Lairg, Sutherland IV27 4HL

Telephone: (05712) 202, Guests 219

Inverness 87, Bonar Bridge 37, Lairg 34, Scourie 21, Ullapool 25

F licence; 28 bedrooms (2 ground floor), 10 with private bathrooms, radio on request; last orders 7.45 p.m.; diets; children welcome; dogs accepted; fishing; lovely walks, wonderful area for botany, hill climbing, birdwatching; Visa, Access and Diners credit cards accepted.

Here in the shadow of the largest mountain in Sutherland, Ben More Assynt, in whose caves antiquarians have discovered traces of Palaeolithic man and some of the oldest rock formations known to exist in the world, is much of interest to geologists, botanists and archaeologists. The hotel enjoys a wide renown both as a quiet and ideal "Anglers' Retreat" and a restful centre for holidays. The prospect from the hotel facing down the length of lovely Loch Assynt is breathtaking. Inchnadamph has been known to *Signpost* for a long time, and all guests receive a true warm Highland welcome from the owners, J. S. and E. Morrison and family, who have run this very homely hotel for many years. This is a house noted for its hospitality, comfort, intimate atmosphere, good food, willing and friendly service. Excellent fishing, which is free to hotel guests comprises salmon, grilse, and beautiful brown trout. Boats are available on ten beats all of which, with one exception, are by the roadside. I can thoroughly recommend Inchnadamph for a peaceful holiday and a fisherman's paradise. Room and breakfast from £27.25 single, £54.50 double. Closed in winter, from the end of October to mid-March, but the office is always open for enquiries. Garage and parking, petrol and oils stocked.

INVER LODGE HOTEL

Lochinver, Sutherland IV27 4LU

Telephone: (05714) 496 *Telex: 75206* *Fax: 05714 395*

London 630, Edinburgh 254, Glasgow 266, Inverness 97, Lairg 47, Ullapool 37

F licence; 20 en suite bedrooms, suites and executive suites available, all with colour TV, telephone, trouser press, tea/coffee making facilities, hairdryer; children welcome; dogs accepted; daily laundry service; billiards room; sauna; solarium; free trout fishing for residents; all major credit cards accepted.

Inver Lodge was commissioned and built to a very high specification in 1988, on a site chosen for the superb views of Lochinver Harbour and the islands dreaming off-shore. It offers its guests traditional highland hospitality, coupled with every modern convenience and luxury. The cuisine, under the expert eye of John Robertson offers a well presented table d'hôte dinner from £24.50, with a wine list to complement his menus. The bedrooms are warm and elegant and equipped to the highest standards, including a trouser press concealed within the wardrobe and a tea tray tucked away in a neat drawer. You will find a bowl of fruit and some shortbreads awaiting you, and should you require anything else, room service offers anything from a snack to a steak. Best of all, the bedrooms face the sea, the exceptions being the Suilvan and Canisp suites, which have views to the mountains and sea. To enjoy even more stunning views, climb the path behind the hotel and stand by the cairn. In three directions, as far as the eye can see, there are mountains of every shape and size, and on the fourth side, the craggy coastline. You can enjoy fishing for salmon and trout on one of the rivers where the hotel has fishing rights, or on one of the lochs. A sea trip to Handa Island is to be recommended. The A837 delivers you to Loch Inver, and the hotel is half way down the village on the left. Room and breakfast from £62.00 single, double £47.00. Closed mid-November–end of April.

THE MANOR HOUSE

Oban, Argyll PA34 4LS

Telephone: (0631) 62087 *Fax: 0631 63053*

Edinburgh 123, Dundee 116, Glasgow 96, Inverness 118, Fort William 50, London 489

F licence; 11 en suite bedrooms, all with telephone, colour TV and full central heating; bar lunches; diets; dogs allowed; sea bathing; sailing and boating ½ mile; indoor heated swimming pool, sauna and solarium, golf, each within 2 mile radius; helipad; Access and Visa cards accepted.

For peace and quiet within walking distance of the bustle of Oban, I recommend the elegant little Manor House Hotel. Built beside the sea on the tip of the bay, it enjoys unrivalled views over the harbour, the adjacent islands and the mountains beyond. The hotel is owned and supervised by Mr and Mrs J. Leroy, along with their managers, Mr and Mrs Patrick Freitag. You can expect hospitality, service, comfort, good food and a very high standard of housekeeping. The house is furnished in keeping with its dignity and age, it offers pretty, well appointed bedrooms, an elegant drawing room and parlour and a well furnished cocktail bar with large windows overlooking the bay, making it a pleasant spot for an aperitif or a bar lunch. The dining room, which has an excellent reputation locally, is styled in pink, and glows with silver and candlelight. Chef Patrick Freitag offers a tempting menu composed of Scottish and continental cuisine, specializing in dishes made from abundant local fish and game in season. Oban is well placed for exploring the scenic West Coast, but for me, its chief delight is the opportunity to take to the sea, either on the car ferry to Mull or on the smaller craft visiting other islands and places of interest. If fishing is your wish you could hardly be better situated. Prices start at £45.00 for dinner, bed and breakfast, per person, weekly rates from £210.00 per person. Open all year except January.

ALLT-NAN-ROS HOTEL

Onich, Nr. Fort William, Inverness-shire PH33 6RY

Telephone: Onich (08553) 210 *Fax: 08553 462*

Fort William 10, Oban 40, Inverness 76, Glasgow 93, Edinburgh 123

F licence; 20 en suite bedrooms (5 ground floor) all with colour TV, radio, telephone, tea/coffee making facilities, hairdryers; late meals to 9.30 p.m.; light lunches available; diets; children welcome, baby listening; dogs accepted; conferences up to 20; children's play area; sea bathing; sailing and boating; shooting and deer stalking can be arranged; fishing (trout and salmon); golf, tennis, squash, riding nearby; lovely walks; all major credit cards accepted.

I was interested to learn that Allt-Nan-Ros is Gaelic for "Burn of the Roses" and derives from the cascading stream which flows through the gardens of the hotel into Loch Leven and Loch Linnhe. Allt-Nan-Ros was originally built as a Victorian Manor House, but has now been upgraded to an attractive hotel, where the amenities of today blend with the best of the past, thanks to the owners, Lachlan, James and Fiona MacLeod, who personally care for this first class place. The public rooms are furnished to a high standard, a new lounge overlooks the loch and features a small library bookcase and board games while the sun lounge has a summer house atmosphere. All overlook the loch and gardens, including the comfortable and nicely appointed bedrooms, newly refurbished in Sanderson fabrics. A recent conversion has provided two very charming and spacious en suite bedrooms with views over the loch to the mountains. The ground floor is particularly suitable for disabled folk. The Allt-Nan-Ros has a high reputation for good food. I thoroughly enjoyed an excellent table d'hôte menu, obviously chosen by a chef with imagination and individuality, dishes were nicely presented and served by a cheerful and efficient staff. A new vegetable and herb garden is being stoutly defended from the local deer and rabbit population, in order to add a home-grown element to this wonderful cooking. There is also a selective and well-chosen wine list comprising 70 wines. Dinner, bed and breakfast from £45.00 including VAT. Other terms on application. Closed end of October to mid-March, but office open for enquiries. "Taste of Scotland" award and Scottish Tourist Board 4 Crown Commended.

CRINGLETIE HOUSE HOTEL

Eddleston, Peebles, Borders EH45 8PL

Telephone: Eddleston (072 13) 233 *Fax: 072 13 244*

Edinburgh 20, Glasgow 50, London 360, Galashiels 19, Lanark 28

F licence; 13 en suite bedrooms all with telephone, remote control colour TV; lift to 1st and 2nd floors only; children welcome; comfortable residents' lounge and also non-smoking lounge; dogs permitted, but not in public rooms, or left unaccompanied in bedrooms; golf 3 miles; tennis; riding 3 miles; putting; croquet; fishing by permit on Tweed; Access, Visa credit cards accepted.

The border country provides the tourist with some of the most lovely and exciting scenery and we are happy to include this hotel for those visiting this area. It is (situated on A703 Edinburgh–Peebles road) approached by a long attractive drive, at the end of which stands this solid well preserved mansion house with marvellous views overlooking Eddleston Valley. The proprietors, Mr. and Mrs. S. L. Maguire, like to provide a personalised service and take no end of trouble to please their guests. The food is supplemented by vegetables and fruit from the walled kitchen garden. The menu, although not large, gives more than adequate choice and most important of all the dishes are freshly prepared. When I visited the hotel the dinner menu that night provided for starters a choice of Gruyère cheese, onion and white wine savoury, Californian avocado salad, and fresh sea trout mousse. The prices seemed very reasonable (starting from £20.00 for dinner) and that also applied to the wine list, and as Edinburgh is only 30 minutes away by car, I can envisage many visitors arriving just for the food, or indeed making this hotel their base for visiting Edinburgh. The public rooms are spacious and attractive and all the bedrooms have been redecorated to a high standard. Room and breakfast from £39.00–£50.00 single, £36.00 per person double/twin with bath, inclusive of VAT at 15%. Sunday lunches £12.50, weekday lunch from £5.00. No service charge. Closed late December to early March, open for Christmas. Enquire about two day Spring/Autumn breaks.

NEWTON HOUSE HOTEL

Glencarse, Nr. Perth, Tayside PH2 7LX

Telephone: (073 886) 250 *Fax: 073 886 717*

Perth 4, Dundee 13, Scone 10, Edinburgh 38, London 458

F licence; 10 en suite bedrooms, all with direct dial telephone, colour TV; tea/coffee making facilities; full central heating; last orders 9.30 p.m. – cold suppers after this time; bar meals; diets & vegetarian meals; children welcome; baby listening; well behaved dogs; conferences and private meals max. 50; over 40 golf courses in vicinity; excellent base for touring dramatic countryside & places of interest such as Scone Palace and Glamis Castle; tennis, riding and shooting nearby; major credit cards accepted.

This former Dower House to the Glencarse Estate is owned by hosts, Carol and Geoffrey Tallis, who pride themselves on offering their guests old fashioned hospitality. Set back from the A85, between Perth and Dundee, it is an ideal location for touring or getting to the major Centres and the famous golf courses. The 10 en suite, individually decorated bedrooms overlook the gardens, and the daily-change menus, presented each evening for your dining pleasure in the Country House Restaurant, feature fresh, local produce cooked in a Scottish / French tradition. The elegant lounges beckon you to enjoy an aperitif or digestif, including Geoffrey's special cocktail which I enjoyed during my visit, though I was unable to discover its secret! The Carse of Gowrie Antique Centre at Rait is a must for the collector, and the fine assortment of Tay pearls at Cairncross the Goldsmith's in Perth, is spectacular. With the home of golf at St. Andrew's (host to the 1990 Open Championship) only 29 miles away, this part of the world is the enthusiast's paradise. Fishing opportunities also abound in the lochs and Tay. The Hotel is open all year, with room and Scottish breakfast from £44.00 single, and £32.00 per person double/twin with 2 day or more Bargain Breaks available.

BALLATHIE HOUSE HOTEL

Kinclaven By Stanley, Nr. Perth, Perthshire PA1 4QN

Telephone: (025 083) 268 *Telex: 76216* *Fax: 025 083 396*

**Edinburgh 1 hour, Perth 20 mins, Pitlochry 40 mins, Gleneagles 45 mins
Rosemount (golf) 10 mins, St. Andrews 1 hour**

F licence; 28 bedrooms (Master Rooms have four poster or canopied beds and fine furniture) and 12 rooms in the Sportsmans Lodge, one ground floor suite suitable for disabled, 2 rooms suited to semi disabled; telephone and colour TV; last orders 8.30 p.m.; light or full luncheon; diets; children welcome; baby listening; dogs accepted in some rooms only; conferences up to 20; putting green and croquet; tennis; rough shooting and clay pigeon shooting; riding, swimming pool, golf, squash, solarium and sauna all nearby; helipad by arrangement 1–8 craft; Master Card, Amex, Diners, Visa cards accepted; hotel closed February.

When describing Ballathie as a country house of distinction, the epithets elegant and comfortable also spring to mind. A rambling "Scottish Victorian" mansion, it is set in the midst of its own estates, and has been beautifully restored. It is furnished with antiques and decorated with colours and fabrics that I find delightful. Its location too, is most enviable, within touring distance of many of Scotland's loveliest areas and with easy access to her cities. Once there, it is hard to believe that there is anywhere other than this private world, where one is tempted by delicious food and generally pampered by a friendly and courteous staff. If golf is your sport, there are courses to test any handicap nearby, and all the traditional Scottish field sports including salmon and trout fishing can be arranged for you by the estate. Whether your mission is business or pleasure, it would be hard to imagine a more suitable venue. Dinner, bed and breakfast from £63.00 to £79.00, weekly rate from £410.00. Sportsmans Lodge, from £25.00 to £31.00, for room and breakfast.

PITTODRIE HOUSE HOTEL

Pitcaple, Grampian AB5 9HS

Telephone: (046 76) 444 *Telex: 739935* *Fax: 046 76 648*

Aberdeen 22, Inverurie 6, Inverness 78, Aberdeen Airport 16

F licence; 27 en suite bedrooms, all with colour TV, radio, telephone, tea/coffee making facilities; central heating; meals to 9.00 p.m.; diets; children welcome; baby listening; dogs accepted; own tennis and squash courts; games room; croquet; clay pigeon shooting; riding; shooting, roe deer stalking and fishing can be arranged nearby; golf 6 miles; badminton 1 mile; large walled ornamental garden; lovely country walks; most credit cards accepted.

On the A96 Aberdeen to Inverness road about 4 miles north of Inverurie turn left and within approximately one mile you will find a long private drive leading to this 17th century castle, now with mid-Victorian additions. It has been in the family since 1900, and remained a family home until 1977, when the present owner, Mr. G. R. T. Smith, opened Pittodrie House as a beautifully furnished country hotel. Antique furniture and pictures belonging to the family remain in the reception rooms and bedrooms which are elegant, spacious and luxurious, with fine views of the gardens. In the gracious dining room, I enjoyed my dinner, the dishes were interesting, well presented and nicely served by a friendly and efficient staff. The wine list was selective and good. A new extension has been commissioned that blends well with the old house. This provides extra very well appointed bedrooms and an attractive suite of rooms designed for functions and conferences having the benefit of their own entrance and car park. I thoroughly commend this lovely house where you can find peace and relaxation. Tariff on application. Special winter terms from 1st October to 30th April. Always open.

GREEN PARK HOTEL

Pitlochry, Tayside PH16 5JY

Telephone: Pitlochry (0796) 3248

Edinburgh 68, Glasgow 83, Braemar 41, Inverness 69, Kingussie 45, Kinloch Rannoch 21, Perth 28

F licence; 37 en suite bedrooms (10 on ground floor), all with telephone, tea/coffee making facilities, colour TV; children welcome; conferences; chess; cards; table tennis; bar billiards; 9 hole putting; swings; sailing and surfing on the loch; pony trekking, golf and fishing by arrangement.

After a long journey, it is a delight to stay in the Green Park Hotel with its breathtaking panoramic views of Loch Faskally and the surrounding green hills. The Hotel is accessible by both car and British Rail Bargain Travel. You can be sure of a warm welcome from the staff, and this attitude pervades throughout. There are bright and spacious lounges, and the Sun Lounge overlooks the Loch. The equally attractive bedrooms are comfortable and well equipped as you would expect in such a well run hotel. Bar lunches and bar dinners are available daily from 12–2.00 p.m. and 7–9.00 p.m. offering The Taste of Scotland Fare. On Friday night, the dinner menu includes the Taste of Scotland for the Scottish Night, and on Saturday, by popular demand, there is the hors d'oeuvres table. A popular feature is the cold buffet served for Sunday dinner. Theatre-goers will appreciate meals being served from 6.30 p.m., with the restaurant closing at 8.30 p.m. With Pitlochry centre only 5 minutes walk away, you can find a variety of pastimes to make your holiday complete. Bed and breakfast from £31.00, inclusive of VAT. Bargain Breaks available and Curling Weekends in October. Closed from the end of October to the end of March, but the office is open for enquiries.

THE LOG CABIN HOTEL

Kirkmichael, Nr. Pitlochry, Perthshire PH10 7NB

Telephone: Strathardle (025 081) 288

Pitlochry 12, Edinburgh 70, Glasgow 85, Blairgowrie 12

F licence; 13 en suite bedrooms, all with radios; TV available; central heating; meals till 9 p.m.; bar meals available lunchtime; supper in the evening; diets; rooms suitable for the disabled; children welcome; dogs welcome; regular dinner dances and Folk nights; fishing; own stocked trout loch, salmon fishing by arrangement; shooting includes blackcock, grouse and use of clay trap; riding by arrangement and pony trekking; stalking by prior arrangement; private tuition for clay shooting and fishing; golf: 40 courses within 2 hrs.

Nine hundred feet above sea-level in a setting of highland heather and forest pine nestles the Log Cabin Hotel. It has a certain charm of its own, built of Norwegian whole logs with natural log walls inside as well. The atmosphere and layout have a continental flavour and it is all presided over by Daphne Kirk and Alan Finch. The cabin-style bedrooms are warm and cosy, mine had en suite facilities with separate bunk room – a boon if you travel en famille. The roomy cafe/bar is very well stocked, particularly with "the malt" for they have over 100 varieties. It has a central log fire with tables to one side where lunches, high teas and bar suppers are served. Another corner houses bar billiards. The restaurant has lovely views and it is not unusual to see deer wandering past. With its rich colours and pine walls it is a pleasing complement to the good, fresh Scottish fare served there. For residents there is a pretty sitting room with a television. This unsophisticated hotel is a pleasant venue from which to enjoy the wealth of outdoor pursuits available in the vicinity. Alan Finch is an expert with both rod and gun and he owns an extensive pheasant shooting and grouse moor. There is stalking for Roe and Fallow deer and excellent fishing on the hotel's loch, tuition is given to beginners. For riders horses are available next door to the hotel and there are miles of moorland roads and tracks threading through the hills. Less than half an hour's drive away there is skiing at Glenshee with special packages arranged for skiers of all abilities. Dinner, room and breakfast from £34.95 per person, including VAT. Reductions for children up to 12, other terms on application, including Winter, Spring, Christmas and New Year breaks.

THE LAKE HOTEL

Port of Menteith, Perthshire FK8 3RA

Telephone: (08775) 258 *Fax: 08775 671*

Glasgow 30, Edinburgh 40, Stirling 18, Oban 84, Perth 50

F licence; 12 bedrooms, all with en suite bathroom, telephone and TV; room and night service; last orders for dinner 9.00 p.m.; bistro for lunches; special diets; children over 10 welcome; dogs by arrangement; golf, riding, shooting and fishing all nearby; hotel open all year except Jan.; Visa and Access welcome.

The Lake Hotel stands on the shore of the Lake of Menteith, with the most romantic of views spread before it. Owned and supervised by Mr. and Mrs. Leroy, and managed by Mr. Peter Bodys, you can expect high standards of hospitality, service, cuisine, comfort and house keeping. The hotel has recently been renovated and refurbished throughout, with a sympathetic eye to the age and style of the building. The bedrooms are comfortable and attractive, with two suites (bedroom, dressing room and large bathroom) overlooking the lake. The mood created in the lakeside restaurant by the view, quiet music – often a live pianist – and discreet service, is just right for the appreciation of the dishes from the well planned menu of Chef, Mark Riva. He uses fresh local fish, meat and game, with vegetables, salads and fruits as they come into season, with delicious results. His breakfasts, too, are something rather special. Drinks and coffee are served in the lounge and conservatory, the former having plenty of books and magazines to enjoy. There is also a smart cocktail lounge, and bistro, serving light meals during the day. From Stirling, take the A84 shortly picking up the A873. After Ruskie, take the A81, and the hotel is ¼ mile on the left hand side. Dinner, room and breakfast per person from £36.00 (low season) £60.00 high season inc. VAT. Weekly from £210.00 low season and £320.00 high season.

CORSEMALZIE HOUSE HOTEL

Port William, Nr. Newton Stewart,
Dumfries and Galloway DG8 9RL

Telephone: Mochrum (098 886) 254

Carlisle 88, Glasgow 94, Dumfries 64, Newton Stewart 13, Port William 6

F licence; 15 bedrooms, 13 private bathrooms, all rooms with radio, room telephone, TV; full central heating; meals to 9.15 p.m.; diets; children welcome; baby listening; dogs accepted; conferences; dancing in winter; sea bathing, sailing and boating, golf, tennis 6 miles, badminton, riding, own shooting; squash 23 miles; own fishing (salmon, trout and coarse fishing); sea angling; croquet and putting.

What a perfect spot in which to spend a holiday, in the depths of the Galloway countryside with facilities from the hotel which include shooting, fishing, riding, tennis, bird watching and hill walking. Local membership is available at two golf courses. The hotel, rather off the beaten track, has been skilfully converted into a very fine and comfortable country house hotel and it has managed to retain the grace and atmosphere of a private mansion. All the public rooms have character and quality and are attractively decorated. The cocktail bar is intimate where people meet to discuss the day's adventures. The dining room offers a relatively small menu, never a bad thing, which has been carefully thought out, and I saw the well stocked larder where fresh produce is the order of the day. The bedrooms are pleasantly decorated with all the necessary modern equipment. The resident proprietors, Mr. and Mrs. Peter McDougall, ensure that you will have an enjoyable stay and receive courteous service. There is a definite appeal for sportsmen as well as guests in search of countrified peace and good living in a lovely setting. Room and breakfast from £34.00 (single), £53.00 (double). Closed mid-January to end February.

BARON'S CRAIG HOTEL

Rockcliffe, By Dalbeattie,
Dumfries and Galloway DG5 4QF

Telephone: Rockcliffe (055 663) 225

Edinburgh 94, Glasgow 94, London 353, Dalbeattie 7

F licence; 27 bedrooms (5 ground floor), all with colour TV, direct dial telephone; 20 private baths; children welcome; cold late meals on request; drying room; dogs accepted; golf, riding, sea bathing, boating, windsurfing, fishing all nearby.

Here is an off the beaten track country house hotel standing in its own twelve acres of mainly wooded ground with views overlooking the Solway Firth. It is an ideal spot for the young and old, family, or rejuvenation of the hard pressed business man, for life moves along at an easy pace and I found a definite charm in this peaceful scenic part of Scotland. You can enjoy complete seclusion and relaxed atmosphere although the amenities include safe sea bathing, boating, fishing and golf, all within easy distance. To these facilities I must add the grace of the grounds which are alive in spring with masses of bulbs and in due season with rhododendrons. On the evening I called for dinner the proprietor, Mr. D. A. Richardson, was always in evidence and at your service, and the owner and his family's attention to their guests' care and comfort is perfectly clear. The attractive dining room fitted with panoramic windows offers good food, together with a sensible wine list. Furnishings throughout the hotel are of a very high standard and the public rooms are spacious, comfortable and include many antiques. Room and breakfast from £34.00 single, £63.00 double. Terms are approximate and include VAT. Closed mid-October to Easter. A "Scotland's Commended Country Hotel".

ST. ANDREWS GOLF HOTEL

St. Andrew, Fife KY16 9AS

Telephone: (0334) 72611 *Fax: 0334 72188*

Dundee 11, Perth 33, Edinburgh 45, Glasgow 83

Hotel licence; 23 en suite bedrooms, all with telephone, radio, TV; full central heating; lift; night service; late meals to 9.30 p.m.; diets; children welcome; baby listening; dogs welcome; conferences; sauna; solarium; dancing in winter; sea bathing; golf close by. All credit cards accepted.

This hotel is situated just a few minutes walk from the headquarters of world golf – the Clubhouse of the Royal and Ancient Golf Club of St. Andrews, and the hotel overlooks St. Andrews Bay. Essentially, it is an hotel with a human touch, and comfortably appointed, inspired, no doubt, by the personal supervision of the owners Maureen and Brian Hughes. I spent a peaceful night in one of the well furnished bedrooms, which in addition to the facilities listed above have tea making facilities and a hair drier. There are four master bedrooms which have lovely sea views, and are spacious with many more facilities. Many local residents and visitors use the candlelit, oak panelled restaurant, which is a reflection on the good food and courteous service. Meals are offered until 9.30 p.m. There is a most carefully selected and comprehensive wine list of more than 100 wines and, as in most Scottish hotels, a well stocked cocktail bar. Part of an advertisement I saw regarding their fare read: "There's life after golf" and, though I am a member of the R and A, I am inclined to agree. Room and breakfast from £54.50 single, £89.00 double. Always open, winter rates on application.

SCOURIE HOTEL

Scourie, Highland IV27 4SX

Telephone: (0971) 2396 *Fax: 0971 2423*

Edinburgh 259, Glasgow 267, Inchnadamph 21, Lairg 43, Ullapool 45, Durness 26

F licence; 21 bedrooms, 19 with private baths, all with TV, telephone, children welcome; well behaved dogs welcome; diets; drying room; fishing on hotel waters; fishing for sea trout and salmon; sea bathing; bird watching; climbing; walking; own petrol pump and oil; Master Card, Diners, Visa cards accepted.

This hotel has been established since 1823 and is situated in the most wonderful part of the South West Coast, not far from Cape Wrath. The forces that threw up the great mountains, scooped out the lochs and fractured the coastline, created a fisherman's paradise. The fishers are usually discerning folk who like their creature comforts, and the Scourie Hotel is here to provide them. Ian and Mary Hay are experienced and successful hoteliers. You will be pleased with the appointments of the hotel; the rooms are warm and restful, with an atmosphere of comfort, enhanced by the antique furnishings and pictures in the main lounge and entrance, and an attractive and popular cocktail bar. The food is good, traditional home cooking, making use of local meat and fish, and is complemented by a well chosen wine list, with a very reasonable price range. The hotel holds fishing rights in lochs and rivers within an area of 25,000 acres, where salmon, sea trout and brown trout are caught. Alternative pursuits include trips out to the islands where seals may be watched; Handa Island is nearby for the ornithologist. The area is a ''mecca'' for geologists, climbers and walkers, and the motorist has an endless variety of places to explore. This is a place of rare character, located on interesting roads that I can highly recommend. Room and breakfast from £30.00 (single with bath), £53.00 double inclusive of VAT. Other terms on application. Open March to October, office always open for enquiries.

PHILIPBURN HOUSE HOTEL

Selkirk, Borders TD7 5LS

Telephone: (0750) 20747 *Fax: 0750 21690*

Edinburgh 40, Peebles 20, Galashiels 6

F licence; 16 en suite bedrooms (3 ground floor), all with telephone, radio, colour TV, baby listening, fire and smoke detectors, hairdryers, trouser press; full central heating; late meals to 9.30 p.m.; diets; children welcome; dogs on application; small conferences; dancing on Saturdays; billiards; games room; outdoor heated swimming pool; playground, adventure area; trampoline; all weather badminton; riding, fishing; 9 hole golf nearby; Visa, Amex, Diners, Master Card credit cards accepted.

Jim and Anne Hill own and run this friendly family hotel. He is a qualified architect and they are both international swimmers and now, through their dedication, successful hoteliers. I was impressed by the happy and relaxed atmosphere, and the many amenities available, especially for the younger generation – this hotel has much to offer. Let's start with food; Jim Hill looks after the kitchen, and the restaurant enjoys a high reputation for its culinary expertise. Looking at the extensive wine list, it is obvious that the owners take a keen interest in purchasing parcels of fine old wines, though sadly many bottles were lost during the severe winter of 1981–2. Hopefully you will meet Davy Fordyce, who is the resident guide for hill walking; he has a wealth of Scottish Borderland knowledge. There are numerous walks, short or long and special children's walks. You might also meet Davy dispensing malt whiskies in the popular Soutars Bar. A variety of bedrooms are available, many being family suites. Room and breakfast from £44.00 (single), £40.00 (twin). Dinner, room and breakfast from £49.00. Open all year.

REDCLIFFE HOTEL

Skelmorlie, Ayrshire PA17 5EH

Telephone: (0475) 521036 *Fax: 0475 521894*

Glasgow 33, Ayr 33, Edinburgh 85

F licence; 9 en suite bedrooms, all with telephone, colour TV; full central heating; last orders 10.00 p.m.; bar meals; diets; children welcome; sea bathing; sailing & boating; fishing; golf 1 mile; credit cards accepted.

A friend of mine recommended this small hotel, which overlooks the Firth of Clyde and the Isle of Bute, for its fine food. The Redcliffe enjoys an enviable reputation for its superb cuisine and the seafood is highly acclaimed. Freshly caught in Scottish seas and lochs, the locally produced delicacies ensure the consistent quality I know, as my lunch was delicious and I have promised myself the fish dinner which sounded quite mouth watering. The wine list has not been neglected and the choice is comprehensive. The bedrooms, all with private bathroom are pleasantly decorated and comfortable with television and telephone. Guido and Irene Bertschy and their family own and run the Redcliffe with care and attention which is reflected in the personalised service and relaxed atmosphere. As French, Italian and German are spoken, there is an international clientele. Tariff on application. Open all year.

DALMUNZIE HOUSE HOTEL

Spittal O'Glenshee, Blairgowrie, Perthshire PH10 7QG

Telephone: (025085) 224

Perth 35, Dundee 37, Braemar 15, Blairgowrie 20

F licence; 17 bedrooms, 15 with private bathrooms; full central heating; lift; late meals by arrangement; light lunches in Cocktail Bar; diets; children welcome; dogs welcome; conferences up to 30; receptions; bar billiards; games room; own 9 hole golf course; hard tennis court; shooting – grouse, pheasant, black cock etc.; deer stalking; clay pigeon; fishing – trout and salmon arranged, also own Rainbow Trout stocked loch; riding nearby; skiing – Glenshee slope 5 miles; 7 self catering cottages on estate, 2 self catering flats in House; most credit cards accepted.

Known as Dalmungie to the locals, this impressive and alluring country house is set in 6,000 acres just 1½ miles off the A93 Perth to Braemar road at The Spittal of Glenshee. Here you will find the entrance gates to the long drive, flanked by the river and golf course. Dalmunzie has been in the Winton family for a long time and is now looked after by Simon and Alexandra Winton – a young, energetic and attentive couple. A warm welcome and courteous friendly service await you at this attractive house. It is warm and cosy with log fires to toast your toes, a home in which to relax and be comfortable and where any problems will be sorted out with a laugh and a kind word. The centrally heated bedrooms are spacious and happily free from the intrusion of telephones, TV and tea making facilities. If you want a warm drink, they will cheerfully make you one at any time. The dining room provides varied and satisfying meals and light lunches are available in the cocktail bar. The family-owned sporting estate can organise almost any shooting holiday, but be sure to enquire early as it is a very popular pastime. Other field sports, trout fishing on the hotel's loch, walking, climbing and golf all await you on the estate. In winter there is skiing for all abilities at nearby Glenshee. Room and breakfast from £27.00 per person, inclusive of VAT. Other terms on application including special rates for 3 nights or more (see Bargain Breaks section). Closed November–December, but office open for enquiries.

PORT-an-EILEAN HOUSE HOTEL

Strathtummel, Perthshire PH16 5RU

Telephone: (08824) 233

Pitlochry 9, Edinburgh 76, Inverness 70, Aberfeldy 19

F licence; 6 en suite bedrooms, full central heating; late meals to 8.30 p.m.; diets; children welcome; dogs accepted; loch bathing; fishing, hotel boats on Loch Tummel, other river or loch fishing for trout or salmon nearby can be arranged; sailing; golf, riding, and shooting nearby; lovely walks.

This historic house built by the sixth Duke of Atholl as a shooting lodge, is situated in 21 acres of natural woodland and formal gardens and is actually on the shore of Loch Tummel, in central Perthshire, 9 miles from Pitlochry on the B8019, start of the legendary "Road to the Isles". This is truly "Queen's View" country. Port-an-Eilean is personally cared for by the resident owners, Mr. and Mrs. Gordon C. Hallewell, who have created a wonderful atmosphere for a peaceful and relaxing holiday in comfortable and restful surroundings. This splendid Country House, a home of distinction and dignity has rooms of character and quality, with superb views of loch and mountains. Downstairs is a friendly cocktail bar, an elegant drawing-room and an attractive sun lounge. In the dining room you are offered an excellent and well thought out table d'hôte menu, which is changed each day. Outside activities are plentiful – many beautiful walks, lots of interesting places to visit, four good golf courses within 15 miles, and trout and salmon fishing can be arranged. Room and breakfast from £30.00 single, £26.00 double (per person) inclusive of VAT. Other terms on application. Closed November to end of April but office open for enquiries.

THE TONGUE HOTEL
Tongue, Sutherland IV27 4XD

Telephone: (084755) 206 *Fax: 084755 353*

Thurso 40, Lairg 40, Inverness 100

F licence; 21 bedrooms (2 suitable for disabled), 14 with en suite bathroom; room telephone and TV; tea/coffee making facilities; room and night service; baby listening; last orders for dinner 8.30 p.m.; bar meals served 12.00–4.00 p.m. and 6.00–9.00 p.m.; special diets; children welcome; dogs accepted; conferences up to 30; Residents' Lounge; laundry service; sea bathing, sailing and boating; bird-watching; riding and fishing; hotel open all year; credit cards accepted.

The Tongue Hotel is one of a fast disappearing breed, the true 'traveller's rest'. After safely traversing the wilderness of mountain and moor on the undeniably narrow roads, guests experience a little of what their forebears must have felt on gaining shelter for the night. Within, bright, warm and cheerful, this Victorian-style hotel maintains the feeling of an outpost of civilization. Furnished with Victoriana, it offers comfortable bedrooms, equipped for the modern traveller, a cosy bar and a residents' sitting room. There is also a cheerful dining room which offers a good dinner, such as local sea-food or game, and all at a moderate price. In contrast to the harsh grandeur of the surrounding countryside, the village of Tongue is set amidst an abundance of greenery. The hotel stands on the hillside overlooking the golden sands of the Kyle of Tongue with its sentinel mountains and dramatic causeway. All roads in this part of Scotland eventually lead to Tongue and most travellers pause for refreshment at its hotel. Approach from the South on the A836 from Lairg, taking the opportunity to stop and listen to the silence of so vast a wilderness, or from East to West on the scenic coastal road that crosses the very top of Scotland. Tariff on application.

HOUSTOUN HOUSE HOTEL
Uphall, West Lothian EH52 6JS

Telephone: (0506) 853831 *Fax: 0506 854220*

Edinburgh 13, Linlithgow 7, Livingston 3, London 419

F licence; 30 en suite bedrooms (10 on ground floor), many featuring traditional four poster beds; all with radio, telephone, tea/coffee making facilities, TV; full central heating; night service; last orders for dinner 9.30 p.m.; diets; children welcome; baby listening; dogs accepted; conferences; golf; all major credit cards accepted.

Sir John Shairp, advocate to Mary Queen of Scots, acquired Houstoun House in 1569 and 400 years later it was converted into an hotel. It is owned by Gleddoch Hotels who also own Gleddoch House (see page 350). This is an extremely comfortable hotel whose reputation for fine cuisine has soared in the space of a short time. It is supported by a wine list which is second to none and makes interesting reading. Around 10,000 bottles lie in the cellar so the choice is – to say the least – comprehensive. Ian MacDonald, the head chef, has introduced a Scottish menu and he uses only fresh produce with herbs and spices from their own garden. It is a pleasure to walk around the well maintained gardens. The bar and reception area have been recently refurbished and are most pleasant and relaxing. All the bedrooms are attractively furnished some with four poster beds, and they have many amenities, including a trouser press. To reach the hotel, from Edinburgh you pass the airport and at Ingliston roundabout take the A89 to Uphall. Open all year. Room and breakfast from £76.00 to £87.00 (single), £100.00 to £130.00 (double), including VAT.

THE ISLANDS

JERSEY

THE ISLE OF MAN

THE ISLE OF WIGHT

ATLANTIC HOTEL

La Moye, St. Brelade, Jersey JE3 8HE

Telephone: (0534) 44101 *Telex: 4192405* *Fax: 0534 44102*

St. Helier 5, Airport 2

F licence; 50 en suite bedrooms including Garden Studio Rooms, and 2 luxury suites, all with telephone, colour TV and radio; late meals to 9.15 p.m.; lift; laundry service; conferences taken; diets available; children welcome; night service; sea bathing; golf nearby; health and leisure centre; indoor heated swimming pool; all major credit cards accepted.

Located amidst the most beautiful gardens, and overlooking the Bay of St. Ouen, the Atlantic Hotel is only 15 minutes from the airport. Since its massive refurbishment programme, the hotel bedrooms have been completely redesigned to capture the atmosphere of the 18th century, in the hand carved mahogany furnishings, and the colour schemes formed by modern variations on a traditional theme, which feature intriguing floral and oriental designs. Modern comforts are not forgotten, however, for instance en suite bathrooms and colour television (English and French), and an up-to-date satellite TV system are provided in all rooms. In the restaurant, new and exciting menus are offered, from table d'hôte to full à la carte, as well as the hotel's ever popular Spuntino menu, also redesigned. The grounds too have been re-landscaped, to introduce yet more trees and shrubs in which guests can wander or just relax by the outside swimming pool after an energetic day's exploring. The new health and leisure centre, known as The Palm Club, includes an indoor heated swimming pool, a spa pool, a fitness centre, saunas and solaria as well as the all weather tennis court. For the sportsminded, a wide variety of activities are available on the island; as well as discovering the romantic and beautiful countryside, there are watersports and horseriding, and the hotel itself overlooks the international standard La Moye Golf Club Course. Whether you are on Jersey for business or pleasure, The Atlantic provides the comfort of an ideal home from home. Room and breakfast from £70.00–£100.00 single, £100.00 to £130.00 double, depending on season. Full terms on application.

HOTEL CHATEAU VALEUSE

St. Brelade's Bay, Jersey

Telephone: (0534) 46281 *Fax: 0534 47110*

F licence; 33 en suite bedrooms, all with telephone, TV, central heating; night service; late meals; diets catered for; children over 5 welcome; no dogs; heated outdoor swimming pool with sea bathing and all sports available nearby. Closed in January and February; Master Card, Barclaycard and Eurocards accepted.

A friendly atmosphere welcomes you at Chateau Valeuse where Mr. and Mrs. Magris run this small hotel which was once the summer residence of the famous Vicomte de St. Juste. Many of the bedrooms overlook St. Brelade's Bay and all are comfortably and tastefully furnished. The Tudor Bar is a cosy meeting place and the sun lounge overlooks the flower terrace, large heated swimming pool and beautifully kept gardens. The hotel is run in association with Manzi's of London and is well known for its fresh sea-food specialities. These are frequently featured on the hotel's table d'hôte menu and also on the extensive à la carte in the Chateau Restaurant which is greatly appreciated by local residents as well as guests. For those who seek quiet relaxation, personal service, excellent food and fine wine – Chateau Valeuse is for you. Room and breakfast from £32.00 single, £60.00 twin.

HOTEL L'HORIZON
St. Brelade's Bay, Jersey

Telephone: (0534) 43101 *Telex: 4192281* *Fax: 0534 46269*

St. Helier 5, Airport 1¾

F licence; 103 en suite bedrooms (16 ground floor), all with radio, telephone and TV; full central heating; lift; night service; late meals; Grill Room; diets; children welcome; baby listening; conferences; sauna, spa pool, steam baths, mini gymnasium; daily dancing in season, twice weekly in winter; indoor heated swimming pool; sea bathing; Visa and Master Card accepted.

L'Horizon is deservedly acknowledged to be one of Europe's leading hotels. It is situated on the south facing edge of the Island's most beautiful bay which has masses of sand and safe swimming. There is an individual style of comfort and service from 160 full-time staff, and unashamed luxury. All bedrooms, many overlooking the sea with breakfast balconies, are tastefully furnished, with certain rooms boasting electrically operated curtains. The renowned Restaurant and popular Star Grill regularly win many awards during the Jersey Good Food Festival, an event with the highest standards. Elegant lounge suites and the choice of two bars afford the ideal atmosphere in which to relax. There is a wide range of facilities including Club L'Horizon and a new Leisure Centre, featuring large, indoor heated swimming pool, sauna, steam and spa baths. There is also an adjacent brasserie. Also available for long or short charters is the Hotel's own 40ft luxury motor sailing yacht, "Clipper L'Horizon", complete with experienced skipper. Manager Gerald Fletcher, whose connection with the hotel goes back some 17 years, personally attends to the requirements of his discerning guests who demand the best. Open all year, room and breakfast from £65.00 single, £130.00 double.

LONGUEVILLE MANOR HOTEL
St. Saviour, Jersey

Telephone: (0534) 25501 *Telex: 4192306* *Fax: 0534 31613*

Airport 6, St. Helier 1½

F licence; 33 en suite bedrooms including 2 luxury suites (6 ground floor); late meals; diets; night service; dogs welcome; TV and radio; drying room; lift; own heated swimming pool; large gardens; sea bathing ¾ mile; golf, tennis and squash ½ mile.

This privately owned 13th century manor house, run by the Lewis and Dufty families, is the perfect setting in which to be pampered. At the foot of one of Jersey's most beautiful valleys, the 15 acres of well kept garden provide most of the produce used in the kitchen, which is under the direction of the new Chef de Cuisine Andrew Baird, recently of Hambleton Hall. There is an excellent wine list to complement the cuisine. Set in the gardens is a heated swimming pool where the day may be idled away with cocktails and lunch. The 31 bedrooms and two luxury suites, all individually decorated, have modern amenities. Only 1½ miles east of St. Helier and within easy reach of the beach, golf course and tennis courts, the Longueville Manor is perfectly situated for your visit to the island. The hotel is also the only one in the Channel Islands to have been granted membership of the Relais et Chateaux. Room and breakfast £68.00 single, £104.00 twin, including service.

GRAND ISLAND HOTEL

Ramsey, Isle of Man

Telephone: (0624) 812455 *Telex: 629849* *Fax: 0624 815291*

Airport 25, Sea Terminal 16, Ramsey 1, Douglas 16, Local Transport 1

F licence; 55 en suite bedrooms all with telephone and colour TV; full central heating; lift; night service; last orders 10.00 p.m.; bistro; bar meals; dietician; children welcome; baby listening; dogs by prior arrangement; conferences 100 max.; snooker; dancing twice weekly; indoor heated swimming pool; sauna; solarium; leisure centre with turkish bath, hair salon and beautician; sea bathing; sailing, boating, tennis, squash, shooting, fishing and golf 1 mile; riding, croquet, helipad; credit cards accepted.

It was a beautiful spring day when I drove over the Snaefell Pass to Ramsey. The hills were yellow with gorse, bluebells and primroses covered the banks and there were marvellous views over the mountains and across the sea. The Grand Island Hotel is magnificently situated, overlooking Ramsey Bay with terraced lawns stretching down to the beach. This original Georgian House was added to in the Victorian era, with further extensions in 1960. The hotel was taken over by its present owners in 1985 and since has been completely refurbished, returning the hotel to its original splendour and adding a wonderful leisure spa and furnishing the rooms with antiques. The main restaurant, with magnificent views over the bay, offers an excellent choice from the à la carte menu, including the famed local fish. Lunch can be served in the bar, or in the Bistro, decorated with red and white tablecloths and many pictures, giving it a warm and cosy atmosphere. The banqueting facilities are excellent and include a ballroom and a dining area with panoramic views. The bedrooms are excellent, all individually and tastefully designed using fabrics from leading English designers. Rooms are equipped with a generous Welcome Pack, plus all amenities associated with a hotel of this standing. There are several luxury suites, some of which include jacuzzi baths. This hotel is an ideal base for a holiday catering for all tastes, from the peace of surroundings with magnificent walks by the sea, through the mountains and glens, to golf, riding, shooting and many other sports. Tariff on application. Open all year.

WINTERBOURNE HOTEL
Bonchurch, Nr. Ventnor, Isle of Wight PO38 1RQ

Telephone: (0983) 852535 *Fax: 0983 853056*

R & R licence; 19 en suite bedrooms (3 ground floor), all with colour TV, telephone and part central heating; last orders 10.00 p.m. by arrangement; bar meals; children welcome; dogs allowed; outdoor heated swimming pool; leisure centre, sauna and sea bathing, squash, badminton, fishing and riding all nearby; Amex, Visa and Access welcome.

This elegant hotel was once the home of Charles Dickens, and he wrote *David Copperfield* here. It is set in lovely gardens with a profusion of colourful flower beds, and a charming stream with pools and waterfalls. There are also private steps and a path down to the beach, altogether an idyllic location, characterized by its peace and tranquillity. Bonchurch enjoys an enviably mild winter climate, being sheltered by St. Boniface Down. The hotel is immaculately run under the personal direction of the proprietors, Pat and Terry O'Connor, and I thoroughly enjoyed my stay here. After a drink in the elegant first floor drawing room, an excellent dinner was served by candlelight in the attractively furnished Copperfield room. The bedrooms are comfortably appointed, with everything the discerning guest could wish for, and most rooms have the most wonderful views over the gardens and sea, whilst others look out over woodland. Hotel closed in winter. Tariff on application.

HOTEL RYDE CASTLE

Ryde, Isle of Wight PO33 1SA

Telephone: (0983) 63755 *Telex: 896466* *Fax: 0983 616436*

Birmingham 151, London 75, Portsmouth 3, Bournemouth 55, Heathrow 72, Southampton Airport 22

F licence; 17 en suite bedrooms, all with colour TV, telephone and full central heating; last orders 10.00 p.m.; bar meals; diets; children welcome; baby listening by arrangement; dogs allowed; conferences up to 200; dinner dances weekly; sea bathing, sailing and boating; leisure centre, tennis and indoor heated swimming pool nearby; squash 2 miles; riding 3 miles; local shooting club; sea and coarse fishing nearby; Mastercard, Visa and Eurocard accepted.

Ryde Castle is a beautiful creeper clad building commissioned by Henry VIII around 1540, to defend Spithead, Southampton Water and Solent from invasion. This eventuality arose later, in the form of the Spanish Armada in the reign of his daughter Elizabeth I. The sea once came up to the car park wall but has gradually receded over the years and you can enjoy magnificent views of the busy Solent, with some of the world's greatest shipping sailing past on world-wide voyages. The castle is steeped in history and is allowed to fly Henry VIII's royal standard from one of its towers. Under the direction of the proprietors, Peter and Patricia Dickins, many exciting period features are being discovered and long neglected moulded ceilings have been carefully restored. The Isle of Wight is a delightful and popular holiday resort with lovely beaches, and of course, excellent sailing. It has a high rate of sunshine, and there is lots to do and see. The hotel bedrooms are well appointed with all modern facilities, and the double rooms have romantic four poster beds. The restaurant offers both table d'hôte and à la carte menus, making full use of the fresh fish caught locally, and Island farm produce. A wide selection of bar snacks and meals is available at lunchtime. Open all year. Room and breakfast from £45.00; Other terms on application, see Bargain Break section.

The English Tourist Board

The network of Tourist Information Centres around the country can help you with planning your holiday, visiting local places of interest and advises you about events and festivals in the region. The English Tourist Board publishes a free director of Tourist Information Centres in the British Isles, available from the English Tourist Board's Networking Unit.

Look Out For This Sign

or write to

ENGLISH TOURIST BOARD,
THAMES TOWER, BLACKS ROAD,
HAMMERSMITH, LONDON W6 9EL
Telephone: 081-846 9000. Telex: 266975 ETBG
Fax: 081 563 0302

LOOK OUT FOR THIS SIGN . . .

Every Hotel that we recommend in our 52nd Edition has been issued with one of these signs and we should be glad to have any comment you wish to make on the Hotel concerned.

1 PHONE CALL FOR 100 HOTELS!

INTER-HOTELS

The way to stay

For 22 years, Inter-Hotels, a consortium of quality hotels, has been offering excellent value for money holidays. Putting the customer first, at over 100 hotels of character and style.

All Inter-Hotels are especially chosen. In addition to finding places to suit your tastes in scenery, we take into account quality, comfort, cuisine and character. You can expect tasteful furnishings, well-equipped bedrooms with private facilities and toilet (most also have colour television).

Send for our holiday brochure so that you can rediscover Britain and Ireland's special appeal and rich variety - a variety encompassing an ever-changing patchwork of landscape, coastline, traditions and places to visit

INTER HOTELS
35 Hogarth Road
London SW5 0QH
Telex: 8951994
Fax: 071 370 7870

CENTRAL RESERVATIONS ☎ 071 373 3241

A Prestige Hotel

RESERVATIONS

GREAT BRITAIN
21 Blades Court,
Deodar Road,
London SW15 2NU.
Tel: 0800 282 124
Toll-Free.
(081) 877 9500
Mkt & Admin.
Telex: 269264
Fax: (081) 877 9477

SCANDINAVIA
Strandvagen 7 C,
Box 14059,
10440 Stockholm,
Telephone: (08)-663 5800
Telex: 17119. Fax: (08) 78366 34

AUSTRALIA & NEW ZEALAND
177-185 William Street
Kings Cross, NSW 2011
Tel: Sydney (02) 360 1666
Elsewhere in Australia:
(008) 251 664 Toll Free.
Telex: 71-127172
Fax: (02) 360 1843
Tel: NZ: (09) 393 814
Fax: NZ: (09) 303 1390

Prestige Hotels

SOUTH AFRICA
P.O. Box 6287
Johannesburg 2000
Tel: (011) 311 2911
Telex: 488196
Fax: (011) 331 2648

JAPAN
21-7 Toranomon 3-Chome,
Minato-Ku, Tokyo, 105.
Tel: (03) 431 6524.
Fax: (03) 578 4060.

NORTH AMERICA
555 Fifth Avenue
New York 10017
Toll Free: (800) 544 7570.
Telex: 170974.
Fax: (718) 786 2350

BARBADOS
Coral Reef Club,
St. James.

FRANCE
Hotel Lancaster,
7 Rue de Berri,
75008 Paris.

GERMANY
Hotel Hessicher Hof,
Friedrich-Ebert-Anlage 40,
6000 Frankfurt-am-Main

Schlosshotel Kronberg
Hainstrasse 25
D – 6242 Kronberg/
Taunus

GREAT BRITAIN
Alexander House,
Fen Place,
Turners Hill,
West Sussex RH10 4QD

Amberley Castle,
Amberley,
Nr. Arundel,
West Sussex BN18 9ND

Auchterarder House,
Auchterarder,
Perthshire,
PH3 1DZ

Bodysgallen Hall Hotel,
Llandudno,
Gwynedd,
North Wales LL30 1RS

Bishopstrow House,
Warminster,
Wiltshire BA12 9HH

The Castle Hotel,
Castle Green,
Taunton,
Somerset TA1 1NF

The Chester Grosvenor,
Eastgate Street,
Chester,
Cheshire CH1 1LT

The Close,
8 Long Street,
Tetbury,
Gloucestershire GL8 8AQ

Clivedon,
Taplow,
Buckinghamshire SL6 0JF

Crabwall Manor,
Mollington,
Chester,
Cheshire CH1 6NE

Culloden House,
Inverness,
Scotland IV1 2NZ

Danesfield House,
Medmenham,
Marlow,
Buckinghamshire SL7 3ES

Dukes Hotel,
St. James's Place,
London SW1A 1NY

Eastwell Manor,
Eastwell Park,
Ashford,
Kent TN25 4HR

The Elms,
Abberley,
Nr. Worcester WR6 6AT

The Fenja,
69 Cadogan Gardens,
London SW3 2RB

Hanbury Manor,
Thunbridge,
Nr. Ware,
Hertfordshire SG12 0SD

Hartwell House,
Oxford Road,
Aylesbury,
Bucks HP17 8NL

The Halkin,
5/6 Halkin Street,
London SW1X 7DJ

Horsted Place,
Little Horsted,
Uckfield,
East Sussex TN22 5TS

Invery House,
Royal Deeside,
Banchory,
Kincardineshire,
Scotland AB3 3NJ

Lainston House,
Sparsholt,
Winchester SO21 2LT

Llangoed Hall,
Llyswen,
Brecon,
Powys,
Wales LD3 0YP

Luckham Park Hotel,
Colerne,
Wiltshire SN14 8AZ

Lower Slaughter Manor,
Lower Slaughter,
Gloucestershire

Middlethorpe Hall,
Bishopthorpe,
York SL4 5UR

Oakley Court Hotel,
Windsor Road,
Water Oakley,
Windsor,
Berkshire SL4 5UR

Pennyhill Park,
College Ride,
Bagshot,
Surrey GU19 5ET

The Ritz,
Piccadilly,
London W1V 9DG

Royal Crescent Hotel,
16, Royal Crescent,
Bath,
Avon BA1 2LS

South Lodge,
Lower Beeding,
West Sussex RH13 6PS

The Stafford,
St. James's Place,
London SW1A 1NJ

Stapleford Park,
Melton Mowbray,
Leicestershire LE14 2EF

Tylney Hall,
Rotherwick,
Nr. Hook,
Hampshire RG27 9AJ

REPUBLIC OF IRELAND
Park Hotel Kenmare,
Kenmare,
County Kerry

Adare Manor,
Adare,
County Limerick

ITALY
Hotel Monaco and
Grand Canal,
San Marco,
1325 Venice

Grand Hotel Villa Cora,
Viale Machiavelli 18,
Florence 50125

SWEDEN
Hotel Diplomat,
Strandvagen 7G,
P.O. Box 14059,
S – 10440 Stockholm

CRUISE SHIPS
Seabourn Pride
Seabourn Spirit
Sea Goddess I
Sea Goddess II

If you would like further information on Prestige Hotels or if you would like to obtain copies of the Prestige Hotels Directory; Short Breaks Brochure; Prestige Magazine; or individual hotel brochures, please write to:
Prestige Hotels, 21 Blades Court, Deodar Road, London SW15 2NU.

BARGAIN BREAKS

Readers are recommended to telephone the hotels to confirm rates and conditions prior to booking.

AVON

FOUNTAIN HOUSE, Lansdown Road, Bath *page* 33

January through to March 1991, any 3 night booking, there is a fourth night free of charge. Prices for four nights start at £162.00 per person.

LANSDOWN GROVE HOTEL, Lansdown Road, Bath *page* 34

£48.00 per person, for dinner, bed and breakfast at weekends only throughout the year. Special seasonal breaks, details on application.

ROYAL CRESCENT HOTEL, Bath *page* 35

Short breaks available. Sunday to Thursday nights inclusive, £70.00 for bed and English breakfast, £95.00 for dinner, bed and breakfast. Friday and Saturday nights £77.00 for bed and English breakfast in a standard room, £110.00 for dinner, bed and breakfast; £93.00 for bed and English breakfast, £125.00 for dinner, bed and English breakfast in a deluxe room; £124.00 for bed and English breakfast, £157.00 for dinner, bed and breakfast in a suite. Rates are per person, per night for a minimum of 2 consecutive nights and include service and VAT.

THE OLD SCHOOL HOUSE, Nr. Bath *page* 36

Two and three day breaks during the period October–March, covering bed, dinner and breakfast. Midweek breaks: 2 days, £60.00 per person. Weekend breaks: 2 days £65.00 per person. Additional days at £25.00 per person.

HUNSTRETE HOUSE, Hunstrete, Bath *page* 128

£175.00 for any 2 nights on a dinner, bed and breakfast basis, per person.

HUTTON COURT, Hutton *page* 129

Reductions available for stays of 2 nights or more. Details on application.

RANGEWORTHY COURT, Rangeworthy *page* 202

Any two days, from £70.00, including dinner, offered all year round.

THORNBURY CASTLE, Thornbury, Nr. Bristol *page* 251

Tariff on application.

BEDFORDSHIRE

THE BEDFORD SWAN, Bedford *page* 37

Weekend break; accommodation for any two nights from Friday evening to Monday morning, £66.00 per person, inclusive of breakfast and a daily allowance of £9.75 towards dinner (à la carte). No supplement for singles, prices not applicable at Christmas and New Year.

BERKSHIRE

ROYAL BERKSHIRE HOTEL, Ascot *page* 19

Champagne Weekend Break £75.00 per person per night, Friday to Sunday. Includes room, morning papers, early morning tea, full English breakfast, dinner, champagne on arrival, service and VAT. Suite supplement of £50.00.

MONKEY ISLAND HOTEL, Maidenhead *page* 172

Weekend Island Breaks, double or twin from £60.00, suite £70.00. Rates are per person, per night and fully inclusive of overnight accommodation, with private bathroom, full English breakfast, early morning tea, four course table d'hôte dinner and free use of all hotel facilities, including fishing and croquet lawn.

BERKSHIRE (Contd.)

REGENCY PARK HOTEL, Nr. Newbury *page* 188

Weekend break – arriving Friday or Saturday, minimum 2 night stay, £49.50 per person per night for dinner, bed and breakfast. Racing weekends at £60.00 per person per night as above, plus entry to Newbury Racecourse, luncheon in Members' dining room and limousine to and from racecourse.

KIRTONS FARM COUNTRY CLUB AND HOTEL, Reading *page* 204

Weekend leisure breaks; two nights accommodation and breakfast, full use of all the sporting facilities, and including a £10.00 allowance towards dinner each night, which may be taken in the Pavilion Restaurant, The Waterfront Bistro or The Members' Bar. £40.00 per person per night, including VAT.

THE SWAN DIPLOMAT, Streatley-on-Thames *page* 241

Special weekend breaks from £126.50 per person to include 2 nights accommodation. Chef's speciality dinner and full English buffet breakfast; VAT included (Friday and Saturday or Saturday and Sunday).

CANTLEY HOUSE HOTEL, Wokingham *page* 279

Weekend rates; single £35.00, double £45.00. Weekend break Fri–Sat, £36.00 per person, per night, to include £12.00 allowance for dinner.

BUCKINGHAMSHIRE

DANESFIELD HOUSE, Marlow *page* 178

Weekend and special activity rates will be available on request towards opening date in March 1991.

CAMBRIDGESHIRE

BUTTERFLY HOTEL, Peterborough *page* 90

Weekend break rate; from £33.50 per guest per night, sharing twin/double room. Applicable one or more nights from Friday to Sunday. Price is for overnight stay, full breakfast and a dinner allowance of £10.50. Offer applies also to sister hotels featured in Guide.

CHESHIRE

THE ALDERLEY EDGE HOTEL, Alderley Edge *page* 2

£35.00 per person including breakfast.

page 39

THE WILD BOAR HOTEL AND RESTAURANT, Beeston, Nr. Tarporley

A two night luxury weekend break comprises Friday dinner and accommodation, Saturday full English breakfast, dinner and accommodation, Sunday full English breakfast, 3 course luncheon. £86.00 per person. One night weekend break £58.00 per person.

MOLLINGTON BANASTRE HOTEL, Chester *page* 74

Special weekends and one-parent family weekends available. Further details on request.

ROWTON HALL HOTEL, Chester *page* 75

Mini Weekend Break – Friday and Saturday dinner, bed and English breakfast £60.00–£76.00 single, £72.00–£82.00 twin or double. Special weekend breaks £47.00 per person per night, which include accommodation, breakfast and table d'hôte dinner.

OLD HALL HOTEL, Sandbach *page* 219

Two nights (to include Saturday). Dinner and breakfast £75.00 per person. £5.00 supplement per person in the four poster room.

CORNWALL

PENHALLOW MANOR, Altarnun *page* 6

Special week long breaks from 1st February to 1st July from £245.00 per person, dinner bed and breakfast, or £280.00 from 1st July to 1st September. Special terms for October and November. For mid-week and weekend breaks, please apply for tariff.

BOSKERRIS HOTEL, Carbis Bay, Nr. St. Ives *page* 67

Low season breaks – two or four days. Prices on application. 5–7 day golfing packages available.

ROYAL DUCHY HOTEL, Falmouth *page* 95

Reduced rates for stays of 2 nights or more. Special rates for children up to 11. Reduced green fees at Falmouth Golf Club and FREE golf at the Carlyon Bay Hotel and Golf Course, our sister hotel in St. Austell. Winter Breaks (November–Easter) from £72.00, Spring Breaks (April–May 24th) from £90.00. Early Summer Breaks (June–July 20th) from £98.00. All prices for 2 nights' half board per person. Autumn Breaks on application.

THE FOWEY HOTEL, Fowey *page* 100

From Friday evening and departing by 11.00 a.m. on Sunday. Two evenings dinner, accommodation and full English breakfast, £140.00 fully inclusive for two persons in a double or twin room with all facilities. Not applicable on Bank Holiday weekends.

HOTEL BRISTOL, Newquay *page* 190

Low season breaks from 22nd September '90–18th May '91 (except Christmas and New Year). Bristol Weekender; two nights £80.00 per person, to be taken Friday/Saturday or Saturday/Sunday, children under 3 no charge. Five day Bristol Break – any five nights, 175.00 per person, children under three no charge. Other children's prices available on application.

HEADLAND HOTEL, Newquay *page* 191

Any length breaks available all season (midweek or weekend) from £70.00 per person low season, £120.00 per person high season for 2 nights, half board in a sea-view room with all facilities. Special interest holidays including champagne hot-air balloon flights, wine tasting, golf and murder weekends. Send for details.

QUEEN'S HOTEL, Penzance *page* 198

Bargain Breaks and special Christmas package available. Rates on application.

PORT GAVERNE HOTEL, Nr. Port Isaac *page* 201

'Breather' breaks off season and 'Tourer' breaks for three or five nights during the season. Terms on application.

CARLYON BAY HOTEL, Nr. St. Austell *page* 214

Open throughout the year, the Carlyon Bay is ideal for early or late breaks, especially with free golf available to residents, making them exceptionally good value to golfers. Winter breaks (November to Easter) from £95.00, Spring breaks (April to Whitsun) from £115.00, Early Summer breaks (June to July 12th) from £125.00. All prices for 2 nights half board per person. Autumn breaks on application.

ST. MORITZ HOTEL, Nr. Wadebridge *page* 265

Low and Winter season breaks, reduced rates on application.

CUMBRIA

LOWBYER MANOR, Alston *page* 5

From January to the end of June inclusive (excluding Bank Holidays), and the beginning of November to the end of December inclusive (excluding Christmas); from £75.00 for any 2 nights.

CUMBRIA (Contd.)

KIRKSTONE FOOT HOTEL, Ambleside page 9
Special Wine Weekends and midweek theme breaks. Open Christmas and New Year. Prices and further details upon application.

NANNY BROW COUNTRY HOUSE HOTEL, Ambleside page 10
Weekend breaks available November to March, Midweek Specials from November to May. Prices and further details on application.

ROTHAY MANOR HOTEL, Ambleside page 11
Between November 1st 1990 and March 28th 1991, but excluding Christmas and New Year, weekend and midweek breaks available, from £54.00 to £78.50 per person per night, inclusive of morning tea, full English breakfast and dinner. Minimum stay of 2 nights at weekend. Courses available include Music of Imperial Russia, Music in Paris 1889–1939, Christmas Preparation, French Cuisine, Wine Evenings and a special Victorian Christmas Dinner. Full details available from the hotel.

WATEREDGE HOTEL, Ambleside page 12
Winter and Spring breaks available from 1st November 1990 until mid May 1991. Mid-week breaks £84.00, Weekend breaks £94.00 per person, for 2 nights dinner, room and breakfast, inclusive of VAT.

SKELWITH BRIDGE HOTEL, Nr. Ambleside page 13
Winter, Spring and Summer breaks available. Tariff on application.

APPLEBY MANOR, Appleby-in-Westmorland page 15
Minimum 2 nights from £42.00 per person nightly, all year, including dinner, room and breakfast, and temporary membership of the leisure club. Scenic cycling breaks, 2 nights from £90.00. Try the romance of the 'Cloud Nine Experience', Champagne, Four Poster, Chocolates and a red rose, from £104.00. 'Hangover Breaks', sample 12 single malt whiskies from a range of over seventy, prices from £96.00.

ROYAL OAK INN, Appleby-in-Westmorland page 16
Two day breaks and fishing breaks available. Tariff on application.

TUFTON ARMS, Appleby-in-Westmorland page 17
Breaks offered all year, subject to availability.

PHEASANT INN, Bassenthwaite Lake, Nr. Cockermouth page 30
Winter breaks available from November to March. Details on application.

OVERWATER HALL, Nr. Bassenthwaite Lake, Ireby page 31
Two day breaks from £66.00.

CUMBRIA PARK HOTEL, Carlisle page 68
October until April, Weekend breaks. Minimum two night stay, dinner, bed and breakfast. Tariff on application.

THE STRING OF HORSES INN, Nr. Carlisle, Faugh page 69
Bargain breaks available – any 2 days or more between October and April, excluding Bank Holidays. Tariff on application.

GRAYTHWAITE MANOR HOTEL, Grange-over-Sands page 105
November–March – up to 25% off seasonal tariff. July and August special terms on application. Please write for details.

NETHERWOOD HOTEL, Grange-over-Sands page 106
Mid-week or weekend breaks, November to March. Any 2 nights, dinner, bed and breakfast £60.00 per person, inclusive of VAT. Additional nights £29.00 per person.

AYNSOME MANOR HOTEL, Nr. Grange-over-Sands page 107
Midweek (Monday–Thursday) 2 days from £67.00, weekend (Friday–Sunday) from £73.00 for dinner, bed and breakfast per person.

CUMBRIA (Contd.)

WORDSWORTH HOTEL, Grasmere *page 108*
2 day break mid week £95.00. Weekend breaks from £120.00. Additional days in each case £45.00.

LANGDALE HOTEL, Great Langdale *page 109*
'Breakaway Breaks' – minimum 2 nights, November–March '91; standard room £48.00 weekday, £65.00 weekend (luxury room £69.00 weekday and £75.00 weekend). April–October '91; standard room £65.00 weekday, £72.00 weekend (luxury room £76.00 weekday, £83.00 weekend).

RIVERSIDE HOTEL, Kendal *page 133*
£80.00 per person for 2 nights, £120.00 for 3 nights, Sunday as an additional night £30.00. Single room supplement £10.00 per night.

page 134
LYZZICK HALL COUNTRY HOUSE HOTEL, Keswick, Underskiddaw
November to March, excluding Christmas and New Year, from £29.50, dinner, bed and breakfast, per person per night. 5% discount on accommodation for stays of over 4 days, 10% discount on accommodation for stays of one week or more.

STAKIS LODORE SWISS HOTEL, Keswick *page 135*
For guests staying a minimum of 2 nights, the holiday rate is applicable. The price includes dinner, bed and breakfast, and prices start from £52.00 per person per night.

ARMATHWAITE HALL, Nr. Keswick, Bassenthwaite *page 136*
5 day breaks May to October. All guests staying for a minimum of 5 nights will be allowed 10% discount on bed and breakfast rate providing dinner is taken in the hotel each evening. Winter weekend breaks from start of November '90 to end of April '91 (excluding Christmas/New Year and Easter). 2 nights, Friday/Saturday or Saturday/Sunday. £110.00 or £125.00 per person, additional days pro rata. Studio Suites £170.00 or £180.00 per person. Rates are for dinner, bed and breakfast. Children sharing parents' room £32.00 per child for high tea, bed and breakfast.

BORROWDALE HOTEL, Nr. Keswick *page 137*
Reduced rates in winter with mid-week breaks of marvellous value. Special winter walking weeends; prices on application. Christmas and New Year packages.

SCAFELL HOTEL, Nr. Keswick, Borrowdale *page 138*
Weekend breaks – dinner, bed and breakfast on Friday and Saturday nights, packed lunch and full afternoon tea on Saturday, Sunday lunch. Midweek breaks also available.

SWAN HOTEL, Newby Bridge *page 189*
Swan breaks – November 2nd to March 23rd 1991, 2 nights dinner, bed and breakfast from £78.00 per person. Can be taken Friday/Saturday or Saturday/Sunday. Includes free bottle of 'Swan Label' wine.

THE BLACK SWAN, Ravenstonedale *page 203*
Bargain breaks available. Details on request.

THE OLD RECTORY COUNTRY HOUSE HOTEL, Torver *page 258*
November–May; stays including dinner, bed and breakfast, mid-week breaks from £27.50, weekends from £30.00. Three days or more 10% discount. Five days, pay for four only (Sunday–Thursday).

GILPIN LODGE, Windermere *page 272*
Special rates for three night weekend breaks or 3–5 night midweek breaks, prices on application.

CUMBRIA (Contd.)

LAKESIDE HOTEL, Windermere *page* 273

1st November–28th March '91, excluding Bank Holidays, 2 nights or more, dinner, bed and breakfast from £39.00 per person, per night; Special Rain Breaks 1st November–30th April. Free sparkling package worth £32.50 if it rains for more than 30 minutes during your stay. (Pre-book as Rain Break) 5 nights for 3, you pay only £132.00, not £220.00 per person. 3 for 2, you pay £88.00 not £132.00. Plus special New Year 3 night package. Details (05395) 31207.

MORTAL MAN HOTEL, Nr. Windermere *page* 275

Winter breaks on request.

WILD BOAR HOTEL, Nr. Windermere, Crook *page* 276

Special two night terms available throughout the year, from £98.00 per person, half board, to include 5 course candlelit dinners on each evening. Dinner dance weekends, winter and autumn. Full details on request.

OLD VICARAGE COUNTRY HOUSE HOTEL, Witherslack *page* 278

Three day bargain breaks available. Discount of £30.00 deducted from normal dinner, bed and breakfast tariff for double occupancy, discount of £15.00 deducted for single occupancy. Bargain breaks are available throughout the year for any three nights, but not during Bank Holiday weekends or from Christmas until the 2nd January. Additional nights charged pro rata.

DERBYSHIRE

IZAAK WALTON HOTEL, Dovedale, Ashbourne *page* 89

1st November to 31st March, 2 and 5 night breaks, details on request.

MAYNARD ARMS, Grindleford *page* 111

£40.00 per person per night, superior twin/four poster, dinner, bed and breakfast. £37.50 per person per night standard double/twin.

RIBER HALL, Matlock *page* 179

Hideaway break; 19th October 1990 to 30th April 1991, 2 nights, two dinners (£22.00 per dinner allowance), two full English breakfasts and one luncheon, from £115.00 per person. Bank Holidays and Christmas excluded.

DEVON

HOLNE CHASE HOTEL, Nr. Ashburton *page* 20

'Let's Go' breaks – any two nights or more throughout the year. Rates approximately 15% lower, early November till the end of March.

DOWNREW HOUSE, Barnstaple *page* 26

Reduced rates out of season, plus special Christmas and New Year packages. Downrew is also the ideal venue for weekend house-parties; details on request, tariff on application.

BOVEY HOUSE HOTEL, Beer, Nr. Seaton *page* 38

30th January–19th May (excluding Easter) and 11th September–29th December, 10% off room rates for two nights or more, applies both weekends and weekdays.

ROYAL HOTEL, Bideford *page* 41

Open throughout the year, Bideford is the ideal base for touring North Devon and Cornwall. Prices from £76.00 per person, TWO NIGHTS' HALF BOARD.

EASTON COURT, Chagford *page* 71

Midweek breaks of 3 nights (Monday–Thursday inclusive, excluding Bank Holidays) £120.00 per person. The above Bargain Breaks are bookable not more than two weeks in advance subject to availability.

DEVON (Contd.)

GREAT TREE, Chagford *page 73*
Getaway Breaks – 2 or more nights including five course dinner from £96.00 per person.

HOOPS INN, Clovelly *page 79*
Short weekend breaks, excluding Christmas and Bank Holidays, November 1990 to March 1991, £45.00 per person. Prices include a minimum of 2 nights' accommodation, morning tea, full English breakfast, dinner and VAT. Book 4 nights and get the fifth free (provided you pay for dinner and breakfast).

ROYAL CASTLE HOTEL, Dartmouth *page 85*
1st November 1990 – 1st May 1991, any two nights Sunday–Thursday, dinner, bed and breakfast, £68.00 standard, £79.00 river view. Weekend breaks (Friday night to Sunday lunchtime) £73.00 standard, £87.00 river view. 2nd May–31st October 1991, any two nights Sunday–Thursday, from £85.00 standard, £104.50 river view. Weekend breaks from £98.00 standard, £115.00 river view.

FINGALS HOTEL AND RESTAURANT, Nr. Dartmouth *page 86*
Three weekday nights from March to end of June, and October to 22nd December £120.00 for two, bed and breakfast.

EBFORD HOUSE HOTEL, Ebford, Nr. Exeter *page 93*
Bargain Breaks from October to May inclusive, excluding Christmas and Easter. Further details on application.

THE ROYAL BEACON HOTEL, Exmouth *page 94*
Getaway Breaks, any day of the week from September 29th 1990 to April 29th 1991 (excluding Christmas, New Year and Easter) from £34.00, dinner, bed and breakfast. Inclusive terms (for guests requiring Carvery Luncheon) from £38.00 including VAT at 15%. Terms quoted are per person per day, for any stay lasting a minimum of two nights.

THE BEL ALP HOUSE, Haytor, Nr. Bovey Tracey *page 119*
Reduced rates for short stays (2–4 nights) and long stays (5 nights or more).

COMBE HOUSE HOTEL, Nr. Honiton, Gittisham *page 126*
1st November to 28th March with the exception of 23rd December 1990 to 2nd January 1991 inclusive, any 2 consecutive nights stay, 10% off the bed and breakfast rate, 3 or more consecutive nights stay, 15% off the bed and breakfast rate. Hotel closed Sundays and Mondays during January and February.

COMMODORE HOTEL, Instow *page 132*
Out of season breaks; October–December (excluding Christmas and New Year), 2 days, dinner, bed and breakfast £72.00 inc. VAT at 15%. January–March 1991, rates from £74.00 per person. Prices are based on 2 people sharing. Single rooms 10% reduction on normal tariff. Special Christmas, New Year and Easter programmes.

THE RISING SUN HOTEL, Lynmouth *page 168*
From January until July, and from October till December inclusive (excepting Bank Holidays), special rates are available for dinner, bed and breakfast for stays of two to five nights, from £44.00 per person per night.

LYNTON COTTAGE HOTEL, Lynton *page 169*
Any two days or more from £51.00 per person, dinner, bed and breakfast. Midweek breaks from October to May from £47.00 per person.

BOLT HEAD HOTEL, Salcombe *page 215*
Getaway Breaks available, details on request.

MARINE HOTEL, Salcombe *page 216*
Special breaks in the off season. Dinner, room and breakfast for a stay of 2 nights, terms on application.

DEVON (Contd.)

TIDES REACH HOTEL, Salcombe *page 217*
Bargain breaks available from 16th March 1991 to 25th May 1991 (excluding Easter) and 1st–31st October 1990. 2 day breaks from £108.00 for dinner, bed and breakfast. 4 day breaks from £202.00 for dinner, bed and breakfast. Extra days pro rata.

SOAR MILL COVE HOTEL, Nr. Salcombe *page 218*
Seasonal breaks available for stays of three nights or more, starting from £147.00 for 3 nights in early spring. Prices are per person sharing a double room. Please enquire for the special Christmas House Party programme.

SAUNTON SANDS HOTEL, Saunton Sands, Nr. Braunton *page 222*
Winter Breaks (November to Easter), from £70.00, Spring Breaks (April to Whitsun) from £119.00, Early Summer Breaks from £125.00. Rates are per person for two nights' half board. Autumn Breaks on application.

THE BELMONT HOTEL, Sidmouth *page 228*
Open throughout the year, The Belmont Hotel is ideal for Spring, Summer or Winter breaks. Winter Breaks (November to Easter) from £72.00, Spring Breaks (Easter to 4th May) from £88.00, Early Summer Breaks (5th May to Whitsun) from £100.00. Rates are per person for 2 nights' half board.

ROYAL GLEN, Sidmouth *page 230*
November until the end of April, excluding Christmas and Easter, details on application.

VICTORIA HOTEL, Sidmouth *page 231*
Open throughout the year, the Victoria is ideal for a relaxing break whichever season you choose. Winter Breaks (November to 1st March) from £86.00, Spring Breaks (1st march to 4th May) from £98.00, Early Summer and Autumn Breaks from £110.00. All prices are per person for 2 nights' half board.

GLENEAGLES HOTEL, Torquay *page 253*
Promotional breaks available during the months of October, November, February and March, at reduced rates. Details on application.

IMPERIAL HOTEL, Torquay *page 254*
2 day breaks available, £98.00 double, £108.00 single. Price is per person per night for a minimum of 2 nights, to include dinner, accommodation in a seaview room, full English breakfast, service and VAT. There is a discount of £12.00 per person per night for inland facing rooms.

PALACE HOTEL, Torquay *page 255*
Minimum 2 day Leisure breaks available all through the year, excluding Christmas, Easter and all Bank Holidays. Also a reduction of 20% on full tariff is available for stays of 7 nights or more. Christmas programmes available. Details on application.

PRINCES HOTEL, Torquay *page 256*
Special short breaks and weekend holiday breaks. Details available on request.

ORESTONE MANOR HOTEL, Nr. Torquay, Maidencombe *page 257*
'Let's Go' Castaway Breaks. Rates for dinner, room and breakfast, any two days on request. We are open throughout the year.

WOODHAYES HOTEL, Whimple *page 270*
Tariff on application.

WATERSMEET HOTEL, Woolacombe, Mortehoe *page 281*
Spring and Autumn breaks, 2–4 days. Terms on application.

DORSET

CARLTON HOTEL, Bournemouth page 53
'Two day break' – tariff available on application.

CHINE HOTEL, Bournemouth page 54
Tariff available on application. Please call (0202) 396234.

CUMBERLAND HOTEL, Bournemouth page 55
'Lazy days' from 1st November 1990 to 1st April 1991. Two or more nights inclusive of four course table d'hôte dinner, accommodation and full English breakfast. Rooms without sea view £35.00, front rooms with sea view and balcony £37.50. Terms are per person per night, inclusive of VAT. Family rooms, four poster rooms and suites are also available.

LANGTRY MANOR, Bournemouth page 56
Welcome Breaks start at £85.00 per person. For Weekend Celebration Breaks, and birthdays or anniversaries, a gift of champagne and chocolates is offered. Four poster rooms and suites are available at a surcharge. All Weekend Breaks include Welcome Champagne Cocktail and special six course Edwardian Dinner Party on Saturday, throughout the year.

QUEEN'S HOTEL, Bournemouth page 57
Mini-breaks, Christmas, New Year and Easter programmes. Details on application.

TROUVILLE HOTEL, Bournemouth page 58
Details on application.

WINTER GARDENS HOTEL, Bournemouth page 59
Special Breaks according to season. Christmas, New Year, Easter Breaks. Free 6 course dinner included. Free accommodation for 1 child per family, subject to availability. All rates provided on application. Please call (0202) 555769.

SUMMER LODGE, Evershot page 92
October–March 1991 (except Christmas, New Year and Easter). Minimum stay 3 days from Sunday–Thursday inclusive. Dinner, full English breakfast, Dorset Cream Tea, morning coffee and newspapers, inclusive of VAT. Single room £210.00, double room from £150.00–£180.00 per person. Service at guests' discretion.

ALEXANDRA HOTEL, Lyme Regis page 164
Spring breaks from Friday 1st February to Thursday 2nd May 1991. Two day breaks from £70.00–£76.00 per person for dinner, full English breakfast, early morning tea tray and VAT, and from the 27th October to 22nd December 1991.

KERSBROOK HOTEL, Lyme Regis page 165
3 day bargain breaks available, from £23.00 per day. Further details on request.

THE SANDBANKS HOTEL, Sandbanks page 221
Tariff available on application, please call (0202) 707377.

EASTBURY HOTEL, Sherborne page 226
£98.00 for any two nights on a dinner, bed and breakfast basis per person.

MANOR HOUSE HOTEL, Studland Bay page 243
Special 3, 4 or 5 night breaks which do not include a Friday or Saturday night. 3 days 10% off daily rate. 4 days 15% off daily rates, 5 days 20% off daily rate.

KNOLL HOUSE HOTEL, Studland Bay page 244/5
Special breaks: Family Five (two adults, one or two children under 13) five nights full board in low season, £654.00. Purbeck Five (single or twin rooms without private bathroom) five nights full board in low season £218.00 per person; September 29th–17th October, two nights full board £91.00–£105.00 per person. Prices include VAT, there is no service charge.

DORSET (Contd.)

KEMPS COUNTRY HOUSE, Nr. Wareham *page* 266
Any 2 nights dinner, bed and breakfast, from £79.00.

MOONFLEET MANOR, Weymouth *page* 268
Weekends from September 1990, Friday and Saturday nights, dinner, room and breakfast, £36.00 per person per night, en suite. Midweek breaks from September 1990, Sunday through Thursday nights, 2–5 nights, including 2 hours bowls play £34.00 per person per night en suite, dinner, room and breakfast.

COUNTY DURHAM

LORD CREWE ARMS, Blanchland, Nr. Consett *page* 50
Breaks from £102.00 per person, in twin/double room, including dinner from à la carte menu (up to £19.50), bed and breakfast. Minimum 2 night stay.

ROSE AND CROWN HOTEL, Romaldkirk *page* 206
Weekend breaks are available from mid-October to mid-May at a special price of £85.00 per person, including dinner, bed and breakfast and VAT.

GLOUCESTERSHIRE

CROWN OF CRUCIS, Ampney Crucis *page* 14
Bed and breakfast at weekends: £27.00 single, £44.00 double per night. Minimum stay 2 nights.

BIBURY COURT, Bibury *page* 40
Winter breaks from November to end of March 1991. Any two days from £89.00 per person to include 2 nights, 2 dinners, continental breakfast and VAT.

THE CROWN INN AND HOTEL, Blockley *page* 51
Minimum of 2 nights stay, with full English breakfast, full 4-course dinner, valued at £17.50 per person. Prices from £52.00 per person per night. (Not inclusive of Christmas, New Year or Cheltenham Gold Cup Week).

COTSWOLD HOUSE, Chipping Campden 76
The Lazy Weekend; a two night stay, available all year – offers you the chance to really unwind. Greeted with welcoming cocktails, and a fruit basket in your bedroom, the weekend includes breakfasts in bed, Gloucestershire Cream Teas, Dinner, Traditional Sunday lunch and champagne as a parting gift. From £72.00 per person, per night. Details of other Speciality Breaks on application.

CHARINGWORTH MANOR, Nr. Chipping Campden 77
Short breaks available mid-week only. Dinner, bed and breakfast for 2 nights, £66.00 per person.

FOSSEBRIDGE INN, Fossebridge *page* 99
Fossebridge Breaks and Champagne Weekends available throughout the year, apart from Public Holiday Weekends and Cheltenham Race Week.

STONEHOUSE COURT HOTEL, Stonehouse *page* 236
£98.00 per person for two nights on a dinner, bed and breakfast basis.

WYCK HILL HOUSE, Stow-on-the-Wold *page* 237
2 day breaks, mid-week or weekend. Room, breakfast, dinner and champagne £135.00 for 2 nights, per person.

AMBERLEY INN, Nr. Stroud *page* 242
Mid-week and weekend breaks available. Golf, riding, hot air ballooning and gliding Getaway Breaks. Summer two night breaks also available, from £82.00 per person.

HARE AND HOUNDS, Nr. Tetbury, Westonbirt *page* 249
Mid-week and weekend breaks available. Golf, riding, hot air ballooning and gliding Getaway breaks. Summer two night breaks also available, from £90.00 per person.

HAMPSHIRE

AUDLEY'S WOOD COUNTRY HOUSE HOTEL, Basingstoke *page 28*
Weekend breaks from £57.50 per person, per night, including room, full English breakfast and table d'hôte dinner. Special activity weekends also available, such as archery, interior design and clay pigeon shooting. Details on request. Four poster rooms and suites available for special weekends away.

BASINGSTOKE COUNTRY HOTEL, Basingstoke *page 29*
Weekend breaks, minimum 2 nights' stay, Friday, Saturday or Sunday, £30.00 per person for bed and breakfast.

CAREY'S MANOR, Brockenhurst *page 65*
Special breaks – any two nights, dinner, bed and breakfast. Tariff on application.

STANWELL HOUSE, Lymington *page 166*
£98.00 for any 2 nights on a dinner, bed and breakfast basis, per person.

PASSFORD HOUSE HOTEL, Nr. Lymington *page 167*
Special 2 day breaks, November to May excluding Bank Holidays from £108.00 dinner, bed and breakfast.

FIFEHEAD MANOR HOTEL, Middle Wallop *page 180*
From November 1990 until Good Friday 1991, and August 1991; Short Breaks at £100 per person for two nights, plus £20 allowance for dinner.

SOUTH LAWN HOTEL, Milford-on-Sea *page 181*
2 day breaks; November–December twin/double £82.50, deluxe £87.50, Single £87.50. January–May twin/double £85.00, deluxe £90.00, single £90.00. Additional days pro rata. Prices are per person and include full English breakfast, dinner and VAT.

CHEWTON GLEN HOTEL, New Milton *page 186*
Winter breaks – November 1990 to March 1991. Inclusive of accommodation, continental breakfast, morning paper, dinner, service and VAT, 2 night minimum stay. Double room from £202.00, suites from £368.00 until March 1991. Tariff on application thereafter. Rates are per room per night, based on two persons sharing accommodation. Not applicable for Friday and Saturday night stays or the Christmas and New Year period.

TYLNEY HALL HOTEL, Rotherwick *page 209*
Weekend breaks 2 nights minimum to include a Saturday night. Prices include full English breakfast, morning newspaper, 3 course table d'hôte dinner and coffee, VAT and service, and are per person per night, from £65.00 per person in a twin room. Use of extensive leisure facilities.

BOTLEY PARK HOTEL, Southampton *page 233*
Two Night Weekend Break £110, including Friday dinner and accommodation, Saturday full English breakfast, dinner, dance and accommodation, Sunday full English breakfast and 3 course luncheon. One Night Weekend Break £80, includes Friday or Saturday dinner/dance, accommodation, full English breakfast and 3 course luncheon.

HEREFORD AND WORCESTER

BROADWAY HOTEL, Broadway *page 62*
Winter terms available 1st November–end of March (excluding Christmas, Easter and Cheltenham Gold Cup). Special rates for periods of more than 7 days. Tariff on application.

THE LYGON ARMS, Broadway *page 63*
Interesting and varied special rates throughout the year, from Champagne and Golf Weekends, to Clay Pigeon Shooting, or the Cotswold Mid-Week Break. Tariff on application.

HEREFORD AND WORCESTER (Contd.)

DORMY HOUSE HOTEL, Broadway *page* 64
Champagne Weekend: £144.00 per person to include Friday and Saturday nights' accommodation, full English breakfast, table d'hôte dinner, champagne on arrival and fresh flowers in the bedroom – available throughout the year.

BROCKENCOTE HALL, Chaddesley Corbett, Kidderminster *page* 70
Any two days £125.00 per person, deluxe double, £149.00 per person super deluxe double.

PENGETHLEY HOTEL, Nr. Ross-on-Wye *page* 208
Bargain breaks from £60.00 per person per day, dinner, bed and breakfast.

THE WHITE LION HOTEL, Upton-upon-Severn *page* 263
November–March £75.00 per person for 2 nights dinner, bed and breakfast. April 1st–November 1991 £80.00 per person for 2 nights, dinner, bed and breakfast. Single room supplement £9.00 per night.

HERTFORDSHIRE

DOWN HALL COUNTRY HOUSE HOTEL, Bishop's Stortford *page* 48
'Country House Weekend' £105.00 per person for 2 nights inclusive of dinner, bed and breakfast. 'Something Special' £120.00 per person, two nights in a four poster or canopied bed, with pink champagne, chocolate and flowers included.

WEST LODGE PARK, Hadley Wood, Nr. Barnet *page* 112
Weekend Breaks: Friday to Sunday or Saturday to Monday. Country House Breaks including country house breakfast and dinner – per person for 2 nights, £120.00 single, £107.50 sharing double room.

REDCOATS FARMHOUSE HOTEL, Redcoats Green, Nr. Hitchin *page* 205
Friday and Saturday, or Saturday and Sunday in this old farmhouse, with open fires, super food and interesting wine list; what more is needed for a Winter Break? Prices from £55.00 per person (2 nights).

BRIGGENS HOUSE HOTEL, Stanstead Abbotts, Nr. Ware *page* 234
Until 30th April 1991; £35.00 per person bed and breakfast, or £49.50 with dinner, From 1st May 1991 to 30th March 1992, £39.00 per person bed and breakfast, or £55.00 with dinner included. Prices are based on a min. 2 night stay and must include a Saturday night.

KENT

EASTWELL MANOR, Ashford *page* 21
Stopover break (Sunday night only); Weekend break (2 nights' accommodation); Midweek break (2 nights' accommodation); 5 nights' break (5 nights' accommodation, Sunday to Thursday nights only). Rates on application.

CASTLEMERE HOTEL, Broadstairs *page* 61
'Let's Go' 2 or 3 nights from a Thursday to Sunday inclusive. 1st October 1990 to 30th March 1991, from £70.50 for 2 nights, £105.75 for 3 nights; 31st March 1991 to September 1991, from £79.00 for 2 nights, £118.50 for 3 nights. Prices are per person inclusive of accommodation in en suite room, full traditional breakfast, four course table d'hôte dinner, newspaper, service and VAT.

THROWLEY HOUSE, Nr. Faversham *page* 97
Honeymoon Special £150.00. Champagne Break £79.00 per person per night, for two nights minimum. Weekend Inclusive rates, £69.50 per person, per night, Friday and Saturday night only.

TUDOR COURT, Hawkhurst *page* 117
Blossom Weekend, Honeymoon breaks and Getaway breaks available. Further details on request.

KENT (Contd.)

SPA HOTEL, Royal Tunbridge Wells page 210

A minimum 2 night stay to include dinner, breakfast and accommodation, available for any Friday, Saturday or Sunday, plus any Bank Holiday Monday. Free use of the Sparkling Health leisure complex is also included. Tariff on application.

LANCASHIRE

THE PICKERINGS, Catterall, Nr. Garstang page 101

One night 'Getaway Breaks' from £45.00 per person, dinner, bed, breakfast and champagne.

COBWEBS COUNTRY HOUSE, Kirkby Lonsdale page 140

Any 2 nights dinner, bed and breakfast, a third night's accommodation free of charge from September onwards (excluding Christmas). Further details on application.

MYTTON FOLD FARMHOUSE, Langho page 142

Special weekend breaks £125.00 per couple, £135.00 from April 1991, including dinner from the à la carte menu.

THE SHIREBURN ARMS, Nr. Whalley page 269

Any 2 nights dinner, bed and breakfast £75.00 per person. Champagne Break, 2 nights dinner, bed and breakfast plus champagne, £85.00 per person.

LEICESTERSHIRE

QUORN GRANGE, Loughborough page 160

Weekend rate; any two nights minimum from Fri–Sun, £35.00 per person, per night, including full English breakfast and VAT.

BARNSDALE COUNTRY CLUB, Nr. Oakham page 196

Weekend breaks Friday–Sunday; any 2 nights for £135.00 per person including breakfast, lunch, dinner and VAT, by prior arrangement only.

NORMANTON PARK HOTEL, Rutland Water page 211

Special Two Day Breaks £78.00 per person per night fully inclusive, third night at £25.00 per person.

THE FALCON HOTEL, Uppingham page 262

Honeymoon Night, includes smoked salmon sandwiches, champagne and flowers, £95.00 per couple. Also 'Explore Rutland Weekends', Friday evening meal, Saturday full English breakfast and 3 course à la carte dinner £79.00 per person. Sunday full breakfast, Sunday night dinner, accommodation and breakfast £25.00 extra per person. Seasonal tariffs and tailor made packages available on request.

LONDON

THE MONTCALM, Great Cumberland Place W1A 2LF page 151

Weekend Breaks £59.00 per person per night sharing a double/twin, £69.00 sharing a duplex suite. Available Friday–Sunday and Bank Holidays for a minimum of 2 nights. Subject to advance booking and availability.

THE PORTLAND, Bloomsbury WC1B 5HB page 153

Weekend Breaks; Friday, Saturday and Sunday, any two nights for £70.00 per person in a double or twin room, bed and English breakfast.

REGENCY HOTEL, 100 Queen's Gate SW7 5AG page 154

Weekend Breaks, £100 per night for two persons sharing a twin/double and £75 per night for a single inclusive of full English Breakfast and VAT at 15%. These rates will be applicable for a minimum 2 night stay from Friday to Monday.

NORFOLK

BLAKENEY HOTEL, Blakeney, Nr. Holt *page 49*

Minimum 2 night stay: Friday and Saturday from £48.00 to £68.00 per person per night. Midweek from £44.00 to £64.00 per person per night. Special four day holidays from £160.00 to £200.00 per person. Tariff includes accommodation, full English breakfast and three course table d'hôte dinner.

SHIPDHAM PLACE, East Dereham *page 91*

Any stay of more than one night, in certain rooms, £58.00 per person, including accommodation, dinner, early morning tea/coffee and breakfast. Sunday as a third or further night £51.00 per person.

LENWADE HOUSE HOTEL, Great Witchingham, Norwich *page 110*

Bargain break weekends and special 3 night terms available.

BUTTERFLY HOTEL, Kings Lynn *page 90*

Weekend break rate; from £33.50 per guest per night, sharing twin/double room. Applicable one or more nights from Friday to Sunday. Price is for overnight stay, full breakfast and a dinner allowance of £10.50. Offer applies also to sister hotels featured in Guide.

NORFOLK MEAD HOTEL, Coltishall, Norwich *page 194*

£85.00 per person sharing a double or twin room for 2 nights dinner, bed and breakfast. £105.00 single room for 2 nights, dinner, bed and breakfast.

SOUTH WALSHAM HALL, South Walsham, Nr. Norwich *page 195*

Weekend breaks – 1 day full board from £85.00 per couple, 2 days full board from £150.00 per couple, weekends only. Special half board terms from £42.00 single, £70.00 double for minimum of 3 nights, from £280.00 single, £450.00 double for any 7 days. All rates apply until March 1991. Further details on application.

NORTHAMPTONSHIRE

STAVERTON PARK HOTEL AND GOLF COMPLEX, Daventry *page 87*

Superb value golfing breaks available all year. Championship 18-hole golf course with extensive teaching facilities. Prices on application.

NORTHUMBERLAND

BISHOPFIELD COUNTRY HOUSE HOTEL, Allendale, Nr. Hexham *page 4*

Off season breaks November–April; any 2 nights, £22.00 bed and breakfast per person, per night. May – any three *nights £22.00 per person per night.*

LORD CREWE ARMS, Blanchland, Nr. Consett *page 50*

Breaks from £102.00 per person, in twin/double room, including dinner from à la carte menu (up to £19.50), bed and breakfast. Minimum 2 night stay.

OXFORDSHIRE

THE GOLDEN PHEASANT HOTEL, Burford *page 66*

2 nights dinner, bed and breakfast, single £60.50, double £90.00, four poster £109.00.

THE MILL HOUSE HOTEL AND RESTAURANT, Kingham *page 139*

Throughout the year, 2 nights dinner, bed and breakfast from £55.00 per person, per night double, single from £65.00 per night.

THE OLD SWAN AND MILL, Minster Lovell *page 182*

Weekend rates available for any two nights minimum stay from £89.00 per double room per night, inclusive of breakfast, service and VAT. Alternatively, £140.00 per double room, per night, inclusive of dinner, breakfast, service and VAT. (Prices subject to change).

OXFORDSHIRE (Contd.)

SPREAD EAGLE HOTEL, Thame *page* 250

Two nights at the weekend £93.50 per person during Autumn 1990; Spring rates from £96.50 per person and Summer from £99.50. Prices include accommodation, full English breakfast and either the house menu or an allowance towards the à la carte menu. Two day Christmas package £195.95 per person. Three days £265.95 with extra days available. Easter and Weekend terms on application. All prices are inclusive of service and VAT.

FEATHERS HOTEL, Woodstock *page* 280

Bargain breaks for 2 nights to include dinner, full English breakfast, and VAT. Tariff on application.

SHROPSHIRE

THE OLD VICARAGE HOTEL, Worfield, Bridgnorth *page* 60

For stays of two nights and longer, throughout the year, why not reserve a leisure break to include room, full English breakfast, 5 course dinner and VAT. Standard double/twin £85.00 per day for two, luxury double/twin £97.00 per day for two.

THE FEATHERS, Bull Ring, Ludlow *page* 163

Bargain breaks available for 2 nights, dinner, bed and breakfast, tariff on application.

PEN-Y-DYFFRYN HALL, Rhydycroesau, Nr. Oswestry *page* 197

Short Breaks – Dinner, bed and breakfast for a minimum stay of two nights, £37.00 per person, then £35.00 per person per night for each additional night, including VAT. Reduced rates available January–Easter. No service charge.

HAWKSTONE PARK, Weston-under-Redcastle, Shrewsbury *page* 227

Full board breaks, minimum 2 nights stay, dinner on arrival until after lunch on departure, inclusive of accommodation, all meals each day and green fees: for 2 nights between 1st November to 31st March 1991 from £99.00 per person. Any 2 night break – dinner, bed and breakfast from £53.00 per person.

SOMERSET

DRAGON HOUSE, Bilbrook, Nr. Dunster *page* 42

Bargain Breaks from £76.00 per person for 2 nights inclusive of accommodation in en suite room, full English breakfast and four course table d'hôte dinner. 'Super Breaks' including golf, riding or shooting also available. Ring 0984 40215 for details.

COMBE HOUSE HOTEL, Holford, Bridgwater *page* 125

Bargain breaks available from September to May from £62.00 for two nights, dinner, bed and breakfast.

KINGS ARMS HOTEL AND RESTAURANT, Montacute *page* 184

All year, Saturday and Sunday nights, plus 3, 4 and 7 night breaks. Prices on application.

ANCHOR HOTEL AND SHIP INN, Porlock Weir *page* 200

Bargain breaks available on application.

CHARLTON HOUSE HOTEL, Shepton Mallet *page* 225

10% reduction on dinner, bed and breakfast for any two or more consecutive days.

ROYAL OAK INN, Winsford *page* 277

Tariff on application.

STAFFORDSHIRE

HOAR CROSS HALL, Hoar Cross *page* 124

Extended stays receive additional beauty treatments.

SUFFOLK

BUTTERFLY HOTEL, Bury St. Edmunds *page* 90

Weekend break rate; from £33.50 per guest per night, sharing twin/double room. Applicable one or more nights from Friday to Sunday. Price is for overnight stay, full breakfast and a dinner allowance of £10.50. Offer applies also to sister hotels featured in Guide.

SURREY

SELSDON PARK HOTEL, Nr. Croydon *page* 83

Bargain weekend breaks for 2 nights or more to include all the hotel's sport and leisure facilities, free golf and dinner dance on Saturday night. Prices on application.

EAST SUSSEX

WINSTON MANOR HOTEL, Crowborough *page* 82

Bargain Break weekends; minimum stay of 2 nights, including dinner, bed and full English breakfast, table d'hôte dinner and 3 course Sunday lunch. Prices on application.

BEAUPORT PARK HOTEL, Hastings *page* 116

Country House Bargain Breaks available all year round. Tariff on application.

THE BRICKWALL HOTEL, Sedlescombe *page* 223

Two day breaks from £66.00, dinner, bed and breakfast all year round.

WEST SUSSEX

EUROPA GATWICK HOTEL, Gatwick *page* 102

Any Friday, Saturday or Sunday night for a minimum 2 night stay, double room, continental breakfast £45.00 (per person) per night. Children under 14 can share parents' room for a supplement of £5.00 per child. Free car parking and complimentary use of the Health Club.

SOUTH LODGE HOTEL, Lower Beeding *page* 161

At weekends, we offer a special rate for 2 nights from Friday to Sunday. This is inclusive of dinner in the restaurant, and full English breakfast. Price on application.

ALEXANDER HOUSE, Turner's Hill *page* 260

48 hour stay, including Saturday night. Full English breakfast and dinner each day. Tariff on application.

WARWICKSHIRE

SALFORD HALL, Abbots Salford *page* 1

Leisure Breaks are available throughout the year at Salford Hall, both mid-week and weekend, ranging from £55.00 per person per night for a five course dinner, accommodation, full English breakfast and VAT.

STRATFORD HOUSE HOTEL, Stratford-upon-Avon *page* 238

2 day Breaks: Winter (November 1st–May 1st) from Monday–Thursday £80 per person, Friday and Saturday £85.00 per person, £10.00 dinner allowance. Summer (May 1st–October 31st) from Monday–Thursday £85.00 per person. Prices are based on twin/double rooms. Single occupancy of double room from £100.00–£120.00 Sun–Thurs, depending on season.

WARWICKSHIRE (Contd.)

WELCOMBE HOTEL AND GOLF COURSE, Stratford-upon-Avon *page* 239
Country House and Golf Weekends £150.00 per person for dinner, bed and breakfast. Both breaks include one free round of golf per day.

BILLESLEY MANOR, Stratford-upon-Avon *page* 240
'Greatstay' bargain breaks: to end April 1991 – bed and breakfast £49.00 (1 night), £98.00 (2 nights), dinner, bed and breakfast £72.00 (1 night), £144.00 (2 nights). From 1st May 1991 – bed and breakfast £52.50 (1 night), £105.00 (2 nights), dinner, bed and breakfast £77.50 (1 night), £155.00 (2 nights).

THE GLEBE, Barford, Nr. Warwick *page* 267
Weekend breaks available throughout the year. Minimum of 2 nights, £48.50 per person (twin bedded room) for dinner, bed and breakfast.

WEST MIDLANDS

FAIRLAWNS HOTEL AND RESTAURANT, Aldridge *page* 3
2 day weekend breaks £65.00 per person, inclusive of dinner, two nights' accommodation, and full English breakfast.

NORTON PLACE HOTEL, Birmingham B30 *page* 44
2 nights dinner, bed and breakfast, with 2 bottles of house wine, £120.00 weekends only. Special Theatre Breaks, £90.00 per person nightly, including English breakfast, pre-theatre supper, coffee liqueurs and petit fours on return. Best seats at Hippodrome (Royal Ballet) or The Royal Shakespeare Theatre.

THE PLOUGH AND HARROW HOTEL, Birmingham B16 *page* 45
Special weekend rates available. Apply for details.

THE SWALLOW HOTEL, Birmingham B16 *page* 46
1st October 1990–31st March 1991. Single room with breakfast, service and VAT £80.00; double room with breakfast, service and VAT £97.50.

MOOR HALL HOTEL, Sutton Coldfield *page* 246
Weekend Getaways; minimum 2 nights to include 3 course table d'hôte dinner, £40.00 per night. Also Romantic Weekends £45.00 per person per night. Rates applicable until March 28th 1991.

WILTSHIRE

CHISELDON HOUSE, Chiseldon, Nr. Swindon *page* 78
Two nights, dinner, bed and breakfast includes a selection from à la carte menu. Any 2 nights, but weekends and August recommended as less busy.

RUDLOE PARK HOTEL, Corsham *page* 81
Leisure Breaks all year, from £100.00 per person for any 2 nights, with dinner, bed and breakfast.

THE OLD BELL, Malmesbury *page* 173
£98.00 for any 2 nights on a dinner, bed and breakfast basis per person.

CRUDWELL COURT HOTEL AND REST., Nr. Malmesbury *page* 174
Bargain breaks available – terms on application.

WHATLEY MANOR, Easton Grey, Nr. Malmesbury *page* 175
2, 3 and 6 night holidays available. 2 nights dinner, room, breakfast and VAT from £120.00 per person.

IVY HOUSE, Marlborough *page* 177
2 day breaks offered throughout the year. 2 nights dinner, bed and breakfast £42.50 per person per night.

WILTSHIRE (Contd.)

BLUNSDON HOUSE HOTEL, Nr. Swindon *page 247*

Luxury and hospitality await you at Wiltshire's first family-owned 4 star hotel. The new £1.2m leisure club is fantastic for the family. Explore Bibury and quaint Cotswold villages or visit Avebury and a host of historic attractions. Getaway weekend breaks from £54.00 per person per night.

CRICKLADE HOTEL AND COUNTRY CLUB, Nr. Swindon *page 248*

Weekend breaks available Friday, Saturday and/or Sunday from £90.00 for 2 nights, £120.00 3 nights inclusive of dinner, breakfast, VAT and use of sporting facilities.

YORKSHIRE

DWELDAPILTON HALL HOTEL, Appleton-le-Moors *page 18*

Spring, Summer and Autumn breaks available from £45.00. Full brochure and tariff available on request. Open for Christmas and New Year special festive breaks.

ROSE AND CROWN, Bainbridge *page 23*

'Let's Go' breaks 1st October to 30th April 1991, excluding Bank Holidays; double/twin room from £72.00 per person. 2 nights' dinner, bed and breakfast with private facilities.

OAKWOOD HALL HOTEL, Bingley *page 43*

Reduced rates are offered at the weekend: Friday, Saturday and Sunday to include full English breakfast and VAT – from £40.00 single, £60.00 double.

DEVONSHIRE ARMS, Bolton Abbey *page 52*

The Devonshire offers a range of weekend breaks including golfing, fly fishing (in season), clay pigeon shooting, bird-watching and hot air ballooning; tariff on application.

MALLYAN SPOUT HOTEL, Goathland, Nr. Whitby *page 103*

Mini breaks out of season: from £45.00 per person per night until 21st May, including dinner, bed and breakfast. Summer breaks from 29th May from £47.50 for dinner, bed and breakfast. Both minimum 2 nights.

GOMERSAL PARK HOTEL, Gomersal *page 104*

Bargain Break Weekends for 2 nights or more, to include all leisure facilities, details on application.

GRANTS HOTEL, Harrogate *page 113*

At certain times throughout the year, 2 nights accommodation for the price of 1 night at full tariff rate. There is a selection of 2 day theme breaks, including a Ski Break, Bric a Brac Break, Green Fingers Break and Fat Rascal Break, all from £37.50 per person per night. Please telephone for the amusing brochure!

NEWTON HOUSE HOTEL, Knaresborough, Nr. Harrogate *page 114*

November–February dinner for 2 included FREE on Saturday nights, with minimum 2 night stay either Friday/Saturday or Saturday/Sunday, for 2 people. November–May £45 per night (double/twin) minimum 2 night stay, 3rd night only £25.00. £5.00 supplement for four poster rooms. Bank Holidays, trade fairs, conferences and exhibitions excluded.

NIDD HALL HOTEL AND COUNTRY CLUB, Harrogate *page 115*

Special rates apply for breaks including Leisure, Health, Gourmet, Riding and Racing Weekends. Prices on application.

THE BLACK SWAN HOTEL, Helmsley *page 120*

Tariff on application. Special rates are available for a minimum of 2 nights' stay. The rates include evening meal, deluxe accommodation, breakfast, service and VAT.

YORKSHIRE (Contd.)

FEVERSHAM ARMS HOTEL, Helmsley *page* 121

Any 2 nights including full English breakfast, four course dinner by candlelight, free tennis and swimming in our sports complex, golf and riding nearby at reduced rates. Prices inclusive of VAT: Winter – £38.00, Spring – £43.00, Summer – £48.00, all per person per night, double occupancy. Four-poster with deluxe bath add £5.00 per person per night.

THE PHEASANT, Harome, Helmsley *page* 122

Tariff £38.50 from 1st November–mid May 1991, thereafter £45.50 per day.

RYEDALE LODGE, Nr. Helmsley *page* 123

2 consecutive nights' stay between 1st October 1990 and 31st May 1991, including room, breakfast and dinner for £109.00 per person. Summer 2 day break between 1st June and 30th September, £119.00.

WORSLEY ARMS HOTEL, Hovingham *page* 127

Any 2 or 3 consecutive days, Winter/Spring Breaks, double or twin, minimum £36.00, maximum £46.00.

COW AND CALF HOTEL, Ilkley *page* 130

Bargain break – minimum 2 nights sharing a double/twin room, from £37.50 to £45.00 per person per night, dinner, bed and breakfast.

ROMBALDS HOTEL AND RESTAURANT, Ilkley *page* 131

2 day breaks year round except for September–October and Christmas, New Year and Easter. Two days' dinner, bed and breakfast with approx. 15% reduction on standard rate. Exact prices depend on room.

AUBURN HILL, Malton *page* 176

Special break rate offers you 2 nights for £41.00 per person per night (double occupancy) and includes 4 course dinner, bed and full English breakfast. Additional nights are pro-rata except January to March when your third nights' accommodation is free.

MONK FRYSTON HALL, Monk Fryston *page* 183

Weekend breaks until 28th March 1991 – £82.00 per person for 2 nights, £123.00 per person for 3 nights. From 29th March £92.00 per person for 2 nights, £138.00 per person for 3 nights.

SOLBERGE HALL, Nr. Northallerton *page* 193

Breaks of 2 nights or more available. Hotel is close to Coxwold where the magnificent church has furnishing carved by the 'Mouse Man' of Kilburn, whose signature was a tiny carved mouse, and also to Laurence Sterne's Shandy Hall.

THE WHITE SWAN, Pickering *page* 199

Low season breaks; 2 or 4 days. Prices on application. Golfing, Walking and 'Bridge' packages available. Also Wine Weekends and Christmas Shopping Breaks.

MILBURN ARMS, Rosedale Abbey, Nr. Pickering *page* 207

Mini-breaks – any two consecutive nights (except bank holidays), accommodation, English or continental breakfast, plus 2 nights gourmet dinner: £80.00 per person. Extra nights pro rata. Special winter discounts – details on application.

FALCON MANOR, Settle *page* 224

2 day breaks (dinner, bed and breakfast) available throughout the year, prices vary according to the season. Winter 2 day breaks from £78.00, summer from £86.00 per person. Longer breaks prices on application.

WHITWELL HALL COUNTRY HOUSE HOTEL, Whitwell-on-the-Hill, York *page* 271

November to April, any 2 days or more from £47.00 per person per night, dinner, bed and breakfast.

YORKSHIRE (Contd.)

BILBOROUGH MANOR, York *page 282*

Breaks from £58.50–£78.50 per person, including early tea, newspaper, dinner up to £19.50 and Bed and Breakfast. Brochure and tariff on application.

SWALLOW CHASE HOTEL, York *page 283*

Breakaway 2 day breaks include 2 nights' accommodation, full English breakfast, table d'hôte dinner each evening and 1 free lunch, which can be taken on either day. Winter rate, 1990/91 £95.00, summer 1991, £115.00 including VAT.

WALES

CLWYD

PEN-Y-DYFFRYN HALL, Rhydycroesau, Nr. Oswestry *page 197*

Short Breaks – Dinner, bed and breakfast for a minimum stay of 2 nights, £37.00 per person, then £35.00 per person per night for each additional night, including VAT. Reduced rates available January–Easter. No service charge.

SOUGHTON HALL, Northop, Nr. Chester *page 290*

Weekend breaks – any Friday and Saturday night in one of our large double or twin rooms. Price to include our traditional dinner each evening or an allowance towards the Gourmet dinner, full English breakfast and VAT. Price on application.

HOTEL SEVENTY DEGREES, Colwyn Bay *page 291*

2 nights. From 5th November 1990 to 28th March 1991 £69.00 twin/double; £45.00 single. PRICE BUSTERS from 1st January 1991 to 28th February 1991. £10.00 off twin/double rate; £7.50 off single rate. From 29th March 1991 to 31st October 1991 £85.00 twin/double; £52.50 single. Rates apply to a minimum of 2 nights, any part of the week and include dinner, accommodation, breakfast, VAT and service.

HAND HOTEL, Llanarmon Dyffryn Ceiriog, Llangollen *page 297*

Tariff on application.

WEST ARMS HOTEL, Llanarmon Dyffryn Ceiriog, Llangollen *page 298*

2 day (or longer) breaks, weekend/midweek, low and high season. Single from £55.00 per day, twin/double from £50.00 per person per day. Inclusive of accommodation in an en suite room, dinner, early morning tea, full English breakfast and VAT.

page 299

TYDDYN LLAN COUNTRY HOUSE HOTEL & RESTAURANT, Llandrillo

Any 2 nights week or weekend throughout the year, £44.00–£47.50 per person sharing, including breakfast and morning newspaper.

LLYNDIR HALL HOTEL, Rossett *page 306*

Weekends available throughout the year at £98.00 per person, including 2 nights accommodation Friday/Saturday or Saturday/Sunday, 2 Welsh breakfasts, 2 dinners (table d'hôte or à la carte allowance), complimentary newspaper, full use of leisure facilities, VAT and service. Children under 12 sharing parents' room free, dinner and breakfast £10.00 per child per day. Special 3rd night option available at £49.00 per person, to include all the above.

DYFED

WOLFSCASTLE COUNTRY HOTEL, Nr. Haverfordwest *page 296*

Bargain breaks – 1st October until 30th June (excluding Bank Holidays) available Friday and Saturday nights. Tariff on application.

DYFED (Contd.)

ST. NONS HOTEL, St. David's page 307

2 nights' dinner, bed and breakfast. Tariff on application.

WARPOOL COURT HOTEL, St. David's page 308

Country House breaks from £42.00, including VAT, per person per night for dinner, bed and breakfast. Available January to early summer. Details on Autumn and Winter breaks on request.

FOURCROFT HOTEL, Tenby page 310

Mini breaks; any 2 or more nights in room with all amenities, evening dinner and full Welsh breakfast. From £40.00 per person per night.

GWENT

THE CROWN AT WHITEBROOK, Nr. Monmouth page 305

10% off dinner bed and breakfast rate, January–March and November–December for any three days.

CWRT BLEDDYN HOTEL AND COUNTRY CLUB, Tredunnock page 311

Weekend, Easter, Christmas and New Year Breaks, available on a dinner, bed and breakfast basis. Prices on application.

GWYNEDD

TREFEDDIAN HOTEL, Aberdyfi page 287

2 day mini breaks, from £35.00 per night, inclusive of dinner, bed, breakfast and VAT. Golfing breaks, please ask for details. Reduced rates for children.

CRAIG Y DDERWEN COUNTRY HOUSE HOTEL, Betws-y-Coed page 288

2 day bargain breaks offered all year to include five course gourmet dinner. Price on application, with a special 15% reduction for winter bookings.

GWYDYR HOTEL, Betws-y-Coed page289

2 days dinner, bed and breakfast from £60.00. 3 days dinner bed and breakfast from £88.00.

BRON EIFION HOTEL, Criccieth page 292

Breaks available all year. Telephone for extra special rates. January–March, Christmas and New Year Breaks.

BONTDDU HALL HOTEL, Nr. Dolgellau page 294

Any 2 consecutive nights, half board £90.00 per person inclusive of service and VAT, excluding bank holidays. Extra nights pro rata. Please specify Bargain Breaks at time of enquiry.

GEORGE III HOTEL, Dolgellau page 295

Any 2 nights (excluding bank holidays) in en suite room, bed, breakfast and allowance on both nights against dinner. £88.00 + 10% service per person. Extra nights pro rata, details on request.

GOGARTH ABBEY HOTEL,, Llandudno page 300

Tariff on application.

CARREG BRÂN HOTEL, Llanfairpwllgwyngyll page 301

Friday–Sunday (excluding Christmas and New Year) any 2 nights £82.00 per person including accommodation, breakfast and table d'hôte dinner inclusive of VAT. Single room supplement £6.00. Child discount available when sharing with two adults.

POWYS

GLIFFAES COUNTRY HOUSE HOTEL, Crickhowell page 293

Short stay and weekly rates on application.

POWYS (Contd.)

BODFACH HALL COUNTRY HOUSE, Llanfyllin *page* 302

From March until mid May, any 2 nights half board £66.00 per person. From mid May until early September, any 2 nights half board £73.00 per person. Autumn breaks until mid November, any 2 nights half board £70.00 per person. Extra nights up to 6 pro rata.

THE LAKE HOTEL, Llangammarch Wells *page* 303

2 days or more, including full breakfast and dinner. Rates on application.

SCOTLAND

BORDERS

CRINGLETIE HOUSE HOTEL, Peebles, Eddleston *page* 356

Spring/Autumn breaks 1991. Saturday, 9th March–Friday, 10th May and Sunday, 20th October–20th December; any 2 or more nights dinner, bed and breakfast will be £47.00 per person per night.

PHILIPBURN HOUSE HOTEL, Selkirk *page* 367

'Scott' Weekend breaks – Friday teatime finishing with a hearty Taste of Scotland lunch on Sunday, full board including afternoon tea (Saturday lunch not included) from £95.00 per person per weekend. 'Buccleuch' Midweek breaks: 2 nights or more from £49.00 per person per night, inclusive of light afternoon tea, dinner and Scottish breakfast. Special 3 day Christmas and New Year breaks. Further details on request.

DUMFRIES & GALLOWAY

BARJARG TOWER, Auldgirth *page* 318

Inclusive terms available throughout the year, for stays of three nights or more.

CORSEMALZIE HOUSE HOTEL, Port William *page* 363

Bargain breaks from £33.50 per person per night for dinner, bed and breakfast for stays of 3 nights or more.

BARON'S CRAIG HOTEL, Rockcliffe by Dalbeattie *page* 364

3 day bargain breaks available throughout the season. Terms on application.

FIFE

FERNIE CASTLE, Nr. Cupar *page* 327

Tariff on application.

ST. ANDREWS GOLF HOTEL, St. Andrews, Fife *page* 365

November '90–March '91, £78.00 for two people, dinner, bed and breakfast per night, minimum two night stay.

GRAMPIAN

DARROCH LEARG HOTEL, Ballater *page* 321

Special rates available for stays of 3 days or more. 20% discount during February, March and April.

KNOCKOMIE HOTEL, Forres *page* 335

Break brochure available, including Falconry, Walking and Gourmet Experiences. Please enquire for details.

MANSION HOUSE HOTEL, Elgin, Moray *page* 334

£200.00 dinner, bed and breakfast for 2 nights' double occupancy. £550.00 dinner, bed and breakfast for 7 nights' double occupancy.

GRAMPIAN (Contd.)

KILDRUMMY CASTLE, Kildrummy *page* 346
Short break holidays on application.

PITTODRIE HOUSE HOTEL, Pitcaple *page* 359
2 day stays, dinner, bed and breakfast. Also special winter terms. Rates on application.

HIGHLAND

LOCH DUICH HOTEL, Ardelve, by Kyle of Lochalsh *page* 316
2 nights or more, prices on application.

CORROUR HOUSE, Aviemore *page* 319
3 day and 5 day breaks. Prices on application.

BALLACHULISH HOTEL, Ballachulish *page* 320
2 nights low season (October to April) £65.00 per person for dinner, bed and breakfast.

ROYAL MARINE, Brora *page* 324
Golfing and fishing packages all inclusive – 2 nights £100.00, 3 nights £150.00. Curling packages in season.

COUL HOUSE HOTEL, Contin *page* 325
Highland breaks: Winter, Spring or Autumn; any 2 or more nights, including full Scottish breakfast, 5 course candle-lit dinner, unlimited golf, or fishing when in season, admission into Inverewe Tropical Gardens and Urquhart Castle. Prices per person, per night £33.00, including VAT; 29th September '90–3rd May '91 and 29th September '91–1st March '92.

GLENMORISTON ARMS, Invermoriston *page* 337
7 day winter breaks from £140.00 per person double, £205.00 single, bed and breakfast. Dinner, bed and breakfast from £295.00 single, £230.00 per person double.

BUNCHREW HOUSE HOTEL, Inverness *page* 338
Three day special package, plus a number of winter breaks which include free evenings at the theatre, etc. Prices are from £225.00 for two people.

KINGSMILLS HOTEL, Inverness *page* 339
2 nights dinner, bed and breakfast, with Sunday lunch. Rates on application.

ROSEDALE HOTEL, Isle of Skye, Portree *page* 340
'Skye Explorer', 4 day holidays inclusive of return ferries, dinner, bed and breakfast and admissions: tariff on application. Also 7 day two-island holiday with Isle of Raasay Hotel, on application and 3 day special.

HOTEL EILEAN IARMAIN, Isle of Skye, Sleat *page* 341
3 day breaks and 7 day breaks. Special rates for conferences. Prices on application.

UIG HOTEL, Isle of Skye, Uig *page* 342
3 day breaks – dinner, bed and breakfast, with or without pony trekking. 7 days, with pony trekking (2 whole, or 4 half days) from May to September, dinner, bed and breakfast. Prices on application.

INCHNADAMPH HOTEL, Loch Assynt, Nr. Lairg *page* 352
Weekly rates on application.

INVER LODGE HOTEL, Lochinver *page* 353
Best Western Getaway breaks, price on application.

ALLT-NAN-ROS HOTEL, Onich, Fort William *page* 355
Spring Breaks, 28th March–20th May: 3 days £140.00, 5 days £225.00, 7 days £299.00. Easter/Summer Breaks, 20th May–30th September: 3 days £181.50, 5 days £302.50, 7 days £380.00. Autumn Breaks, 1st October–2nd November: 3 days £155.00, 5 days £247.00, 7 days £335.00.

HIGHLAND (Contd.)

SCOURIE HOTEL, Scourie *page 366*

Bargain breaks – any 3 nights dinner, bed and breakfast for the cost of 2 (low season rates). Any 7 nights dinner, bed and breakfast for the cost of 5 (low season rates). This offer applies to selected rooms only. Prices on application.

LOTHIAN

CALEDONIAN HOTEL, Edinburgh *page 332*

Special Weekend Breaks are offered subject to availability.

ROXBURGHE HOTEL, Edinburgh *page 333*

Tariff on application.

HOUSTOUN HOUSE, Uphall *page 372*

Special weekend break, minimum 2 nights Friday to Sunday, inclusive of dinner, full Scottish breakfast, and VAT (not available certain weekends), tariff on application.

STRATHCLYDE

INVERCRERAN HOUSE, Appin *page 315*

Tariff on application.

LOCH MELFORT HOTEL, Arduaine, by Oban *page 317*

£47.50 dinner, bed and breakfast, for minimum stay of two nights, September 25th–December 22nd and March 1st–May 3rd. Christmas and New Year full board terms.

THE KILDONAN HOTEL, Barrhill *page 322*

Any 2 consecutive nights £120.00, or 5 nights £280.00. These rates are per person, and include dinner, bed and breakfast in a standard, double or twin room. On all rates, a single supplement of £10.00 per day is charged.

TAYCHREGGAN HOTEL, Kilchrenan *page 345*

Out of season tariff of £34.00 per person. Set dinner, bed and breakfast, must be pre-booked. Special events weekends in Spring and Autumn, please enquire for further details.

GLEDDOCH HOUSE, Langbank *page 350*

Any 2 nights Friday to Sunday, dinner, bed and breakfast including golf and leisure facilities £66.00 per person, per night.

BRISBANE HOTEL, Largs *page 351*

Special rates available on request.

MANOR HOUSE, Oban *page 354*

November–March, April, May and October, for 2 nights, tariff on application. Includes free entry to indoor heated swimming pool, sauna, solarium and golf club.

TAYSIDE

THE OLD MANSION HOUSE, By Dundee *page 329*

January, February, March weekend breaks, prices on application.

CASTLETON HOUSE, Nr. Glamis *page 336*

Reduction offered for stays of 3 nights or more. Details on application.

NEWTON HOUSE HOTEL, Nr. Perth, Glencarse *page 357*

Special rates for dinner, bed and breakfast. Minimum stay 2 nights, from £44.00 per person per night. Christmas and New Year programme available plus special weekends throughout the year.

TAYSIDE (Contd.)

BALLATHIE HOUSE HOTEL, Kinclaven by Stanley, Nr. Perth *page* 358

Rates on application – reduced after 3 and 7 nights. Also 'Getaway Breaks', minimum 2 nights during March to June and November to 20th December, subject to availability. Please specify 'Getaway Breaks' at time of enquiry.

GREEN PARK HOTEL, Pitlochry *page* 360

Bargain breaks on application, including Curling weekends in October.

LOG CABIN HOTEL, Nr. Pitlochry, Kirkmichael *page* 361

Two days or more, room, dinner and breakfast from April to June. Special Autumn and New Year packages, details on application.

DALMUNZIE HOUSE HOTEL, Spittal O'Glenshee *page* 369

Bargain breaks for low season; dinner, bed, breakfast and tea from £43.50 per person, per night. High season, from £47.50 per person per night.

HOLIDAY ISLANDS

CHANNEL ISLANDS

JERSEY

THE ATLANTIC HOTEL, La Moye, St. Brelade *page* 374

Winter breaks (November, December and March, excluding Christmas, New Year and Easter). For a minimum 3 night stay in a Golf View Room, £50.00 per person per day, dinner, bed and breakfast. Subject to availability, all winter breaks will be automatically upgraded to Sea View at no extra charge.

HOTEL CHATEAU VALEUSE, St. Brelade's Bay *page* 375

Winter weekend breaks available (excluding Christmas and New Year). Rates on application.

HOTEL L'HORIZON, St. Brelade's Bay *page* 376

£195.00 per person, for any 3 nights, on a dinner, bed and breakfast basis. Inclusive of return air fare from the south coast.

LONGUEVILLE MANOR HOTEL, St. Saviour *page* 377

Winter weekend breaks from 20th October 1990 to 25th March 1991 (excluding Christmas and New Year). A Saturday night must be included. With flights: £210.00 (single), £195.00 (standard double), £221.00 (medium double), £239.00 (large double) £303.00 (suite). Without flights: £125.00 (single), £110.00 (standard double), £136.00 (medium double) £154.00 (large double), £218.00 (suite). Rates are per person for two nights and include accommodation, full English breakfast, dinner, and service. Further details on request.

ISLE OF MAN

GRAND ISLAND HOTEL, Ramsey *page* 378

Tariff on application.

ISLE OF WIGHT

HOTEL RYDE CASTLE, Ryde *page* 380

A wide variety of different Bargain and Weekend Breaks, from £59.00 per person. Please enquire for further details.

HOTELS WITH OWN GOLF COURSES

WALES

SCOTLAND

HOTELS WITH OWN TENNIS COURTS

HOTELS WITH OWN TENNIS COURTS (Contd.)

WALES

SCOTLAND

HOTELS WITH INDOOR SWIMMING POOLS AND LEISURE CENTRES

HOTELS WITH INDOOR SWIMMING POOLS AND LEISURE CENTRES (Contd.)

WALES

SCOTLAND

ISLANDS

SPORTING FACILITIES

Sporting facilities to be found at *Signpost* hotels are listed on the following pages. This section is arranged by country (England, Wales, Scotland, Islands) and by county within those countries.

KEY

A	Facilities available *at hotel*
b	Facilities available *within 5 miles* of hotel
c	Special arrangements can be made with local clubs/organisations

page		golf	tennis	croquet	pitch & putt	boating	fishing	riding	billiards/ snooker	swim/pool	sea/river bathing	sailing	squash	badminton	shooting	leis. centre	solarium	sauna	other
	ENGLAND																		
	AVON																		
32	Combe Grove Manor Hotel and Country Club, Bath	A	A							A			A			A	A	A	gymnasium, hydrospa.
33	Fountain House, Bath	b	b					b					b	b	b				
34	Lansdown Grove, Bath	c	c			c	c	c				c	c	c	c				
35	Royal Crescent, Bath	b	b			b							b		b				Plunge pool, jacuzzis.
36	The Old School House, Bathford, Bath	b	b					b		b			b			b	b	b	
28	Hunstrete House, Hunstrete		A							A									
129	Hutton Court, Hutton	b					b	b			b	b			c				
202	Rangeworthy Court Hotel, Rangeworthy	b						b											
251	Thornbury Castle, Thornbury	b	b				b	b					b	b					Clay pigeon shooting.
	BEDFORDSHIRE																		
37	The Bedford Swan Hotel, Bedford	b	b							A									
98	Flitwick Manor, Flitwick		A																Games room.
	BERKSHIRE																		
19	Royal Berkshire, Ascot		A	A				b		A			A			A	A	A	
171	Fredrick's Hotel and Restaurant, Maidenhead	b	b																
172	Monkey Island Hotel, Maidenhead	b	b	A			A						b						
204	Kirtons Farm Country Club and Hotel, Reading		A				A		A	A			A				A	A	water-skiing, windsurfing.
241	Swan Diplomat, Streatley on Thames	b	b			c	b	b		A		c			b	A	A	A	
279	Cantley House, Wokingham	b	A	A				b											
	BUCKINGHAMSHIRE																		
177	Danesfield House, Marlow	b	A			b	b	c		A		b			c				
	CHESHIRE																		
2	Alderley Edge Hotel, Alderley Edge																		Many sporting facilities can be arranged by hotel.
39	Wild Boar Hotel, Beeston	b				b	c					b			c				

page		golf	tennis	croquet	pitch & putt	boating	fishing	riding	billiards/ snooker	swim/pool	sea/river bathing	sailing	squash	badminton	shooting	leis. centre	solarium	sauna	other
	CHESHIRE (continued)																		
74	Mollington Banastre Hotel, Chester							A		A			A		A	A	A	A	
75	Rowton Hall Hotel, Chester		b				b	b		A			b	b		A		A	Steam room, gymnasium.
170	Sutton Hall, Nr. Macclesfield	b	b					b											
219	Old Hall Hotel, Sandbach	b														b			
	CORNWALL																		
6	Penhallow Manor, Altarnun	b					b	b											
67	Boskerris Hotel, Carbis Bay	b	b			b				A	b								
80	Treglos Hotel, Constantine Bay	c	c			A	A	b	A	A	A	A							surfing, spa bath.
95	Royal Duchy Hotel, Falmouth	c	c				c	b	A	A	A	A	c			A		A	spa bath.
96	Budock Vean Hotel, Nr. Falmouth	A	A				A	b		A		A							windsurfing, games room.
100	The Fowey Hotel, Fowey	b				A	A	b			A	A							
190	Hotel Bristol, Newquay	b	b			b	A	A	A	A	A	b	b	b		A	A	A	
191	Headland Hotel, Newquay	A	A	A			b	b		A	A		b		b	A	A	A	
192	Tredragon Hotel, Nr. Newquay	b	b				b	b		A	A	A	b	b	b	A	A	A	games room.
198	The Queen's Hotel, Penzance	c				A	A	b			A	A	c				A	A	
201	Port Gaverne Hotel, Port Isaac					A	A	A			A								
213	Boscundle Manor, St. Austell		b	A		b		b		A	b	b	b						gymnasium, 2-hole practice course.
214	Carlyon Bay Hotel, Nr. St. Austell	A	A						A	A	A	b				A	A	A	
264	The Nare Hotel, Veryan	b	A			A	b	b	A	A	A	A				A	A	A	gymnasium, games room.
265	St. Moritz, Nr. Wadebridge	b					b	c			A	b					A		
	COUNTY DURHAM																		
84	Hall Garth Country House Hotel, Darlington		A		A					A							A	A	
206	Rose and Crown Hotel, Romaldkirk	b					b						b		b				
	CUMBRIA																		
5	Lowbyer Manor Country House Hotel, Alston	b				b	b	b				b			b				
9	Kirkstone Foot Hotel, Ambleside	b	b			b	b	b				b	b						

page		golf	tennis	croquet	pitch & putt	boating	fishing	riding	billiards/ snooker	swim/pool	sea/river bathing	sailing	squash	badminton	shooting	leis. centre	solarium	sauna	other
	CUMBRIA (continued)																		
10	Nanny Brow Country House Hotel, Clappersgate, Ambleside	b	b			b	b	b		b	b	b	b						spa bath.
11	Rothay Manor Hotel, Ambleside	b	b	A		b	b	b				b	b	b					
12	Wateredge Hotel, Ambleside					A	A				A	A							
13	Skelwith Bridge Hotel, Nr. Ambleside	b	b			b	A	A		b	A	b	b				b	b	Pony trekking, sail-board for hire.
15	Appleby Manor Hotel, Appleby in Westmorland ..	b					b	b	A	A			b			A	A	A	games room, jacuzzi.
17	Tufton Arms Hotel, Appleby in Westmorland ..	b					b			b			b		b				
30	Pheasant Inn, Bassenthwaite Lake	b					A	b											
31	Overwater Hall, Nr. Bassenthwaite Lake	b				b	b	b	A			b							games room.
68	Cumbria Park Hotel, Carlisle	b	b				b						b	b					
69	String of Horses Inn, Nr. Carlisle						b	b		A		b	b	b			A	A	whirlpool spa.
105	Graythwaite Manor Hotel, Grange-over-Sands ..	b	A					b	A	b									
106	Netherwood Hotel, Grange-over-Sands	b	b			b	b	b		A	A	A	b	b	b	A			leisure centre opening 1991.
107	Aynsome Manor Hotel, Nr. Grange-over-Sands ..	b	b				b	b		b	b								
108	Wordsworth Hotel, Grasmere	c					b	b		A			b			A	A	A	games room, mini-gym. jacuzzi.
109	Langdale Hotel, Great Langdale	b	b			A	A	b		A		A	A	c	c	A	A	A	pool, games room, Jacuzzis, Health and Beauty Salon, trim trail.
133	The Riverside Hotel, Kendal						b	b		b			b				b		
134	Lyzzick Hall Hotel, Keswick						b	b		A		b							
135	Stakis Lodore Swiss Hotel, Keswick	c	A			b	c	b		A		b	A			A	A	A	
136	Armathwaite Hall Hotel, Keswick, Bassenthwaite ..	b	A			b	b	b		A	b		b			A	A	A	spa, gymnasium.
137	Borrowdale Hotel, Nr. Keswick	b				b	b	b		b	A	b							
138	Scafell Hotel, Nr. Keswick					b	b	A			b								
162	Scale Hill Hotel, Loweswater	b				b	b	b				b							

page		golf	tennis	croquet	pitch & putt	boating	fishing	riding	billiards/ snooker	swim/pool	sea/river bathing	sailing	squash	badminton	shooting	leis. centre	solarium	sauna	other
	CUMBRIA (continued)																		
185	The Mill, Mumgrisdale, Penrith	b				b	b	A	A			b		A	A				darts, games room, clay pigeon shooting.
189	Swan Hotel, Newby Bridge					A	A	b			A	A							marina.
203	The Black Swan, Ravenstonedale	b	A				A												
232	Skinburness Hotel, Silloth-on-Solway	b	b				b	b	A	b			b				A	A	gymnasium.
251	The Old Rectory Hotel, Torver						b	b				c			c				
261	Sharrow Bay Country House Hotel, Ullswater	b				A	A	A			A								
272	Gilpin Lodge, Windermere	b	b	A															
273	Lakeside Hotel, Windermere	b	b			A	A	b			A	A	b						boat launching and mooring
274	Langdale Chase Hotel, Windermere		A			A	A	b											
276	Wild Boar, Crook, Nr. Windermere	b	b				b	b					b		b				
278	Old Vicarage Country House Hotel, Witherslack	b	A				b	b		b	b	b	b	b					
	DERBYSHIRE																		
24	Hassop Hall Hotel, Hassop, Nr. Bakewell	b	A				b	b											
88	Kedleston Country House Hotel, Derby	b					b	b								b	A	A	
89	Izaak Walton, Dovedale						A	c			A		b						
111	Maynard Arms, Grindleford	b					c			b									
179	Riber Hall, Matlock	b	A				c			b									clay pigeon shooting by arrangement.
	DEVON																		
20	Holne Chase Hotel, Nr. Ashburton						A	b											
26	Downrew House, Nr. Barnstaple	A	A	A			b	b	A	A			b	b		b	b		games room.
27	Halmpstone Manor, Bishops Tawton, Nr. Barnstaple		b				b	b					b		b	b			
38	Bovey House, Beer					b		b			b								
41	Royal Hotel, Bideford	b				b					b	b							
71	Easton Court, Chagford	b					b	b							b				
72	Mill End Hotel, Chagford	b	b				b												bird watching.
73	Great Tree Hotel, Nr. Chagford	b				b	b	b				b			b				

page		golf	tennis	croquet	pitch & putt	boating	fishing	riding	billiards/ snooker	swim/pool	sea/river bathing	sailing	squash	badminton	shooting	leis. centre	solarium	sauna	other
	DEVON (continued)																		
79	Hoops Inn, Horns Cross, Nr. Clovelly	b				b	b				b	b		b	b				
85	Royal Castle Hotel, Dartmouth					A	A					A							
86	Fingals Hotel and Restaurant, Nr. Dartmouth		A			b	b	b	A	A		b							games room, jacuzzi.
93	Ebford House Hotel, Nr. Exeter	b	b			b	b	b			b		b	b	b	A	A	A	
94	The Royal Beacon Hotel, Exmouth	b	b			A	c	c	A		A	A			c	b	A	A	
119	Bel Alp House, Haytor	b						c	A										
126	Combe House Hotel, Nr. Honiton	b	b	A			A	c											
132	The Commodore Hotel, Instow	b	b					b			A	A	b						water skiing, 3 moorings.
168	Rising Sun Hotel, Lynmouth	b	b			A		b			A	A			b				
169	Lynton Cottage Hotel, Lynton		b				b	A			A				b				
215	Bolt Head Hotel, Salcombe		b			A	A	b	b	A		A	b				b	b	private moorings.
216	Marine Hotel, Salcombe	b	b			A	b		A	A	A					A	A	A	own slipway and boat mooring, beauty and massage salon.
217	Tides Reach Hotel, Salcombe	b	b			A	A	b	A	A	A	A	A			A	A	A	spa bath, steam bath, massage therapy, gym, wind surfing, water sports from own boat house.
218	Soar Mill Cove Hotel, Soar Mill Cove, Nr. Salcombe	c	A					c		A	A					b			
222	Saunton Sands Hotel, Saunton Sands	c	A				b	b	A	A		A	A		b	A	A	A	Children's paddling pool.
228	Belmont Hotel, Sidmouth	b	b				b	b		b	b	b					b	b	
229	Hotel Riviera, Sidmouth	c	b			b	b	b			b	b			c				
230	The Royal Glen Hotel, Sidmouth	b	b							A	b								
231	The Victoria, Sidmouth						c	b	A	A	A	A	b	b			A	A	games room, spa bath, 18-hole putting green.
235	Gabriel Court Hotel, Stoke Gabriel	b		A			A	b		A	A								
252	Devonshire Hotel, Torquay	b	A			b	b	b		A	b		b						
253	The Gleneagles Hotel, Torquay	b	b				b		A	A	b	b	b	b			A		spa bath, games room.

page		golf	tennis	croquet	pitch & putt	boating	fishing	riding	billiards/ snooker	swim/pool	sea/river bathing	sailing	squash	badminton	shooting	leis. centre	solarium	sauna	other
	DEVON (continued)																		
254	Imperial Hotel, Torquay	c	A	A		A	c	c		A	A		A		c	A	A	A	
255	The Palace Hotel, Torquay		A	A	A	b	b	b	A	A	b	b	A			A		A	games room.
256	Princes Hotel, Torquay	b	b				b			A	A	A	b						
257	Orestone Manor House, Nr. Torquay	b	b			b	b	c		A	b	b	b						games room.
270	Woodhayes Country House Hotel, Whimple		A	A															
281	Watersmeet Hotel, Mortehoe, Woolacombe	b	A			b	b	b	A	A	A	b							games room, surfing, clay pigeon shooting arranged.
	DORSET																		
53	Carlton Hotel, Bournemouth	b	b				b		A	A	A		b	b		A	A	A	
54	The Chine Hotel, Bournemouth	b	b			A				A	A	A					A	A	
55	The Cumberland Hotel, Bournemouth	b	b				c	b	A	A	A	A	b				A		games room (pool – high season only).
56	Langtry Manor, Bournemouth		b			b	b	b			b	b			b				
57	Queen's Hotel, Eastcliff, Bournemouth					b						b							games room.
58	Trouville Hotel, Bournemouth	b	b			b	b				b	b	b		b		A	A	spa pool, gymnasium.
59	Winter Gardens Hotel, Bournemouth	b	b			b	b	b		A	b	b			b	A	A	A	2 fitness rooms, Ski-Master Simulator.
92	Summer Lodge Hotel, Evershot		A				b	b		A									
164	Alexandra Hotel, Lyme Regis	b	b			b	b	b			A	b	b						
165	Kersbrook Hotel, Lyme Regis	b				b	b	b			b	b			b				wind surfing.
220	Haven Hotel, Sandbanks	b	b			A		b		A	A	A	A			A	A	A	gymnasium.
221	Sandbanks Hotel, Sandbanks	b	b			A		b		A	A	A				A	A	A	trimnasium.
226	Eastbury Hotel, Sherborne	b	b				b	b					b	b	b				
243	Manor House Hotel, Studland Bay	b	A			A		A			A	A							
244/5	Knoll House, Studland Bay	A	A			b	b	b		A	A	b				A	A	A	Health spa, games rooms, adventure playground, windsurfing.

page		golf	tennis	croquet	pitch & putt	boating	fishing	riding	billiards/ snooker	swim/pool	sea/river bathing	sailing	squash	badminton	shooting	leis. centre	solarium	sauna	other
	DORSET (continued)																		
266	Kemps Country House Hotel and Restaurant, Nr. Wareham	b	b				b	b		b	b		b			b			
268	Moonfleet Manor Hotel and Country Club, Nr. Weymouth		A						A	A			A			A	A	A	gymnasium, table tennis, toddlers' indoor play area. 4 indoor bowls rinks, adjacent country club.
	GLOUCESTERSHIRE																		
14	The Crown of Crucis, Ampney Crucis	b	b																
40	Bibury Court, Bibury						b												
76	Cotswold House, Chipping Campden	b	c																
99	The Fossebridge Inn, Fossebridge	b					A								A				
237	Wyck Hill House, Stow-on-the-Wold			A				b											clay pigeon shooting.
242	The Amberley Inn, Nr. Stroud	b						b											
249	Hare & Hounds, Nr. Tetbury	b	A	A					A				A						
	HAMPSHIRE																		
7	Alton House Hotel, Alton	b	A				b	b	A	A			b		b	b	b	b	'Skirmish' 1 mile.
8	The Grange Hotel, Alton			A						A									
28	Audley's Wood, Basingstoke	b																	
29	Basingstoke Country Hotel, Basingstoke	b	b				b	b		A			b	b	b	A			
65	Carey's Manor, Brockenhurst	c					b	b		A	b	b	b	b	b	A	A	A	Jacuzzi, steam room, impulse shower & gym.
166	Stanwell House Hotel, Lymington	b	b				b	b			b		b	b	b				
167	Passford House, Lymington	b	A	A		b	b	b	A	A	b	b				A	A	A	multi-gym, table-tennis.
180	Fifehead Manor, Middle Wallop						b	b							b				
181	South Lawn Hotel, Milford-on-Sea	b	b			b	b	b	b	b	b	b	b		b				
186	Chewton Glen Hotel, New Milton	A	A	A		b	b	b		A	b	b	b			A			
209	Tylney Hall Hotel, Rotherwick	c	A	A				c	A	A					c	A	A		multi-gym.

page		golf	tennis	croquet	pitch & putt	boating	fishing	riding	billiards/ snooker	swim/pool	sea/river bathing	sailing	squash	badminton	shooting	leis. centre	solarium	sauna	other
	HAMPSHIRE (continued)																		
233	Botley Park, Southampton	A	A	A		b	b	b	A	A		b	A			A	A	A	pétanque, gymnasium.
	HEREFORD and WORCESTER																		
62	The Broadway Hotel, Broadway	b	b					b											
63	The Lygon Arms, Broadway	b	A					c	A	A			c			A		A	clay pigeon shooting, hot air ballooning and archery all by arrangement.
64	Dormy House Hotel, Broadway	b	b					b					b	b	b				
208	Pengethley Hotel, Nr. Ross-on-Wye	b	b	A	A		A	b		A			b						
263	The White Lion Hotel, Upton-upon-Severn	b						b											
	HERTFORDSHIRE																		
48	Down Hall Country House Hotel, Nr. Bishops Stortford		A					b		A						A	A	A	games room.
112	West Lodge Park Hotel, Hadley Wood	b	b	A				b		b			b						fitness trail.
212	St. Michael's Manor, St. Albans	b	b										b						
234	Briggens House Hotel, Stanstead Abbots	A	A	A			A												boules.
259	Pendley Manor Hotel, Tring	b	A				b	b	A	A			b		b	A	A	A	gymnasium; motorized polo, war games and gliding close by.
	KENT																		
21	Eastwell Manor, Nr. Ashford		A				A	c	A						A				
61	Castlemere Hotel, Broadstairs	b	b			b	b	b	b	b	A	b							
117	Tudor Court, Hawkhurst	b	c					b					b						ballooning by arrangement.
210	The Spa Hotel, Royal Tunbridge Wells	b	A			b	b	b		A		b	b	b	c	A	A	A	spa pool.
	LANCASHIRE																		
101	The Pickerings, Garstang	b																	
140	Cobwebs Country House, Kirkby Lonsdale	b					b								b				

page		golf	tennis	croquet	pitch & putt	boating	fishing	riding	billiards/ snooker	swim/pool	sea/river bathing	sailing	squash	badminton	shooting	leis. centre	solarium	sauna	other
	LANCASHIRE (continued)																		
142	Mytton Fold Farm Hotel, Langho	b						b											
269	Shireburn Arms, Nr. Whalley						A	b							c				
	LEICESTERSHIRE																		
160	Quorn Grange, Loughborough	b	b			b	b	b					b	b	b	b	b	b	
196	Barnsdale Country Club, Nr. Oakham	b	A			A	b	b	A	A		A	A			A		A	games room, gym, netball, minigolf, bowls.
211	Normanton Park Hotel, Rutland Water	b				A	A	b				A			A				bird watching, cycling, wind-surfing.
262	Falcon Hotel, Uppingham	c	c			c	c	c				c	c		c		A	A	gymnasium.
	LONDON																		
144	The Beaufort, Beaufort Gardens																		health club.
150	Le Méridien Hotel, Piccadilly	b							A	A			A			A	A	A	Turkish bath, Jacuzzi, health club, dancing classes, massage.
154	Regency Hotel, 100, Queen's Gate															A	A	A	floatarium.
	MIDDLESEX																		
118	Edwardian International, Hayes									A						A	A	A	gymnasium.
	NORFOLK																		
49	Blakeney Hotel, Blakeney	b	b			A	b	b		A	A	A	b	b	b			A	games room, Jacuzzi.
91	Shipdham Place, East Dereham	b					b	b							b				
110	Lenwade House, Great Witchingham	b	b				A			A			b		b		A		gymnasium.
194	Norfolk Mead Hotel, Norwich	b	A			A	A	b		A		b	b						
195	South Walsham Hall, Nr. Norwich		A			b	A	A		A		b	A				A	A	pétanque.
	NORTHAMPTONSHIRE																		
87	Staverton Park Hotel and Golfing Complex, Daventry	A					A		A						A				leisure centre planned.

page		golf	tennis	croquet	pitch & putt	boating	fishing	riding	billiards/ snooker	swim/pool	sea/river bathing	sailing	squash	badminton	shooting	leis. centre	solarium	sauna	other
	NORTHUMBERLAND																		
4	Bishopfield Country House Hotel, Allendale	b	b				b	b	A						b				bicycles available.
25	Waren House Hotel, Bamburgh	b	A			b	c	A			A	b			c				local bird watching.
50	The Lord Crewe Arms, Blanchland	b				b	b	b				b							
	OXFORDSHIRE																		
66	The Golden Pheasant Inn, Burford	b					b							b					
139	Mill House Hotel and Restaurant, Kingham	b	b				b	b											
182	The Old Swan and Mill, Minster Lovell	b	A	A			A	b	A										punting.
280	Feathers Hotel, Woodtock	b	b				b	b					b	b	b				
	SHROPSHIRE																		
163	The Feathers at Ludlow	c						c		b									
197	Pen-y-Dyffryn Hall, Rhydycroesau, Nr. Oswestry . .	b					A	c								b			
227	Hawkstone Park Hotel, Shrewsbury	A	A	A			c	c	A	A					c		A	A	games room, trimnasium.
	SOMERSET																		
42	The Dragon House, Bilbrook						b				b								
125	Combe House, Holford		A	A				c		A							A		
184	The King's Arms Hotel, Montacute														c				
200	The Anchor Hotel & The Ship Inn, Porlock Harbour	b					b	b				b							
225	Charlton House Hotel, Shepton Mallett	b	A					b		A			b					A	
277	Royal Oak Hotel, Winsford						A	b							c				
	STAFFORDSHIRE																		
124	Hoar Cross Hall, Hoar Cross		A	A			c	c						A	c		A	A	dance studio, hydrotherapy pool, gym, golf improvement facility, health/beauty spa.
	SURREY																		
83	Selsdon Park Hotel, Sanderstead, Nr. Croydon . .	A	A	A				b	A	A			A			A	A	A	Jacuzzi, gymnasium, steam bath, boules.

page		golf	tennis	croquet	pitch & putt	boating	fishing	riding	billiards/ snooker	swim/pool	sea/river bathing	sailing	squash	badminton	shooting	leis. centre	solarium	sauna	other
	EAST SUSSEX																		
82	Winston Manor Hotel, Crowborough	b						b		A			b	b		A	A		gymnasium.
116	Beauport Park Hotel, Hastings	b	A	A			b	A		A	b	b	b		c				
223	Brickwall Hotel, Sedlescombe	b	b					b				b							
	WEST SUSSEX																		
102	Europa Gatwick Hotel, Gatwick							b		A						A	A	A	
161	South Lodge, Lower Beeding	b	A				A								A				
260	Alexander House, Turners Hill	b	A				b		b										
	WARWICKSHIRE																		
1	Salford Hall Hotel, Abbots Salford, Nr. Stratford . .		A						A								A	A	
239	Welcombe Hotel, Stratford-upon-Avon	A	A																
240	Billesley Manor, Nr. Stratford-upon-Avon		A	A	A		c	c		A					c				
	WEST MIDLANDS																		
3	Fairlawns Hotel, Aldridge	b																	
44	Norton Place Hotel, Kings Norton, Birmingham . .																		fitness centre, laser and clay-pigeon shooting.
46	The Swallow Hotel, Five Ways, Birmingham									A						A	A		gymnasium, beauty salon.
246	Moor Hall, Sutton Coldfield	b	b					b		A			b	b		A	A	A	leisure centre/pool opening Jan. 1991.
	WILTSHIRE																		
78	Chiseldon House, Chiseldon	c					c	c		A			c	c	c				
81	Rudloe Park Hotel, Corsham	b	b	A			b	b		b			b	b	b				sports centre 1 mile.
173	The Old Bell Hotel, Malmesbury	b						b											
174	Crudwell Court, Nr. Malmesbury	b	b	A			b	b			A	b	b		b	b			
175	Whatley Manor, Nr. Malmesbury	b	A	A			A	b	A	A			b				A	A	golf net, Jacuzzi, putting green.
177	Ivy House, Marlborough	b	b				c						b		c				

page		golf	tennis	croquet	pitch & putt	boating	fishing	riding	billiards/ snooker	swim/pool	sea/river bathing	sailing	squash	badminton	shooting	leis. centre	solarium	sauna	other
	WILTSHIRE (continued)																		
247	Blunsdon House, Nr. Swindon		A						A	A			A			A	A	A	gym, spa bath.
248	Cricklade Hotel, Nr. Swindon	A	A				c		A	A					c	A	A		spa bath, steam baths.
	YORKSHIRE																		
18	Dweldapilton Hall Hotel, Appleton-le-Moors	b					c	b											
23	Rose and Crown Hotel, Bainbridge						A		A										
52	Devonshire Arms Country House Hotel, Bolton Abbey	c	c				A	c					c	c	A				
103	Mallyan Spout Hotel, Goathland						b												
104	Gomersal Park Hotel, Gomersal	b						b		A						A	A	A	spa pool, gymnasium.
113	Grants Hotel, Harrogate	b	b					b											
114	Newton House Hotel, Knaresborough, Nr. Harrogate	b	b				b	b	b						b	b			
115	Nidd Hall Hotel and Country Club, Nidd, Nr. Harrogate	b	A			A	A	b	A	A		A	A		A	A	A	A	gymnasium.
121	Feversham Arms Hotel, Helmsley	b	A				b	A		A					b				games room.
122	The Pheasant, Helmsley	b	b				b	b		b									
123	Ryedale Lodge, Nr. Helmsley	b					A	b							c				
127	Worsley Arms Hotel, Hovingham	b	b				b	b					A		b				
130	Cow and Calf Hotel, Ilkley	b	b				b	b	A	b			b	b	b				games room.
131	Rombalds Hotel, Ilkley	b	b					b		b			b			b	b	b	
141	Lastingham Grange Hotel, Nr. Kirkbymoorside ..	b						b											
176	Auburn Hill Hotel, Malton	b					b			b					b		b	b	
193	Solberge Hall, Nr. Northallerton	b					c	b	A										
199	White Swan, Pickering		b				b	b					b						
207	Milburn Arms, Rosedale Abbey						b	b				b							
224	Falcon Manor, Settle	b	c				A	A					c		c		A		crown green bowling.
271	Whitwell Hall Country House Hotel, Whitwell on the Hill		A							A						A		A	games room.
282	Bilbrough Manor Country House Hotel, York ..	c					c	c							c				many racecourses nearby.
283	Swallow Chase Hotel, York									A						A	A	A	

page		golf	tennis	croquet	pitch & putt	boating	fishing	riding	billiards/ snooker	swim/pool	sea/river bathing	sailing	squash	badminton	shooting	leis. centre	solarium	sauna	other
	WALES																		
	CLWYD																		
290	Soughton Hall, Northop, Nr. Chester	c	A				b	b	A				b	b	A				games room.
291	Hotel 70°, Colwyn Bay	b	b			b	b	b			b	b	b		b				
297	Hand Hotel, Llanarmon D.C.		A				A	c							c				
298	The West Arms Hotel, Llanarmon D.C.		b				A	c							c				
299	Tyddyn Llan Country House Hotel and Restaurant, Llandrillo	c		A		b	A	c				b			c				
306	Llyndir Hall Hotel, Rossett	b	b				b	b		A					b	A	A		trymnasium, steam room.
	DYFED																		
296	Wolfscastle Country Hotel, Nr. Haverfordwest . .		A					b					A						
307	St. Nons Hotel, St. David's	c				b	b	c			b								
308	Warpool Court, St. David's	b	A		b	b	b	c	A	A	b	b				A		A	wind surfing, clay pigeon shooting.
310	Fourcroft Hotel, Tenby	b	b				b	b	A	A	A				b	A		A	gymnasium.
	GWENT																		
305	The Crown at Whitebrook, Nr. Monmouth	b	b				b	b							b				
311	Cwrt Bleddyn Country Hotel, Tredunnock	b	A			b	b	b	A	A		b	A		c	A	A	A	games room, steam room, fitness room.
	GWYNEDD																		
287	Trefeddian Hotel, Aberdyfi	A	A			b	b		A	A	b	b	b	A		A	A		wind surfing, games room.
288	Craig-y-Dderwen Country House Hotel, Betws-y-Coed	b					b	b							b				
289	Gwydyr Hotel, Betws-y-Coed	b					A	b									A	A	hotel controls 20 miles salmon fishing.
292	Bron Eifion Country House Hotel, Criccieth	b	b				b	b			b								
294	Bontddu Hall, Nr. Dolgellau	b						b			b								
295	George III Hotel, Nr. Dolgellau	b	b				A	b					b						wind surfing.

page		golf	tennis	croquet	pitch & putt	boating	fishing	riding	billiards/ snooker	swim/pool	sea/river bathing	sailing	squash	badminton	shooting	leis. centre	solarium	sauna	other
	GWYNEDD (continued)																		
300	Gogarth Abbey Hotel, Llandudno			A		b		b		A	b					A	A	A	games room.
301	Carreg Brân Hotel, Llanfairpwyllgwyngyll	b	A			b	b	b	A	A	b	b	A		c		A	A	steam room, fitness room.
304	Anglesey Arms Hotel, Menai Bridge	b	b			b	b			b	b	b							
309	Tynycornel Hotel, Tal-y-Llyn, Tywyn						A			A	b				A		A	A	
	POWYS																		
293	Gliffaes Country House Hotel, Crickhowell	b	A	A		b	A	b	A	b		b							hang gliding nearby.
302	Bodfach Hall Country House Hotel, Llanfyllin . .	b	b										b			b			
303	Lake Hotel, Llangammarch Wells	A	A				A	b	A						b				clay pigeon shooting.
	SCOTLAND																		
	BORDERS																		
343	Sunlaws House Hotel, Kelso	b	A				A	A							A				
356	Cringletie House Hotel, Peebles	b	A	A			c	b											
367	Philipburn House Hotel, Selkirk	b					c	c	A	A				A					games room, playground, adventure area, trampoline.
	DUMFRIES and GALLOWAY																		
318	Barjarg Tower, Auldgirth	b					b	b							c				
363	Corsemalzie House Hotel, Port William			A		b	A	b			b	b		A	A				
364	Baron's Craig Hotel, Rockcliffe by Dalbeattie . .	b				b	b	b			b								wind surfing.
	FIFE																		
327	Fernie Castle Hotel, Nr. Cupar						A								A				
365	St. Andrews Golf Hotel, St. Andrews	b									b						A	A	
	GRAMPIAN																		
321	Darroch Learg Hotel, Ballater	b	b				b	b											
323	Braemar Lodge, Braemar	b					b								b				wild-life and skiing nearby.

page		golf	tennis	croquet	pitch & putt	boating	fishing	riding	billiards/ snooker	swim/pool	sea/river bathing	sailing	squash	badminton	shooting	leis. centre	solarium	sauna	other
	GRAMPIAN (continued)																		
326	Craigellachie Hotel, Craigellachie	b	b				b	b	A						b		A	A	gymnasium, skiing nearby.
334	Mansion House, Elgin	b	b				b	b		A		b	b		b	A			
335	Knockomie Hotel, Forres	b	b	A		b	b	b			b	b	b		c				
346	Kildrummy Castle Hotel, Kildrummy	b					b	c	A										
359	Pittodrie House Hotel, Pitcaple		A	A			c	c					A	b	c				clay pigeon shooting, games room.
362	The Lake Hotel, Port of Menteith	b					b	b							b				
	HIGHLAND																		
315	Loch Duich Hotel, Ardelve					b	A	A			b								
319	Corrour House Hotel, Nr. Aviemore	b	b			b	b	b				b	b		b				
320	Ballachulish Hotel, Ballachulish	b	b			A	b	b	A		A	A			b				skiing, mountaineering, hill walking.
324	Royal Marine Hotel, Brora	b	b				b	b	A	A	b	A	b	b	b	A	b	A	games room, curling.
325	Coul House Hotel, Contin	b					A				A	A			b				games room.
330	Dundonnell Hotel, Dundonnell					b					b	b							
337	Glenmoriston Arms Hotel, Invermoriston	b					b	b							b				
338	Bunchrew House Hotel, Inverness	b	b			b	A	A		b	b				A				
339	Kingsmills Hotel, Inverness	b	c			c	c	c		A		c			c	A	A	A	
340	Rosedale Hotel, Isle of Skye		b			A					A								
341	Hotel Eilean Iarmain, Sleat, Isle of Skye	b					A	b			A				A				stalking.
342	Uig Hotel, Isle of Skye					b	b	b			b				c				
344	The Holly Tree, Kentallen					A	b	b			A	A			b				
347	The Kinlochbervie Hotel, Kinlochbervie					c	A	c			A	c			c				
348	Lochalsh Hotel, Kyle of Lochalsh					b	c	c			b	c			c				clay pigeon shooting.
349	Achany House, Nr. Lairg	b					c	b						c					stalking red and sika deer – by arrangement.
352	Inchnadamph Hotel, Loch Assynt						A												
353	Inver Lodge Hotel, Lochinver						A				A						A	A	

page		golf	tennis	croquet	pitch & putt	boating	fishing	riding	billiards/ snooker	swim/pool	sea/river bathing	sailing	squash	badminton	shooting	leis. centre	solarium	sauna	other
	HIGHLAND (continued)																		
355	Allt-nan-Ros Hotel, Onich	b	b			A	A	b			A	A	b		c				walking.
366	Scourie Hotel, Scourie						A				b								bird watching, climbing, walking.
371	Tongue Hotel, Tongue					A	A	A			A	A							bird watching.
	LOTHIAN																		
332	Caledonian Hotel, Edinburgh	b	b							b	b			b		b	b	b	
372	Houstoun House Hotel, Uphall	b																	
	STRATHCLYDE																		
315	Invercreran House, Appin						b	b	A		b	b						A	gliding nearby.
317	Loch Melfort Hotel, Arduaine, by Oban					A	A				A	A							
322	The Kildonan Hotel and Country Estate, Barrhill	A	A			c	A	c	A	A		c	A		A	A	A	A	gymnasium.
328	Dolphinton House Hotel, Dolphinton	b	A				A	b											
345	Taychreggan Hotel, Kilchrenan	b				A	A	b			A				c				stalking.
350	Gleddoch House, Langbank	A						b	A	A			A					A	
351	The Brisbane Hotel, Largs	b	b			b	b	b		b	b	b			b	b			
354	Manor House, Oban	b				b				b	A	b	b			b	b	b	
368	Redcliffe Hotel, Skelmorlie	b				A	A				A	A							
	TAYSIDE																		
329	Old Mansion House, by Dundee	b	A	A						A			A						
331	Stakis Dunkeld House, Dunkeld	b	A	A			A	b		A					A	A	A	A	multigym, shooting academy, archery.
336	Castleton House Hotel, by Glamis	b					c	c							c				ski slopes nearby.
358	Ballathie House Hotel, Nr. Perth		A	A			A								A				helipad and putting green.
357	Newton House, Nr. Perth	b	b					b							b				
360	Green Park Hotel, Pitlochry	c					c	b			A	A				A			chess, cards, bar billiards, 9 hole putting.

page		golf	tennis	croquet	pitch & putt	boating	fishing	riding	billiards/ snooker	swim/pool	sea/river bathing	sailing	squash	badminton	shooting	leis. centre	solarium	sauna	other
	TAYSIDE (continued)																		
361	The Log Cabin, Nr. Pitlochry	b					A	c		b					A				walking, pony trekking, stalking, clay pigeon.
369	Dalmunzie Hotel, Spittal O'Glenshee	A	A				c	b							A				skiing, games room, stalking.
370	Port-an-Eilean Hotel, Strathtummel	b				A	A	b			A	A			b				
	ISLANDS																		
	JERSEY																		
374	Atlantic Hotel, La Moye	b	b							A	b		b			A			
375	Hotel Chateau Valeuse, St. Brelade's Bay	b	b			b	b	b		A	b	b	b	b					
376	Hotel L'Horizon, St. Brelade's Bay	b				A	b	b		A	A	A				A	A	A	wind surfing.
377	Longueville Manor Hotel, St. Saviour	b	b							A	b		b						
	ISLE OF MAN																		
378	Grand Island Hotel, Ramsey	b	b	A		b	b	A	A	A	A	b	b		b	A	A	A	
	ISLE OF WIGHT																		
379	Winterbourne Hotel, Bonchurch						b	b		A	b		b	b		b	b		
380	Hotel Ryde Castle, Ryde			b		A	b	b		b	A	A	b		b	b			

CITY CENTRE HOTELS

ENGLAND

BATH

FOUNTAIN HOUSE, *see page 33*

LANSDOWN GROVE HOTEL, *see page 34*

ROYAL CRESCENT, *see page 35*

BIRMINGHAM

NORTON PLACE HOTEL, *see page 44*

THE PLOUGH AND HARROW HOTEL, *see page 45*

THE SWALLOW HOTEL, *see page 46*

THE COPTHORNE BIRMINGHAM, Paradise Circus, Birmingham B3 3HJ

Telephone: 021-200 2727 *Telex: 339026 COPBHX-G*

F licence; 215 en suite bedrooms, all with radio, telephone, TV, mini-bar; full central heating; lift; lounge service; indoor swimming pool; whirlpool; solarium, sauna, team room, leisure room, gymnasium; conference facilities max 184; major credit cards accepted.

ROYAL ANGUS THISTLE HOTEL, St. Chad's Queensway, Birmingham B4 6HY

Telephone: 021-236 4211 *Fax: 021-233 2195*
Telex: 336889

F licence; 135 en suite bedrooms, all with radio, telephone and TV; full central heating; lift; full night service; meals to 10.00 pm; lounge service; conferences up to 180; major credit cards accepted.

BRIGHTON

COURTLANDS HOTEL, The Drive, Brighton/Hove BN3 3JE

Telephone: (0273) 731055

F licence; 58 en suite bedrooms, 8 ground floor, all with direct dial telephone, radio, colour TV, central heating; 3 family rooms; executive suite with spa bath; lift; night service; late meals in restaurant to 9.30 pm, cold meals by arrangement; diets; children welcome; baby listening; dogs in rooms only; conferences; solarium, games room; pool; covered swimming pool (heated); sea bathing 400 yards; sailing Brighton Marina; 6 golf courses nearby; tennis, squash, badminton all ½ mile; fishing 1 mile; riding 1½ miles; car park; credit cards accepted.

GRANVILLE HOTEL, 123/125 King's Road, Brighton BN1 2FA

Telephone: (0273) 18302

F licence; 25 en suite bedrooms (3 ground floor), all with telephone, radio, TV; full central heating; lift; night service; late meals to 10.30 pm; vegetarian diets; children at Manager's discretion, baby listening; conferences; jacuzzi in two rooms, solarium; sea bathing, sailing; golf, tennis, squash, badminton, riding, fishing, all nearby; all credit cards accepted.

WHITEHAVEN HOTEL, Wilbury Road, Brighton/Hove BN3 3JP

Telephone: (0273) 778355 *Telex: 877159 Ref. Whitehaven*

R & R licence; 17 en suite bedrooms (8 ground floor) all with telephone, colour television, radio, trouser press, hairdryer and tea/coffee making facilities; full central heating; late meals till 9.30 pm; diets; children over 8 welcome; solarium; heated swimming pool, sea bathing, sailing, tennis, squash, badminton, riding, golf all nearby and fishing can be arranged; open all year; Access, Diners, Amex, Visa credit cards accepted.

BRISTOL

AVON GORGE HOTEL, Sion Hill, Clifton, Bristol, Avon BS8 4LD
Telephone: (0272) 738955 *Fax: 0272 238125*
F licence; 76 en suite bedrooms, all with room telephone and TV; full central heating; lift; night porter; late meals to 10.00 pm; lunch time bar buffet; conferences maximum 100; all credit cards accepted; street parking; tariff on application. Ground floor, 2 basement prestige flats; jacuzzis and four poster beds available.

THE GRAND HOTEL, Broad Street, Bristol, Avon BS1 2EL
Telephone: (0272) 291645 *Fax: 0272 227619*
F licence; 180 en suite bedrooms, all with radio, room telephone and TV; full central heating; lift; 24-hour room service; late meals to 10.30 pm; Brass Nails Restaurant; conferences 5–500; Amex, Diners, Access and Visa cards accepted; NCP parking facilities for residents; tariff on application.

CAMBRIDGE

GARDEN HOUSE HOTEL, Granta Place, Mill Lane, Cambridge CB2 1RT
Telephone: (0223) 63421 *Fax: 0223 316605*
Telex: 81463
F licence; 117 en suite bedrooms (7 on ground floor), all with colour TV, refrigerated mini-bar, tea/coffee tray, hairdryer, direct dial telephone; restaurant meals to 9.30 pm, light meals in lounge to 10.30 pm; 24-hour room service; parking for 200 cars; conferences max. 200; special weekend rates; major credit cards accepted.

CARLISLE

CUMBRIA PARK HOTEL, *see page 68*

THE CUMBRIAN HOTEL, Court Square, Carlisle CA1 1QY
Telephone: (0228) 31951
F licence; 110 bedrooms, all with private bathroom, radio, direct dial telephone, 6 channel TV; full central heating; lift; night service; late meals to 10.00 pm; coffee shop open to 11.00 pm; conferences maximum 300; free entry to snooker club; Access, Barclaycard, Visa, Amex, Diners Club, Travel Key all accepted; parking for 80 cars; tariff on application.

CHELMSFORD

PONTLANDS PARK COUNTRY HOTEL, Great Baddow, Nr. Chelmsford, Essex CM2 8HR
Telephone: (0245) 76444 *Fax: 0245 478393*
R & R licence; 17 en suite bedrooms with telephone & TV; meals till 10.00 pm; children welcome; no dogs unless in kennels; conferences; indoor swimming pool; sauna, solarium; credit cards accepted.

CHESTER

MOLLINGTON BANASTRE HOTEL, *see page 74*

ROWTON HALL HOTEL, *see page 75*

COVENTRY

THE BRANDON HALL, Brandon, Nr. Coventry CV8 3FW
Telephone: (0203) 542571
F licence; 60 en suite bedrooms with colour TV and telephone; night service; last orders 9.30 pm; bar meals; children welcome; dogs accepted; conferences max. 90; 6 squash courts; credit cards accepted.

DARLINGTON

BLACKWELL GRANGE MOAT HOUSE, Blackwell Grange, Darlington DL3 8GH
Telephone: Darlington 380888
F licence; 98 en suite bedrooms, 29 ground floor, all with radio, TV, telephone; full central heating; lift; night service; late meals to 10.00 pm; conferences maximum 300; credit cards accepted; parking for 150 cars; tariff on application.

DAVENTRY

STAVERTON PARK HOTEL, *see page 87*

DERBY

INTERNATIONAL HOTEL, Burton Road, Derby DE3 6AD
Telephone: (0332) 369321 *Fax: 0332 294430*
R & R licence; 51 en suite bedrooms with telephone & colour TV; lift; night service; last orders 10.00 pm; coffee shop; children welcome; dogs by arrangement; conferences max. 80; credit cards accepted.

DUNSTABLE

OLD PALACE LODGE HOTEL, Church Street, Dunstable LU5 4RP
Telephone: (0582) 62201
F licence; 49 en suite bedrooms (15 ground floor) all with telephone, TV, hairdryer and trouser press; full central heating; lift; 24 hour room service; diets; children welcome; baby listening; dogs by arrangement; conferences max. 36; several golf courses nearby; Amex, Visa, Access and Diners cards accepted.

EXETER

ROYAL CLARENCE HOTEL, Cathedral Yard, Exeter, Devon EX1 1HD
Telephone: (0392) 58464 *Fax: 0392 439423*
F licence; 56 en suite bedrooms all with colour TV & video, telephone, hairdryer & trouser press; lift; night service; last orders dinner 9.45 pm; bar meals; children welcome; no dogs; conferences max. 100; sporting facilities nearby; credit cards accepted.

EBFORD HOUSE HOTEL, Nr. Exeter, *see page 93*

GUILDFORD

THE ANGEL, High Street, Guildford GU1 3DR
Telephone: (0483) 64555
F licence; 27 en suite bedrooms including de-luxe suites, all with radio, colour TV, telephone and tea/coffee making facilities; coffee shop open 7.00 am till 10.00 pm; night porter; children welcome; conference facilities; car parking close by; credit cards accepted.

HARROGATE

GRANTS HOTEL, *see page 113*

NEWTON HOUSE HOTEL, *see page 114*

NIDD HALL HOTEL & COUNTRY CLUB, *see page 115*

OLD SWAN HOTEL, Harrogate, N. Yorkshire HG1 2SR
Telephone: (0423) 500055 *Fax: 0423 501154*
137 en suite bedrooms with telephone, colour TV; lift; night service; last orders dinner 10.00 pm; bar meals; diets; children welcome; dogs accepted; conferences 30–300; putting green; tennis; credit cards accepted.

HULL

STAKIS PARAGON HOTEL, Paragon Street, Hull, Humberside HU1 3UF
Telephone: (0482) 26462 *Telex: 52450*
F licence; 124 bedrooms, all with private bathroom, radio, room telephone and TV; individual heaters; 2 lifts; night service; late meals available on request; conferences maximum 240; all credit cards accepted; tariff on application.

IPSWICH

BELSTEAD BROOK HOTEL, Ipswich, Suffolk IP2 9HB
Telephone: (0473) 684241 *Fax: 0473 68124*
F licence; 78 en suite bedrooms with telephone & colour TV; night service; last orders dinner 9.30 pm; bar meals; diets; children welcome; no dogs; conferences max. 50; credit cards accepted.

LEEDS

HAYLEY'S HOTEL & RESTAURANT, Shire Oak Road, Headingly, Leeds LS6 2DE
Telephone: (0532) 784446 *Fax: 0532 753342*
F licence with restrictions; 22 en suite bedrooms with satellite TV, direct-dial telephone; night service; dinner till 9.45 pm – suppers till 10.30 pm; lounge food service; conferences max. 25; children welcome; no pets; car parking; Visa, Master Card & Amex cards accepted.

QUEEN'S HOTEL, City Square, Leeds LS1 1PL
Telephone: (0532) 431323 *Telex: 55161*
F licence; 190 en suite bedrooms, all with radio, room telephone and TV; full central heating; lift; 24 hr room service; late meals to 10.00 pm; lounge snacks; conferences maximum 600; all major credit cards accepted; parking facilities nearby; tariff on application.

LEICESTER

BELMONT HOTEL, De Montfort Street, Leicester LE7 7GR
Telephone: (0533) 544773 *Telex: 34619*
F licence; 56 en suite bedrooms, 10 ground floor, all with radio, telephone, colour TV; full central heating; lift; night service; late meals to 10.00 pm; conferences maximum 100; Amex, Visa, Access and Diners cards accepted; parking for 40 cars; tariff on application.

GRAND HOTEL, Granby Street, Leicester LE1 6ES
Telephone: (0533) 555599 *Fax: 0533 544736*
F licence; 92 bedrooms, all with private bathroom, radio, telephone and TV; full central heating; lift; night service; late meals to 9.30 pm; coffee shop; conferences maximum 400; credit cards accepted; own parking facilities; tariff on application. Reduced weekend rates.

LIVERPOOL

BRITANNIA ADELPHI HOTEL, Ranelagh Place, Liverpool L3 5UL
Telephone: (051) 709 7200 *Telex: 629644*
F licence; 344 en suite bedrooms, all with radio, direct dial telephone, colour TV; full central heating; three lifts; night service; late meals to 11.00 pm in Cromptons French Restaurant and 2.00 am in Overstuffed Pizza; Kicks Disco Bar, Saturday discotheque; coffee shop; conferences maximum 800; swimming pool, sauna, solarium, jacuzzi, squash courts, fully equipped health club; credit cards accepted; own parking facilities. Tariff on application.

LONDON

THE ALEXANDER HOTEL, Sumner Place, *see page 143*
THE BEAUFORT HOTEL, Beaufort Gardens, *see page 144*
THE BERKSHIRE HOTEL, Oxford Street, *see page 145*
THE COBURG HOTEL, Bayswater Road, *see page 146*
THE DIPLOMAT HOTEL, Chesham Street, *see page 147*

LONDON (Contd.)

DUKES HOTEL, St. James's Place, *see page 148*
THE GORING HOTEL, Grosvenor Gardens, *see page 149*
LE MERIDIEN, Piccadilly, *see page 150*
THE MONTCALM, Great Cumberland Place, *see page 151*
NUMBER FIVE SUMNER PLACE, South Kensington, *see page 152*
THE PORTLAND HOTEL, Bloomsbury, *see page 153*
THE REGENCY HOTEL, Queen's Gate, *see page 154*
THE RITZ, Piccadilly, *see page 155*
ROYAL GARDEN HOTEL, Kensington High Street, *see page 156*
SHERATON PARK TOWER, Knightsbridge, *see page 157*
THE STAFFORD HOTEL, St. James's Place, *see page 158*
WHITE'S HOTEL, Lancaster Gate, *see page 159*

THE CHURCHILL HOTEL, Portman Square W1A 4ZX
Telephone: 071-486 5800 *Telex: 264831*
F licence; 489 bedrooms and suites, all fully air conditioned with private bathroom, direct dial telephone, radio, colour TV, complementary in-house films, mini-bars; 24 hour room service; guest business service suite; children welcome; dogs at discretion of management; valet service; hairdressing salon and barber shop; theatre desk; garage; all major credit cards accepted.

THE HAMPSHIRE HOTEL, Leicester Square WC2H 7LH
Telephone: 071-839 9399 *Telex: 914848*
F licence; 124 en suite bedrooms with colour TV & telephone; 2 lifts, room service, last orders 11.00 pm except Sunday 10.00 pm, wine bar meals; children welcome, no dogs, conferences max. 100; most credit cards accepted.

INN ON THE PARK, Park Lane W1A 1A2
Telephone: 071-499 0888 *Fax: 071-493 1895*
Telex: 22771
F licence; 228 bedrooms (including 26 suites), all with private bathroom, radio, satellite TV, 3 telephones; lift; 24 hour room service, same day laundry, one hour pressing; 2 restaurants; bar; lobby lounge serving light meals; diets on application; air conditioning; children welcome; meeting/private dining facilities; pre- or after-theatre dinners; parking for 60 cars; major credit cards accepted.

THE MOUNTBATTEN HOTEL, 21 Monmouth Street, Covent Garden WC2H 9HD
Telephone: 071-836 4300 *Fax: 071-240 3540*
127 en suite bedrooms with telephone & colour TV; 2 lifts, night service; snacks in Wine Bar; children welcome; no dogs; conferences max. 80; pre- and post-theatre menu; all major credit cards accepted.

NORFOLK HOTEL, Harrington Road, London SW7 3ER
Telephone: 071-589 8191 *Fax: 071-581 1874*
Telex: 268852
F licence; 97 en suite bedrooms, all with jacuzzi, radio, telephone, remote control colour TV, free in-house movies, mini bar, trouser press, hair dryer; full central heating; lift; night service; meals to 9.30 pm, 10.00 pm weekends; 4 Star Restaurant, Wine Bar, Real Ale Tavern; all major credit cards accepted.

ROYAL COURT HOTEL, Sloane Square, London SW1W 8EG
Telephone: 071-730 9191
F licence; 102 en suite bedrooms (7 suites), all with radio, telephone, TV and video; full central heating; lift; night porter; meals to 10.30 pm; Courts Café Bar; Real Ale Tavern, 4 Star Restaurant; conferences up to 30; all major credit cards accepted.

MANCHESTER

HOTEL PICCADILLY, PO Box 107, Piccadilly Plaza, Manchester M60 1QR
Telephone: (061) 236 8414
F licence, 255 bedrooms, all with private bathroom, radio, telephone, TV; tea and coffee making facility, trouser press, hair dryer; full central heating; lift; night service; late meals to 11.00 pm; conferences maximum 700; hairdressing salon; credit cards accepted; own parking facilities. Reduced rate at weekends.

NEWCASTLE

GOSFORTH PARK HOTEL, High Gosforth Park NE3 5HN
Telephone: (091) 236 4111 *Telex: 53655*
178 en suite rooms with direct dial telephone & colour TV; 24 hour room service; leisure centre with indoor swimming pool; helipad; children welcome; credit cards accepted.

NORWICH

THE NORFOLK MEAD HOTEL, *see page 194*
SOUTH WALSHAM HALL, *see page 195*
SPROWSTON HALL HOTEL, Wroxham Road, Norwich NR7 8RP
Telephone: (0603) 410871
F licence; 41 en suite bedrooms (11 on ground floor), all with radio, telephone, TV; full central heating; night service; meals to 9.30 pm; diets; children welcome; baby listening; dogs welcome;conferences; golf next door; sauna, solarium, billiards, indoor heated swimming pool, tennis, squash, badminton, fishing all 4 miles; riding 5 miles; all major credit cards accepted.

NOTTINGHAM

STRATHDON THISTLE HOTEL, 44 Derby Road, Nottingham NG1 5FT
Telephone: (0602) 418501 *Fax: 0602 483725*
Telex: 377185
F licence; 70 en suite bedrooms, all with radio, direct dial telephone and TV, video feature films, hair dryer, trouser press; full central heating; lift; 24 hr room service; late meals to 10.30 pm; coffee shop to 10.30 pm; conferences maximum 120; all credit cards accepted; few parking spaces, and NCP approximately 100 yards; tariff on application.

OXFORD

THE RANDOLPH HOTEL, Beaumont Street, Oxford OX1 2LN
Telephone: (0865) 24781
F licence; 109 en suite bedrooms with telephone, colour TV; full central heating; 2 lifts; night service; last orders – restaurant 10.00 pm, coffee shop 10.30 pm; diets; children welcome; dogs accepted; conferences max. 350; credit cards accepted.

PLYMOUTH

THE COPTHORNE HOTEL, The Armada Centre, Plymouth PL1 1AR
Telephone: (0752) 224161 *Fax: 0752 670688*
F licence; 135 en suite bedrooms, all with radio, telephone, TV/video, tea/coffee making facilities, mini-bar; full central heating; lift; night service; meals until 10.30 pm; coffee shop; diets; children welcome; dogs accepted; conferences; indoor heated swimming pool; sauna, solarium; credit cards accepted.

MAYFLOWER POST HOUSE HOTEL, Cliff Road, The Hoe, Plymouth PL1 3DL
Telephone: (0752) 662828
F licence; 106 en suite bedrooms, all with radio, telephone and TV, and tea and coffee making facilities; full central heating; two lifts; night service; late meals to 10.30 pm; coffee shop; conferences maximum 85; swimming pool; Amex, Diners, Visa, Access, THF Gold Card accepted; parking for 149; tariff on application.

READING

CAVERSHAM HOTEL, Caversham Bridge, Reading RG1 8BD
Telephone: (0734) 391818 *Fax: 0734 391665*
F licence; 114 en suite bedrooms, all with telephone, colour TV; full central heating; 2 lifts; night service; last orders 10.30 pm; diets; children welcome; Tavern Bar; conferences max. 200; leisure centre with heated pool, gymnasium, boating on river; credit cards accepted.

SHEFFIELD

ASTON HALL, Worksop Road, Aston, Sheffield S31 0EE
Telephone: (0742) 872309 *Fax: 0742 873228*
R & R licence; 22 en suite bedrooms including 3 suites all with telephone & colour TV; full central heating; night porter; last orders 9.45 pm; conferences max. 200; jacuzzi in suites; car parking for 160; Access and Visa accepted. Tariff on application.

GROSVENOR HOUSE HOTEL, Charter Square, Sheffield, South Yorks. S1 3EH
Telephone: (0742) 720041 *Telex: 54312*
F licence; 103 en suite bedrooms, all with radio, direct dial telephone, TV; full central heating; lift; night service; late meals to 11.00 pm; coffee shop and restaurant; conferences maximum 400; all credit cards accepted; 80 indoor parking spaces; tariff on application.

SOUTHAMPTON

BOTLEY PARK HOTEL, *see page 233*

POLYGON HOTEL, Cumberland Place, Southampton SO9 4GD
Telephone: (0703) 330055 *Telex: 47175*
F licence; 4 Star Hotel; 120 en suite bedrooms, all with radio, telephone, TV; two lifts; late meals to 10.00 pm; 24 hour room service; conferences maximum 500; Barclaycard, Access, Diners, JCB, Amex cardholders welcome; parking for 120; tariff on application.

ST ALBANS

ST MICHAEL'S MANOR HOTEL, *see page 212*

STOKE-ON-TRENT

HAYDON HOUSE HOTEL, Basford, Stoke-on-Trent ST4 6JD
Telephone: (0782) 711311
R & R licence; 27 bedrooms most with private bathroom; suites, all with telephone & TV; meals till 10.30 pm; bistro; children welcome; dogs accepted; conferences; most credit cards accepted.

SWINDON

BLUNSDON HOUSE HOTEL, *see page 247*

CRICKLADE HOTEL & COUNTRY CLUB, *see page 248*

POST HOUSE HOTEL, Marlborough Road, Swindon SN3 6AQ
Telephone: (0793) 24601
F licence; 104 en suite bedrooms, 51 on ground floor, all with radio, telephone and colour TV; full central heating; health and fitness club with pool, sauna, solarium and gym; late meals to 10.00 pm; conferences maximum 100; children's play area; all credit cards accepted; free parking; tariff on application.

WILTSHIRE HOTEL, Fleming Way, Swindon SN11 1TN
Telephone: (0793) 28282
F licence; 85 bedrooms, all with private bathroom, radio, room telephone and TV; full central heating; two lifts; night service; late meals to 10.30 pm; conference facilities; beautiful Georgian style restaurant; Access, Visa, Diners and Amex cards accepted; parking provided; tariff on application.

WASHINGTON

GEORGE WASHINGTON HOTEL, Stonecellar Road, High Usworth, District 12 NE37 1PH
Telephone: (091) 417 2626 *Fax: 091 415 1166*
F licence; 106 bedrooms, 25 ground floor, all with private bathroom, radio, telephone and TV, trouser press, hairdryer, tea/coffee making facilities; full central heating; night service; late meals to 10.15 pm; coffee shop; conferences maximum 180 resident, 180 non-resident; swimming pool, sauna, solarium, jacuzzi, snooker room, 18 hole golf and 9 hole par three, gymnasium, driving range and 2 squash courts; credit cards accepted; own parking facilities.

WINCHESTER

THE ROYAL HOTEL, St Peter Street, Winchester SO23 8BS
Telephone: (0962) 840840 *Fax: 0962 841582*
F licence; 59 en suite bedrooms, with telephone, colour TV & satellite channels; night service; last orders dinner 9.30 pm; bar meals; children welcome; dogs accepted; conferences max. 120; major credit cards accepted.

WESSEX HOTEL, Paternoster Row, Winchester SO23 9LQ
Telephone: (0962) 61611
F licence; 94 bedrooms, all with private bathroom, radio, telephone and TV; full central heating; two lifts; night service; late meals to 10.00 pm; all day coffee shop; conferences maximum 100; board room; Access, Amex, Diners, Visa, THF, Carte Blanche accepted; own parking.

GREAT YARMOUTH

THE CARLTON HOTEL, Great Yarmouth NR30 3JE
Telephone: (0493) 855234
F licence; 97 bedrooms all with radio, telephone and TV; full central heating; night service; meals till 21.30; coffee shop; children welcome; dogs accepted; conferences; most credit cards accepted.

THE STAR HOTEL, Hall Quay, Great Yarmouth NR30 1HG
Telephone: (0493) 842294
F licence; 42 en suite bedrooms, all with radio, telephone, TV, tea/coffee making facilities, full central heating; lift, night service; late meals to 9.45 pm; conferences maximum 80/100; pool table; Amex, Visa, Diners, Access accepted; own parking; tariff on application.

YORK

SWALLOW CHASE HOTEL, Tadcaster Road, York, *see page 283*

MOUNT ROYALE, York, N. Yorks. YO2 2DA
Telephone: (0904) 628856/7/8/9 *Fax: 0904 611171*
Telex: 57414
R & R licence; 23 en suite bedrooms, 6 ground floor, all with radio, telephone and TV, trouser press, tea/coffee making facilities; full central heating; late meals to 9.30 pm; swimming pool; large enclosed garden; all credit cards accepted; own parking; tariff on application.

ROYAL YORK HOTEL, Station Road, York, N. Yorks. YO2 2AA
Telephone: (0904) 653681 *Telex: 57912*
F licence; 148 bedrooms, 113 with private bathroom, all with radio, direct dial telephone and TV; full central heating; lift; night service; choice of two restaurants and two bars; conferences maximum 180; credit cards accepted; 9 hole putting green; own parking; tariff on application.

WALES

CARDIFF

THE ANGEL HOTEL, Castle Street, Cardiff CF1 2QZ
Telephone: (0222) 232633 *Fax: 0222 396212*
F licence; 91 en suite bedrooms with telephone & colour TV; 2 lifts; night service; children welcome; dogs accepted; conferences max. 300; gymnasium, sauna; solarium; credit cards accepted.

THE PARK HOTEL, Park Place, Cardiff CF1 3UD
Telephone: (0222) 383471 *Telex: 497195*
F licence; 108 en suite bedrooms, all with radio, telephone and TV; full central heating; night service; 24 hour meals; conferences maximum 300; all credit cards accepted; own parking; tariff on application.

LLANDRINDOD WELLS

HOTEL METROPOLE, Temple Street, Llandrindod Wells, Powys LD1 5DY
Telephone: (0597) 2881 *Telex: 35237*
F licence; 121 en suite bedrooms, all with radio, TV, direct dial telephone, tea/coffee making facilities, trouser press, hairdryer, full central heating; 2 lifts; 24 hour porter service; dogs welcome; no charge for children sharing parents' room; conferences 500 max; banqueting 250 max; spa waters; bowls; concessionary golf at Llandrindod Wells golf course; free coarse fishing in season, also salmon/trout fishing on the Wye and Ithon; most major credit cards accepted.

SWANSEA

DRAGON HOTEL, Swansea, West Glamorgan SA1 5LS
Telephone: Swansea 51074
F licence; 118 bedrooms, all with private bathroom, radio, telephone and TV; full central heating; lift; night service; late meals to 10.00 pm; coffee shop; conferences maximum 300; Access, Amex and Visa cards accepted; own parking facilities.

SCOTLAND

ABERDEEN

BUCKSBURN MOAT HOUSE HOTEL, Old Meldrum Road, Bucksburn, Aberdeen AB2 9LN
Telephone: (0224) 713911 *Telex: 73108*
F licence; 98 en suite bedrooms (25 ground floor) all with radio, telephone and TV; tea/coffee making facilities; full central heating; lift; night service; late meals to 10.30 pm; conferences max. 180; swimming pool; multi-gym; credit cards accepted; own parking; courtesy bus to and from airport. Tariff on application.

CALEDONIAN THISTLE HOTEL, 10 Union Terrace, Aberdeen AB9 1HE
Telephone: (0224) 640233
F licence; 80 bedrooms, all with private bathroom, alarms, radio, direct dial telephone, TV, in-house movies, tea/coffee making facilities, trouser press, hair dryer; full central heating; lift; night service and late bar; late meals to 11.45 pm; 2 restaurants; conferences maximum 60; sauna; sunbed; all credit cards accepted; own parking; tariff on application.

DUNDEE

QUEEN'S HOTEL, 160 Nethergate, Dundee DD1 4DU
Telephone: (0382) 22515
F licence; 31 en suite bedrooms, all with radio, direct dial telephone, TV, and tea/coffee making facilities; full central heating; lift; night service; late meals to 11.00 pm; conferences maximum 200; two bars; Access, Amex, Diners and Visa accepted; free parking for 40 cars; special weekend and conference rates; tariff on application.

EDINBURGH

CALEDONIAN HOTEL, *see page 332*

ROXBURGHE HOTEL, *see page 333*

BRUNTSFIELD HOTEL, Bruntsfield Place, Edinburgh EH10 4HH
Telephone: 031-229 1393 *Telex: 727897 DOOCOT-G*
F licence; 52 bedrooms, 5 ground floor, all with private bathroom, radio, direct dial telephone, colour TV, trouser press, hairdryer; full central heating; lift; 24 hr laundry service; late meals to 10.00 pm; one restaurant, two bars; seminar facilities for 70; Visa, Amex, Access and Diners cards accepted; own parking; swimming pool, sauna, solarium and gym.

GLASGOW

ALBANY HOTEL, Bothwell Street, Glasgow G2 7EN
Telephone: 041-248 2656 *Telex: 77440*
F licence; 251 bedrooms, all with private bathroom, radio, telephone and TV; full central heating; lift; night service; late meals to 11.00 pm; carvery; conferences maximum 800; credit cards accepted; own parking facilities.

CENTRAL HOTEL, Gordon Street, Glasgow, Strathclyde G1 3SF
Telephone: 041-221 9680 *Telex: 777771*
F licence; 217 bedrooms, 167 with private facilities, all with direct dial telephone, radio and TV, majority with trouser press, hair dryer; two lifts, night service; late meals to 10.00 pm; coffee shop open to 11.00 pm; conferences maximum 600; all standard credit cards accepted; tariff on application.

INVERNESS

KINGSMILLS HOTEL, Culcabock Road, Inverness, *see page 339*

ENGLISH INDEX

ENGLAND INDEX

ENGLAND INDEX

ENGLAND INDEX

WELSH INDEX

ISLANDS

SCOTTISH INDEX

ALPHABETICAL INDEX

Hotels in Britain and the Channel Islands, which are fully described in *Signpost* are entered below alphabetically according to location.

ALPHABETICAL INDEX

ALPHABETICAL INDEX

ALPHABETICAL INDEX

ALPHABETICAL INDEX

ALPHABETICAL INDEX

Reader's Notes

Reader's Notes